Geo-Mexico:

the geography and dynamics
of modern Mexico

Geo-Mexico:
the geography and dynamics
of modern Mexico

Richard Rhoda and Tony Burton

SB

SOMBRERO BOOKS, B.C., CANADA

First published 2010
by Sombrero Books
P.O. Box 4, Ladysmith, BC V9G 1A1, Canada

Library and Archives Canada Cataloguing in Publication
Rhoda, Richard, 1945-
Geo-Mexico : the geography and dynamics of modern
Mexico / Richard Rhoda and Tony Burton.
Includes bibliographical references and index.
ISBN 978-0-9735191-3-6
1. Mexico--Geography. 2. Mexico--Economic
conditions--1994-. 3. Human geography--Mexico.
I. Burton, Tony, 1953- II. Title.
F1210.9.R46 2010   917.204'842   C2009-906836-2

ISBN 978-0-9735191-3-6

Contents

Figures

Tables

Text boxes

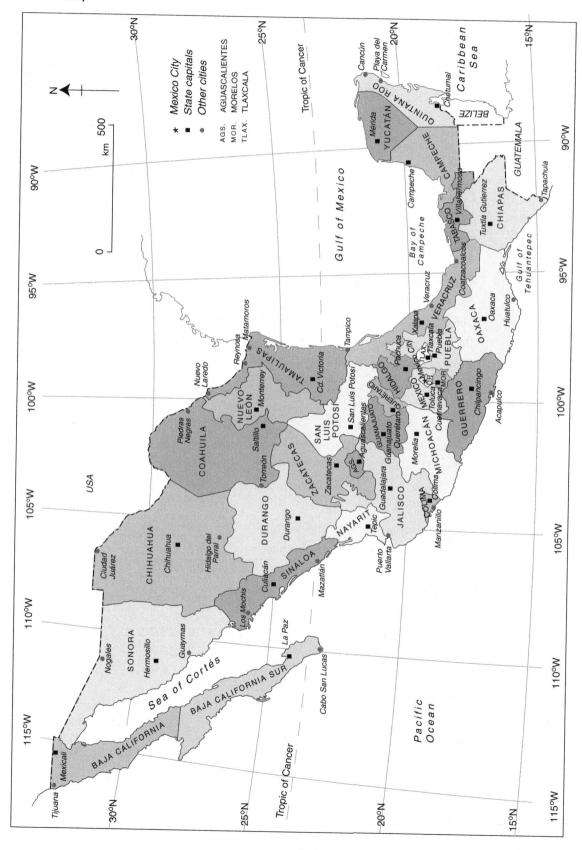

1
The dynamics of Mexican geography

This book's aim is to explore some of the fascinating diversity that makes Mexico as varied and interesting as any place on earth. Patterns, disparities, inequities and trends are all analysed and discussed, enhancing an understanding of the complex geography of Mexico.

A basic premise of this book is that the United Mexican States (the country's official name is *Estados Unidos Mexicanos*) is an important country that does not always receive the respect or study it merits.

Mexico is divided into 31 states and a Federal District. For simplicity, we refer to the latter as a state throughout this book. Mexico's largest state—Chihuahua—is about the size of the US state of Georgia. The Federal District, the smallest, is about a quarter the size of Prince Edward Island but ten times the size of Washington D.C. Despite its name, the Federal District is not entirely urban; it also contains several steep mountains and volcanoes.

Mexico is commonly associated with cacti, tequila, poverty, beach resorts and workers migrating to the USA. These perceptions may have some degree of truth but fail to capture the ecological and cultural richness and global importance of the country.

Mexico's population of about 110 million makes it the 11th largest nation on earth; an additional 31 million Mexicans currently reside in the USA. Mexico is one of only six countries in the world that rank in the top 15 for gross domestic product (GDP/PPP)[1], population and land area (Table 1.1). China, India, the USA, Brazil and Russia are the other members of this exclusive group.

Mexico's diverse economy produces about $1.6 trillion in goods and services every year, more than Canada or South Korea. Several Mexican corporations, brands and entrepreneurs are emerging as world leaders in their respective fields. On the down side, Mexico's per person GDP is far from equitably distributed. The income of the wealthiest 10% is almost 25 times that of the poorest 20%. Mexico has both extremes: some of the poorest rural areas in the Americas alongside some of the wealthiest urban neighborhoods on the planet.

Like Mexico, geography as a subject is also often under-appreciated, equated with memorizing the names of countries, capitals, mountain ranges and rivers. 'Real' geography is much more exciting! It focuses on the interactions between individuals, societies and the physical environment in both time and space. Geography looks at the processes behind these interactions and how human activities have helped define them. It also seeks to explain similarities and differences between places. In fact, it was early geographers who helped provide the essential foundation for many physical and social sciences, ranging from geology, meteorology and climatology to cultural anthropology, demography and economics.

Mexico has a long tradition of geography. Modern geography was given a jump-start in the country by the brilliant Prussian traveler Alexander von Humboldt, who explored Mexico for twelve months in 1803–04.

The Mexican Society of Geography and Statistics was founded in 1833, only three years after the UK's Royal Geographical Society and fully 55 years before the National Geographic Society. Geography remains a popular and respected subject in Mexican high schools and universities.

Modern geography encompasses four major traditions: earth science; human-environment relationships; area or regional studies; and spatial or locational analyses.

The earth science tradition looks at the nature and effects of processes related to landforms, climatology, and the earth's biosphere. The human-environment tradition explores how human activities impact the natural environment and vice versa. The area studies tradition concentrates on specific regions, be they natural or human. The spatial tradition analyzes the locational patterns of activities. This book is mindful of all four traditions, adopting all four of them at different points in our exploration of the diverse geographies of Mexico.

We also delve into all five of the themes identified by the Association of American Geographers and National Council for Geographic Education in 1984 to facilitate the teaching of geography.[2] These five themes are location, place characteristics, human–environment interaction, movement and region.

Location includes both absolute location and relative locaton. The absolute location of Tijuana is 117.0°W longitude, 32.5°N latitude. Its relative location concerns questions such as, "Is Tijuana closer to Juneau, Alaska, or Cancún, Mexico?" (The correct answer is Juneau.)

Place characteristics include both physical and human aspects. A physical characteristic of Mexico's ecology is that it has 30,000 different species of flowering plants, compared to 18,000 species in the USA and 12,000 species in Europe. A human characteristic would be that, on average, women living in Mexico City have 1.8 children during their lifetime, compared to 2.1 for women in the USA.

An example of the human-environment theme is the building of cities in Mexico which has changed the microclimate by producing heat islands. Between 1920 and 1997, the temperature of Guadalajara increased by 5.7°C (10.3°F) This theme might question why the 1985 earthquake in the Pacific Ocean which caused an estimated 10,000 deaths in Mexico City resulted in very few casualties in Acapulco, which was much closer to the quake's epicenter.

Movement, whether of people, things or ideas, is a critical topic, falling within the spatial or locational analysis tradition of geography. We investigate a variety of movements, or spatial interactions, such as trade, travel times, internal and international migration, and the spread of languages, religions and other aspects of culture. All these movements are dependent on the behavior of those making the spatial decisions and their perceptions of alternative routes and destinations.

Region as a theme for teaching geography is directly linked to the area studies tradition. In this book, we delineate and discuss numerous functional regions within Mexico, identified on the basis of variations in such characteristics as landforms, climates, ecosystems, indigenous languages, urban landuses, quality of life and political voting behavior.

Throughout the book, we introduce geographic models and theories which help explain the patterns and processes connected to each specific topic and how they relate to findings elsewhere. In several cases, we suggest how the model or theory can be adapted to be more appropriate to Mexico.

Each chapter in this book focuses on a particular geographical subject, discusses broad generalizations and looks at how these play out in various areas of

Physical geography

Poctépec = hill that smokes (volcano)

Economic geography

Michmaloyan = place to fish

Human geography

Teocalcingo = where the temple is

Figure 1.1 Three examples of Aztec place glyphs from the 16th century Codex Mendoza. The Aztecs knew their geography!

Table 1.1 Some basic facts about Mexico

		World Rank
Area	1,964,375 km² (758,449 mi²)	14
Population, 2008	106,682,518	11
Economy: GDP (PPP*), 2008	US$1.58 trillion	11
GDP per person, 2008	US$14,810	70+
Length of coastline	11,122 km (6911 mi)	14
Highest point: Pico de Orizaba	5610 m (18,406 ft)	na

*PPP = purchasing power parity

Mexico. We look at how current geographic patterns have evolved, and how they are still evolving.

Chapters 2 through 7 examine Mexico's physical geography. Chapter 2 discusses how plate tectonics have shaped Mexico and given rise to numerous volcanoes and earthquakes. Chapter 3 is devoted to Mexico's diverse landforms and its basic physiographic regions. Chapter 4 investigates the general factors influencing climate and how they determine Mexico's wide variety of climatic zones as well as hazards such as hurricanes. Urban microclimates and global climate change are also introduced. In chapter 5, we discuss Mexico's biodiversity and varied ecosystems. Water availability, the focus of chapter 6, looks at coastal resources, rivers, lakes, and aquifers. Chapter 7 builds on this by examining freshwater issues, including the potential for floods and droughts.

The next two chapters deal with population dynamics. Chapter 8 discusses Mexico's population growth since 1520, its late 20th century population explosion, issues of population density, and the reasons why some areas are growing so much faster than others. Chapter 9 looks toward the future by presenting the demographic transition model and Mexico's anticipated population dynamics between now and 2050.

Chapter 10 is the first of four chapters about Mexico's cultural geography. It focuses on Mexico's very large and diverse indigenous population, concentrated mainly in the south of the country. Over 60 indigenous languages are still spoken everyday in Mexico; only India, Papua New Guinea, and Indonesia have a greater diversity of languages. Chapter 11 discusses the distribution and growth trends of Mexico's religions. Our discussion in chapter 12 of political geography starts by tracing the historical evolution of Mexico's international and internal

borders before discussing the spatial significance of support for particular political parties and voting behavior in recent elections. The patterns of ethnicity, language, religion and other cultural traits allow us, in chapter 13, to examine one possible division of Mexico into distinct cultural regions.

Economic processes and characteristics are the focus of the next seven chapters. Chapter 14 compares Mexico's total economic production with other major countries and asks the question, "Is Mexico a world player?" In considering this, we explore the issues of Mexico's inequitable income distribution and production levels in different states. Chapter 15 looks into patterns and trends of primary economic activities (agriculture, forestry, fishing, mining). The location and importance of manufacturing and service activities are the subject of chapter 16. Chapter 17 takes an in-depth look at transportation of people and goods and its impacts on Mexico's development. The movement of information and ideas are analyzed in chapter 18 where examples include cell phones, the internet, comic books and TV soap operas. In chapter 19, we examine Mexico's massive tourism industry and include a wide-ranging discussion of its economic, social and environmental consequences. Chapter 20 covers the services and commodities that make up Mexico's economic base as well as flows of exports and imports. We end this chapter by considering what globalization means and just how globalized Mexico is compared to other countries.

The next three chapters deal with processes of urbanization. Chapter 21 outlines Mexico's 500-year transition from a predominately rural society to a heavily urbanized one. Chapter 22 presents a general model of urban spatial growth and the distribution of residential, industrial, and commercial land uses within cities. The focus is primarily on the growth and evolution of Mexico City, but case studies of Guadalajara and Monterrey are also presented. In chapter 23, we focus on current urban issues and likely future trends.

The dynamics and characteristics of Mexico's rural areas are the subject of chapter 24, which also discusses market centers and central place theory.

The next three chapters cover migration dynamics. Chapter 25 looks at the many factors that influence migration behavior and help explain the patterns of internal migration in Mexico. In chapter 26, we turn our attention to international migration, specifically to the massive movement of Mexican workers to jobs in the USA and the implications of this migration. Chapter 27 analyses the characteristics and implications of the Mexican diaspora in the USA.

The following two chapters are concerned with quality of life. Chapter 28 investigates the factors affecting quality of life such as education, health, crime, political rights and income. Mexico is compared with other countries. Chapter 29 compares variations in the quality of life between states and at the municipal level. The differences are enormous—the quality of life in some municipalities is similar to that in France, Germany or the United Kingdom, while in others it is more like that in Ethiopia or Burundi.

Chapter 30 presents a synthesis of Mexico's progress in environmental matters and its stance on key global issues. In our final chapter, we look forwards to consider some of the crucial issues pertaining to Mexico's future and offer some suggestions on what to watch for in the coming decades.

Mexico's place names

Mexico's place names, or toponyms, offer many clues about geography. Mexico's indigenous peoples spoke languages that had no formal alphabet. For place names, they used combinations of pictographs, ideographs and phonetic symbols. Spanish explorers recorded the names provided by the locals as best they could, resulting in some inevitable confusion and distortion. For instance, it is sometimes claimed that "Yucatán" actually derives from Maya Indians responding, "I don't know!" when asked to name a nearby place.

Suffixes derived from indigenous (mostly Nahuatl) words include:
- -apan = in/near water or river
- -calco = in the house of
- -can = place
- -cingo, -tzingo = (small) place of settlement
- -huacan, -oacan = place where they have
- -pan = in/on [Zapopan]
- -ro = place
- -tepec = hill
- -tepetl = mountain
- -titlan = near
- -tla = abundance
- -tlan = in or near [Ocotlán: near the pines;]

The Spanish language is at least as rich as English when describing landscapes. Common Spanish geographical terms relating to landscape include:
- cerro = hill
- montaña = mountain
- sierra = elongated mountain range
- mesa = flat-topped (table) hill
- cumbre = summit or peak
- pico = sharp peak
- valle = valley
- barranca = canyon
- cenote = limestone sinkhole
- cabo = point or cape
- punta = point or headland
- arroyo = brook
- río = river
- lago = lake
- salto, cascada = waterfall
- ojo (de agua) = spring
- presa = reservoir (and dam)
- mar = sea
- salinas = salt flats or salt works
- golfo = gulf
- bahía = bay
- puerto = port (inland, puerto = pass)

2
Earthquakes and volcanoes

Mexico has a complex system of landforms, dominated by mountains. While Mexico's two large North America neighbors, the USA and Canada, have vast expanses of flat, relatively low land, most of Mexico is mountainous and relatively high. About 75% of Mexico's land area is above 1000 m (3300 ft) compared to about a quarter of the USA and roughly an eighth of Canada. More importantly, about 80% of Mexicans live above 1,000 m compared to less than 5% in the USA or Canada.

Mexico's relief and landforms can best be understood by looking at their historical evolution during the past 200 million years. At the start of that time, the world's land masses formed one massive world continent named Pangaea. Pangaea stretched almost from one pole to the other and was surrounded by an enormous ocean, over twice as big as the current Pacific Ocean.

The northern and southern parts of this gigantic landmass slowly drifted apart. By 135 million years ago, there were two gigantic land masses: Laurasia in the north which contained the North American and Eurasian continents, and Gondwana in the south which included South America and Africa, together with most of India, Australia and Antarctica. At this time, Mexico was at the extreme southwest corner of Laurasia.

To explain these movements and to predict future movements of the continents and oceans, geologists have developed the theory of plate tectonics. The earth's crust or lithosphere is from 5 to 65 km (3 to 40 mi) thick and divided into about a dozen large tectonic plates, tabular blocks that drift across the Earth in different directions and at various speeds (up to a few centimeters or inches per year), probably as a result of thermal convection currents in the Earth's molten mantle. Most plates consist of a combination of both ocean floor and continent, though some are entirely ocean floor.

Each tectonic plate is moving relative to other plates. The movements are not independent because the plates smash into and scrape against one another. Areas in the center of tectonic plates, far from the boundaries, have relatively little seismic activity, but the boundaries between plates are seismically very active, creating earthquakes and volcanoes. The level of seismic activity depends on the relative speed and direction of the plates at the boundary.

There are three distinct kinds of boundaries between plates. At divergent boundaries, along mid-ocean ridges, plates are being steadily pushed apart, with new crust being added by volcanic activity to the rear of each plate as it moves. At convergent boundaries, plates collide and parts of the plates either buckle or fracture or are subducted back down into the molten mantle. The third kind of boundary is where plates are neither created nor destroyed but are moving side by side. The resulting friction as they rub against each other can produce large earthquakes.

Almost all of Mexico sits atop the south-west corner of the massive North American plate (Figure 2.1). Immediately to the south is the much smaller Caribbean plate. The North American plate extends westwards from the Mid-Atlantic Ridge, which runs through Iceland and down the middle of the Atlantic Ocean, to the western edge of North America. In a north-south direction, it extends from close to the North Pole as far south as the Caribbean.

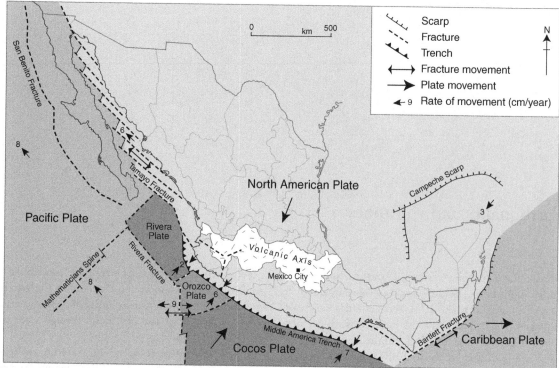

Figure 2.1 The tectonic plates influencing Mexico[1]

While most of Mexico rests on the North American plate, it is also influenced by several other plates. Baja California is on the gigantic Pacific plate, which is moving northwest and under the North American plate. The intersection of these plates under the Gulf of California causes parallel faults which are part of the famous San Andreas Fault system. Thus, the Gulf of California is an area of heavy seismic activity.

The small Rivera plate, between Puerto Vallarta and the southern tip of Baja California, is moving in a southeasterly direction and rubbing against the Pacific plate; it, too, is moving under the North American plate.

The Cocos plate is an ocean crust plate located off the south coast of Mexico. As we shall see shortly, the collision of the Cocos plate and the North American plate has had several far-reaching consequences.

How have tectonic plates affected Mexico?

To the east of Mexico, in the last 100 million years, outward expansion from the Mid Atlantic Ridge (a divergent boundary) first pushed South America ever further apart from Africa, and then (slightly more recently) forced the North American plate (and Mexico) away from Eurasia. The Atlantic Ocean continues to widen, expanding the separation between the

New World and the Old World, by about 2.5 cm (1 in) each year.

Meanwhile, to the west of Mexico, an analogous situation is occurring in the Pacific Ocean, where the Cocos plate is being forced eastwards away from the massive Pacific plate, again as a result of mid-ocean activity. The Cocos plate is effectively caught in a gigantic vice, its western edge being forced ever further eastwards while its leading eastern edge smacks into the North American plate.

The junction between the Cocos and North American plates is a classic example of a convergent plate boundary. The collision zone is marked by a deep ocean trench, variously known as the Middle America trench or the Acapulco trench. Off the coast of Chiapas, this trench is a staggering 6662 m (21,857 ft) deep. The trench is formed where the Cocos plate is forced to dive beneath the North American plate. As the Cocos plate is subducted, its leading edge fractures, breaks and is partly re-melted into the surrounding mantle. Any cracks in the overlying North American plate are exploited by the molten magma, which is under immense pressure, and as the magma is forced to the surface, volcanoes form. The movement of the plates also gives rise to earthquakes. The depth of these earthquakes will vary with distance from the deep ocean trench. Those close to the trench will be relatively shallow, whereas those occurring further away from the trench (where the subducting plate is deeper) will have deeper points of origin.

As the plates move together, sediments, washed by erosion from the continent, collect in the continental shallows before being crushed upwards into fold mountains as the plates continue to come together. A line of fold mountains stretches almost continuously along the west coast of the Americas from the Rocky Mountains in Canada past the Western and Southern Sierra Madres in Mexico to the Andes in South America. Almost all Mexico's major mountain ranges—including the Western Sierra Madre, the Eastern Sierra Madre and the Southern Sierra Madre— formed as a result of these processes during the Mesozoic Era, from 245 to 65 million years ago. We look at each of these regions in chapter 3.

However, no sooner had they formed than another momentous event shook Mexico. About 65 million years ago, a giant iridium-rich asteroid slammed into the Gulf of Mexico, close to the Yucatán Peninsula, causing the Chicxulub Crater, and hastening the demise of the dinosaurs. An estimated 200,000 km³ of crust was pulverized; most of it was thrown into the air. The resulting dust cloud is thought to have contributed to the extinction of up to 50% of all the species then on Earth. Not only did this event have an enormous impact on all life forms on Earth, it also left a legacy in the Yucatán. The impact crater is about 200 km (125 mi) across. Its outer edge is marked by a ring of sinkholes (locally known as *cenotes*) and springs where the fractured crust provided easy access to ground water. These locations include the ria (drowned river valley) of Celestún (now a UNESCO Biosphere Reserve), where fresh water springs mingle with salt water to create an especially rich habitat for birdlife.

In the 65 million years since the asteroid impact (the Cenozoic period), the remainder of Mexico has been formed, including many of the plateaus and plains, and the noteworthy Volcanic Axis, which owes its origin to on-going tectonic activity at the junction of the North American and Cocos plates.

Earthquakes

The boundaries of the North American Plate are seismically quite active, while most of the rest is relatively quiet. This means that the eastern part of Mexico is seismically quiet, while the western and southern

The west coast breaks up: a new island forms

Geologists believe that in the not too distant (geologically speaking) future, the coastline of western Mexico will be completely different from today.

They have recognized and mapped three important major sets of fault lines that are slowly cracking western Mexico apart. The first set forms an east-west rift valley, occupied by Lake Chapala, Mexico's largest natural lake. These parallel faults caused the section of land between them to fall, creating a basin large enough to temporarily impound the inflowing River Lerma to form the lake.

The second set of parallel faults extends westwards from Guadalajara towards Tepic in the state of Nayarit. Highway 15 follows this line of faults, and movements here have allowed several noteworthy volcanoes to form including Tequila, Sanganguey and Ceboruco. The third line of faults has caused the long shallow depression, much of it covered by a thin sheet of water during the rainy season, running south from Guadalajara to Colima and Manzanillo on the Pacific coast.

These three sets of faults intersect just west of Lake Chapala. Assuming current trends continue, a small triangular chunk of the North American plate, including the resort town of Puerto Vallarta, will eventually split off from the rest of Mexico before drifting slowly westwards, at a speed of about 2.4 cm/yr, into the Pacific Ocean towards Hawaii. The coastline of western Mexico will be forever changed.

The pattern of earthquakes in the region supports this idea. The epicenter of the largest earthquake in historic times (estimated magnitude 7.0) near Lake Chapala was immediately under the town of Zacoalco, precisely where the three rift valleys intersect. The quake on 27 December 1568 damaged churches, houses and friaries throughout the region.

Furthermore, several much more recent earthquakes have also had epicenters under the land, rather than under the ocean, supporting the idea that this section of Mexico is subject to some extreme geological stresses.

coastal areas, from Baja California to Chiapas, are very active.

In the last hundred years, Mexico has experienced 36 earthquakes of Richter Magnitude 7.0 or greater. This is about the size of the 1989 San Francisco or 1994 Los Angeles earthquakes, which killed many people and destroyed sections of freeway. Since 1910, Mexico has had five quakes greater than 8.0, which is ten times larger, and comparable to the 1906 San Francisco or 1964 Anchorage earthquakes. Almost all Mexico's earthquakes occur close to the west coast, from Jalisco in the north to Guatemala in the south.

While the precise location and timing of earthquakes can not yet be predicted, seismic gap theory suggests that a significant earthquake is now overdue for that section of the Cocos plate boundary opposite the Guerrero coast. The last major earthquake in this region was in 1911, and pressure for another earthquake is believed to be building. On either side of this gap, the pressure has already been released by more recent earthquakes.

Volcanoes

Mexico's active seismic zones have created numerous volcanoes, many of which are still active.

Virtually all the country's active and recently dormant volcanoes are located in a broad belt of high relief which crosses Mexico from west to east: the Volcanic Axis (Figure 2.2). Altitudes in this region vary from a few hundred to several thousand meters. The principal peaks are shown on the map. They include many of Mexico's most famous mountains, such as Popocatepetl and Iztaccihuatl, near Mexico City; Pico de Orizaba, Mexico's highest peak; Paricutín, the only completely new volcano in the Americas in recent times; and Colima, considered the most active at present. Many of the volcanoes are surprisingly young. For instance, a study using Carbon-14 dating

The 1985 Mexico City earthquakes

The worst earthquake disaster in modern Mexican history occurred in September 1985. The magnitude 8.1 earthquake at 7:19 a.m. on Thursday 19 September 1985 lasted a full two minutes. It was followed by a 7.5 earthquake 36 hours later. These earthquakes resulted from the Cocos Plate pushing under the North American Plate. While the epicenters were 50 km off Mexico's Pacific coast near the Michoacán-Guerrero border, most of the damage occurred 350 km (215 mi) away in Mexico City because the city center's subsoil, being former lakebed, is very unstable. The clay and silt beneath the city is up to 50 m thick in the area that received most damage. Geologists have likened the effects of the earthquake to the shaking of a bowl of jelly.

Further damage was caused by liquefaction, a process in which water is squeezed rapidly through the pore spaces in soil, dramatically reducing its cohesion. The sediments beneath Mexico City amplified the ground motions during the earthquakes and many buildings were stressed well beyond building code limits.

Damage estimates range upward to 10,000 deaths, 50,000 injured and 100,000 homeless. More than 500 buildings collapsed, and a further 600 of the 3000 damaged structures were subsequently razed to the ground. The destruction was concentrated in a relatively small area near the city center and included many public buildings, such as government offices, as well as 11 hospitals and clinics, numerous multi-story apartment blocks, 11 hotels and 10 banks. More than 1600 school classrooms were damaged. Buildings of between 6 and 15 stories were especially hard hit. The underbelly of the city was exposed; dozens of textile sweatshops were destroyed. The damages revealed many instances of poor construction standards and of poor enforcement of building codes. Well-built high rises such as the Latin American tower, designed to be earthquake-proof, were unscathed.

The total cost to the Mexican economy was estimated to exceed $5 billion, equivalent to 2% of the country's GDP (Gross Domestic Product).

The disastrous 1985 earthquakes led to much tighter building codes, equal or superior to anywhere in the world, and to the formation of well-trained emergency search and rescue brigades. They also resulted in the establishment of a Seismic Alarm System which provides a 50-second warning for any earthquake measuring over 6.0 on the Richter scale occurring off the coast of Guerrero or Michoacán.

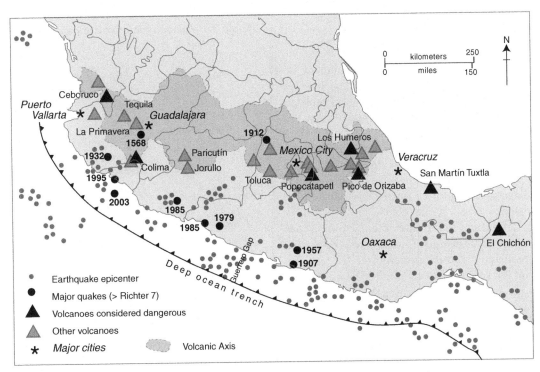

Figure 2.2 The Volcanic Axis[2]

on the palaeosols (ancient soils) under 12 volcanoes in the Toluca area yielded ages ranging from 38,600 to 8400 years before present.

It is unclear precisely why this broad belt of Mexico should be so active. Elsewhere in the world all major tectonically active areas have been linked in terms of their location to the margins or meeting-zones of tectonic plates. Some Mexican geologists believe that Mexico's Volcanic Axis is a rare example of activity associated with a gently dipping plate margin, one where the edge of the Cocos plate is subsumed, but at only moderate gradient, beneath the North American plate.

Almost all the volcanic activity in this zone has taken place in the last 25 million years, from the upper Oligocene period, through the Miocene and Pliocene and up to Recent. Two distinct periods of activity are recognized by some geologists. The first, in the late Oligocene and early Miocene, produced volcanic rocks often found today tightly folded by later earth movements. The second, responsible for all the major composite cones as well as dozens of ash and cinder cones, started in the Pliocene and continues today.

Starting in the west, the first active volcanoes are Everman and Barcenas in the Revillagigedo Islands.

Two of the westernmost volcanoes on the mainland are near Colima. At 4260 m (13,976 ft), the inactive Ne-

vado of Colima is as tall as the highest mountains in the contiguous USA. Its younger brother, Colima Volcano (or Volcán de Fuego) is lower (3820 m) but highly active and considered potentially very dangerous. It has erupted in cycles for several hundred years, and is capped by a dacitic plug characteristic of a silica-rich Pelean volcano. Such volcanoes have the potential to erupt suddenly, not emitting vast quantities of molten lava, but shooting out less spectacular, but far more devastating, clouds of red-hot asphyxiating gasses.

Tequila volcano, overlooking the town where the beverage is distilled, is also in Jalisco. In neighboring Michoacán state, the most noteworthy volcanoes are Jorullo (which last erupted in 1759) and Paricutín, which began life in a farmer's field in 1943 and ceased activity in 1952, but only after its lava had overwhelmed several small villages.

Closer to Mexico City, the Nevado of Toluca (4680 m) has a drive-in crater and is a favored destination for Mexico City families in winter to take their children to play in the snow.

The most famous volcano in the Volcanic Axis is the still active Popocatepetl ("Popo"), which rises to 5500 meters (18,045 feet). Alongside Popo is the dormant volcanic peak of Iztaccihuatl (5220 m or

El Chichón[4]

Not all volcanoes give any warning of impending activity. On 29 March 1982, in Chiapas, the El Chichón volcano erupted completely without warning and with unexpected fury. Vulcanologists later worked out that its last previous eruption had been 1200 years earlier. Two further eruptions followed in early April. The lack of warning caused heavy loss of life among local villagers who had been unable to evacuate their villages.

El Chichón forced more than 7 million tons of sulfur dioxide and 20 million tons of particulate material into the stratosphere. The resultant cloud of volcanic gases circled the Earth in three weeks and was still dissipating three years later. It was expected that the additional particulates in the atmosphere would reduce the solar radiation reaching the earth and cause the following summer to be cooler than usual. However, in an unlikely coincidence, an El Niño event began that same year, negating any significant cooling effect. The El Chichón eruption was one of the largest volcanic eruptions of the 20th century, exceeded only by the 1991 Mt. Pinatubo eruption in the Philippines in terms of the amount of volcanic gases and particulates entering the stratosphere. Ash fell over a wide area, from Campeche to San Cristóbal de las Casas in Chiapas.

By the time the eruption was over, the volcano, whose summit was 1260 m (4134 ft) prior to the eruption, had lost 200 m in height. The Chiapanecan Volcanic Arc, which includes El Chichón, is thought to be related to the subduction of the edge of the Cocos Plate underneath the North American plate.

Table 2.1 Mexico's major volcanoes[3]

Volcano	States	Height	
		meters	feet
Pico de Orizaba	Veracruz; Puebla	5 610	18 406
Popocatapetl	México; Morelos; Puebla	5 500	18 045
Iztaccihuatl	México; Puebla	5 220	17 126
Nevado of Toluca	México	4 680	15 354
Malinche	Tlaxcala; Puebla	4 420	14 501
Nevado of Colima	Jalisco	4 260	13 976
Cofre de Perote	Veracruz	4 200	13 780
Tacaná	Chiapas	4 080	13 386
Telapón	México	4 060	13 320
El Ajusco	Federal District	3 930	12 894
Colima Volcano	Jalisco; Colima	3 820	12 533

17,126 ft). On a smog-free day, both are clearly visible from Mexico City. The southern suburbs of Mexico City are overshadowed by a smaller active volcano, Ajusco, which reaches 3930 m (12,894 ft).

The Pico de Orizaba, a dormant volcano on the border between states of Veracruz and Puebla, is Mexico's highest mountain. At 5610 m (18,406 ft) it is the third highest peak in North America.

Only a few volcanoes appear to be in an anomalous location to the general pattern. They include two volcanoes in Chiapas which lie south of the Volcanic Axis: El Chichón (see box) and Tacaná (4080 m).

3
Relief and landforms

The relief and landforms of Mexico have been greatly influenced by the interaction of tectonic plates. The relief patterns are so complex (Figure 3.1) that it is often claimed that early explorers, when asked what the country was like, simply crumpled up a piece of parchment by way of response.

Figure 3.2 shows Mexico's main physiographic regions. The core of Mexico (both centrally located, and where most of the population lives) is a high plateau rimmed by mountain ranges to the west, south and east. Coastal plains lie between the mountains and the sea. The long Baja California Peninsula parallels the west coast. The low Isthmus of Tehuantepec separates the Chiapas Highlands and the low Yucatán Peninsula from the rest of Mexico. The following sections provide more detail on each of these areas.

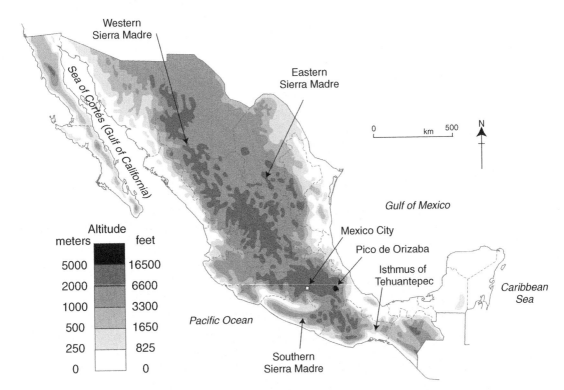

Figure 3.1 Mexico's relief [1]

1 Baja California

Baja California is a very long, narrow peninsula which stretches for about 1150 km (700 mi). In the north, it is composed of mostly granite, while the south is mostly marine sediments and lava. The Gulf of California is a trough resulting from a series of faults which are part of the famous San Andreas Fault in California. Prior to the opening up of the Gulf of California, the peninsula was attached to the mainland. There are several volcanic islands in the Gulf. The backbone of the peninsula is a crystalline mountain system with many peaks exceeding 1500 m (5000 ft) and some reaching as high as 3000 m (10,000 ft). The mountains have longer, gentler western slopes and steeper more rugged eastern slopes. Thus, as viewed from the Gulf of California, the Baja Mountains and the Western Sierra Madre look steep, foreboding and very rugged, while from the other side they look more subdued.

2 Sonoran Basin and Range

This basin and range landscape trends north-north-west to south-south-east. Parallel faulted blocks are separated by alluvial bajadas (broad, debris-covered slopes) and plains, which become wider approaching the coast. Despite being a desert area, this region exhibits many features, such as wadis and salt flats which have resulted from water action. The build-up of sediments in the delta of the Colorado River blocked the upper part of the Gulf of California (Sea of Cortés) and formed California's Salton Sea and Imperial Valley basin. This region also includes the Sierra of Pinacate with its distinctive volcanic cones, craters and lava flows.

3 Western Sierra Madre (Sierra Madre Occidental)

The Western Sierra Madre forms the western border of the Central Plateau. This rugged, broad Mesozoic

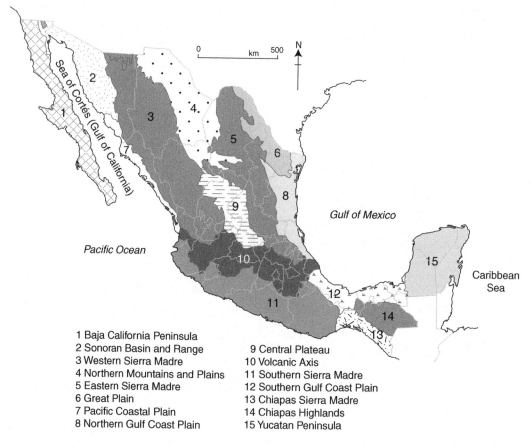

1 Baja California Peninsula
2 Sonoran Basin and Range
3 Western Sierra Madre
4 Northern Mountains and Plains
5 Eastern Sierra Madre
6 Great Plain
7 Pacific Coastal Plain
8 Northern Gulf Coast Plain
9 Central Plateau
10 Volcanic Axis
11 Southern Sierra Madre
12 Southern Gulf Coast Plain
13 Chiapas Sierra Madre
14 Chiapas Highlands
15 Yucatan Peninsula

Figure 3.2 Mexico's physiographic regions[2]

mountain range stretches about 1200 km (750 mi) from south of Nogales nearly all the way to Nayarit, where it meets the Volcanic Axis. Its width varies considerably but averages about 150 km (95 mi). The mountain summits mostly exceed 2000 meters (6500 ft) with some above 3000 m (almost 10,000 ft), clear evidence that vast quantities of sediments and volcanic materials were folded by plate movements. From the high central plateau, the mountains appear relatively gentle. But from the low western coastal plain, they appear quite rugged, dissected by deep canyons such as the Copper Canyon, which rivals the US Grand Canyon in size and splendor (see box).

The Western Sierra Madre has proven to be a serious barrier to east-west transportation in northern Mexico. Before the second half of the 20th century, there was no efficient way to cross these mountains. Historically, Spanish exploration, settlement, urbanization and commercial development on either side of the mountains developed independently. Thus, relatively close settlements on either side, such as Chihuahua and Ciudad Obregón, or Durango and Mazatlán, were worlds apart. Communications between the two sides were via Guadalajara, far to the south. No rail line crossed the mountains until 1961, though efforts to construct rail lines were initiated in the 19th century. Prior to the mid 1970s, there was only one paved road through the mountains connecting Mazatlán to Durango. Clearly, the Western Sierra Madre has had an enormous impact on the human and economic geography of Mexico.

4 Northern Mountains and Plains

Uplift and erosion have molded this arid and semi-arid section of the Chihuahuan desert, which continues northwards into the USA. Steep but low hills are separated by wide bajadas from former lake beds and alluvial plains, occupying inland basins known as bolsons. Many parts form closed, interior basins with no external drainage. South of Ciudad Juárez, at Samalayuca, is one of Mexico's most extensive areas of sand dunes. This is one of the most arid parts of the country; the soils exhibit all the signs of high levels of salinization.

5 Eastern Sierra Madre (Sierra Madre Oriental)

East of the Central Plateau is the Eastern Sierra Madre, which runs about 1200 km (750 mi) from about Tlaxcala east of Mexico City all the way north to the Río Bravo del Norte, which is also known as

the Río Grande. The mountains north of Monterrey have eroded significantly and now are relatively gentle. Summit elevations are similar to those of the Western Sierra Madre. Unlike its western counterparts, the Eastern Sierra Madre does not constitute a serious barrier between the plateau and the Gulf Coast Plain because there are several accessible passes through these older, more eroded mountains.

6 Great Plain

This is the southernmost extension of the physiographic province of gently sloping hills and plains

---

Is Mexico's Copper Canyon bigger than the US Grand Canyon?

According to a local Tarahumara Indian legend, the canyons were formed when "a giant walked around and the ground cracked." Geologists believe that a sequence of volcanic rocks varying in age from 30 to 135 million years were slowly uplifted to an average elevation of 2275 m (7500 ft) and then dissected by pre-existing rivers.

These antecedent rivers retained their courses, cutting down over 1400 m into the plateau surface, forming deep canyons and dividing the former continuous plateau into separate giant blocks. Centuries of erosion by the Urique river and its tributaries have resulted in the present-day landscape of structurally-guided plateau remnants, termed mesas, buttes and pinnacles, depending on their size.

Strictly speaking, the name Copper Canyon refers only to one small part of an extensive network of canyons comprising the Urique Canyon system. Table 3.1 compares some measurements of the Urique Canyons and the US Grand Canyon.

	Urique Canyons	US Grand Canyon
Total length of rivers (km)	540	446
Depth (m)	1250–1870	1480
Height of rim (m above sea level)	2250–2540	2000–2760
Maximum width (km)	4	15

that extends northwards as far as Canada. In Coahuila between Piedras Negras and Monclova are substantial coal deposits. Also found are deposits of silver, zinc, lead, mercury and gold.

7 The Pacific Coastal Plain

The Pacific Coastal Plain between the Western Sierra Madre and the Gulf of California runs for about 1500 km (1000 mi) from the port of Guaymas southwards to San Blas on the Nayarit coast. The plain varies in width from about 80 km (50 mi) in the south to about 200 km (125 mi) in the north. The coast is relatively straight, low, and sandy, but there are a few deep bays which have become major ports. These include Guaymas and the sheltered harbor of Topolobampo near Los Mochis. The southern section of this coastal plain has extensive salt marshes.

8 Northern Gulf Coast Plain

East of the Eastern Sierra Madre lies the Northern Gulf Coast Plain, which extends into Texas and Louisiana. It is widest in the north near the Rio Bravo del Norte (Rio Grande) but narrows towards the south. This flat and swampy region, dominated by lagoons and marine sediments, represents an emergent coastline that originated in the Cenozoic period. Two ranges of calcareous rocks, forming the Sierras of Tamaulipas and San Carlos, arise from the plain. There are no good natural harbors along this coast, but the Laguna de Tamiahua south of Tampico provides some shelter for smaller craft.

9 Central Plateau

Immediately north of the Volcanic Axis and sandwiched between the Western Sierra Madre and the Eastern Sierra Madre is the Central Plateau. This region is composed mostly of folded Mesozoic strata formed as Pangaea was breaking apart and the Pacific Plate was moving under the North American Plate. The elevation of the plateau increases from north to south, reaching heights of about 1800 m (6000 ft) at its southern edge near Querétaro. This region includes the highly industrialized Bajío region. The Bajío ("lowlands") region is the mid-altitude, largely flat, area comprising most of the state of Guanajuato, as well as parts of Querétaro, Michoacán and eastern Jalisco. The soils in the major valleys, such as that of the Lerma River, benefit from their proximity to volcanic deposits further south and are quite fertile. For more than a thousand years this region has supported intensive agriculture and relatively high population densities. The southern section is characterized by numerous landlocked alluvial basins whose drainage to the sea has been blocked by volcanic lava.

10 Volcanic Axis

The formation and main features of this region were analyzed in the previous section. The Volcanic Axis lies south of the Central Plateau, and traverses Mexico from Nayarit and Colima in the west right across the country to Veracruz. The Volcanic Axis has Mexico's newest mountains, all of which have developed in the last few million years. Erosion has had little time to work on these volcanic peaks, some of which are still developing. As a result, this region includes

---

The world's largest natural crystals[3]

Early in 2001, news emerged of a truly extraordinary discovery in 300 m deep caverns in the state of Chihuahua. Miners tunneling through the Naica Hills, south of Chihuahua City, in search of silver and zinc, found huge mineral crystals, far larger than any natural crystals previously seen anywhere on the planet.

The Naica Hills are comprised of 97 million year old (Early Cretaceous) limestones. Pressure from a chamber of superheated molten rock (magma) deep underground forced mineral-rich fluids upwards into cracks in the limestone. Over time, deposition from these fluids filled the cracks with sulfide-rich ores of metals such as gold, silver, lead and zinc.

Caves formed in some places, providing the perfect habitat for monster sword-shaped crystals, some over 6 meters long. The crystals are made of selenite, a crystalline form of the mineral gypsum, the main ingredient in blackboard chalk. The air temperature in the main cave is a suffocating 60°C (140°F). The owners hope that eventually this will become an important geo-tourist attraction.

Geologists are still debating precisely how such large crystals could form. Did they grow very slowly in pre-existing steam-filled caverns as a direct result of the same hydrothermal fluids that formed the ore deposits, or were they formed later from the slow percolation of rainwater through the surrounding limestone?

Mexico's highest mountains, reaching over 5500 m or 18,000 ft. Thick, lava-rich volcanic soils make this one of the most fertile areas in North America. Though the area is very rugged, it has supported relatively high population densities for hundreds of years, including the current large metropolitan areas of Mexico City, Guadalajara, and Puebla. Legacies of previous volcanic activity are found in craters, mud-volcanoes, geothermal activity, and the numerous hot springs (and spa towns) scattered throughout the Volcanic Axis.

11 Southern Sierra Madre (Sierra Madre del Sur)

This complex region is an area of considerable seismic activity. High mountains composed of a variety of different rock types hug the coastline and extend from near Puerto Vallarta in the north to Tehuantepec in the state of Oaxaca in the south. The peaks normally rise to about 2000 m (6500 ft), with a few as high as 3000 m (10,000 ft). Sections of these older volcanic peaks have been seriously eroded, leaving a very dissected and rugged landscape with limited flat land. Broader accessible valleys such as the Oaxaca Valley are densely settled. This region also includes the rugged yet fertile Balsas basin, which stretches almost 600 km (400 mi) through Guerrero and Michoacán. Despite the preponderance of mountains, there are some excellent natural harbors such as Acapulco. The Southern Sierra Madre is a serious barrier to transportation, though the Spaniards did manage to build an acceptable route south from Mexico City to Acapulco. This passage enabled Spanish galleons to bring the riches of Asia to the port of Acapulco for onward transport overland by pack mule to Mexico City and Veracruz for shipment back to Spain.

12 Southern Gulf Coast Plain

This plain of marine and fluvial sediments narrows in the north to about 16 km (10 mi) in Veracruz, where a small island provides some protection for ocean vessels but widens considerably further south in Tabasco. Deep alluvial deposits have accumulated in the adjacent deltas of some of Mexico's largest rivers, including the Grijalva-Usumacinta, the Coatzacoalcos and the Papaloapan. These extensive deltas, crossed by numerous braided, meandering river channels, are year-round marshes, posing challenges for permanent settlement but offering potentially rich, fertile soils if drainage schemes are carried out. The flood

The world's deepest water-filled sinkhole[4]

The El Zacatón sinkhole on El Rancho Azufrosa, near the town of Aldama in Tamaulipas, is the deepest water-filled sinkhole anywhere on the planet. A 2007 NASA-funded study proved that it is a staggering 335 m (1099 ft) deep. The sinkhole is one of several located in the same general area, though they apparently share no underground connections. The surface of the lake is 16 m below the sinkhole's rim; the lake is 319 m deep at its deepest point.

Most sinkholes form as a result of the collapse of the ceilings of underground cavities which have formed from the gradual dissolution of limestone due to percolating acidic rainwater. However, volcanism is thought to have played a major part in the formation of El Zacatón. The pit began to form in the Pleistocene period when subterranean volcanic activity increased the acidity of water deep underground. This acidic water then gradually ate away at the surrounding limestone in a process known as hypogenic karstification. As the underground caverns grew larger, the overlying rock ceiling periodically collapsed, eventually leaving giant pits extending to the surface above.

risk is high in many parts of this region, including in the city of Villahermosa, the state capital of Tabasco. Along the coast, the marine processes of littoral drift and deposition have smoothed the coastline, creating a series of long and very narrow sandbars and sandspits, such as that protecting the Laguna de Términos. The coastal plains are interrupted between Coatzacoalcos and Veracruz by the volcanic Sierra de los Tuxtlas, which has numerous small cones, and a 10 km diameter volcanic caldera, the largest in Mexico, now occupied by Lake Catemaco.

13 Sierra Madre de Chiapas

This region, also known as the Central American range, extends across Mexico's border into Guatemala and Central America. Apart from a narrow coastal plain, it is mainly volcanic mountains which have resisted erosion. While most peaks are near 1500 m (5000 ft), the Tacaná Volcano, near the Guatemala border is over 4000 m (13,000 ft).

The western boundary of this region, where it meets the Southern Sierra Madre, coincides with the Isthmus of Tehuantepec, which was lifted out of the ocean only during the past few million years, and where the land is much flatter and lower. This natural gap in the mountains is exploited by both a railroad and a highway to link the Pacific coast with the Southern Gulf Coast Plain. Several proposals have been made to construct either an advanced intermodal transportation system or a canal across this narrow 250 km long isthmus; either would almost certainly take traffic away from the Panama Canal further south.

14 Chiapas Highlands

The Chiapas Highlands, which also extend into Guatemala, are composed largely of limestones and sandstones. Prior to the construction of the Pan American highway, this relatively rugged area was quite isolated. Trending northwest to southeast through these highlands are several valleys, including the Chiapas Valley, drained by the headwaters of the River Grijalva, which has been dammed to create the massive Angostura reservoir. Another dam on the Grijalva, close to Tuxtla Gutierrez, is responsible for the flooding of the lower parts of the impressive Sumidero Canyon.

15 Yucatán Peninsula

This low, flat limestone platform is the most recently formed part of Mexico. The low topography, which is quite similar to western Cuba and southern Florida, is virtually all below 150 m (500 ft). The submerged western and northern portion of this platform is known as the Campeche Bank. The peninsula was connected to Cuba until the bridging section sank below sea level forming the Yucatán Channel. The west and north coasts are marked by lagoons, mangrove swamps and sand bars. The emergence and infilling of coastal lagoons in the southeastern and southwestern extremities of the peninsula have resulted in areas of marshland interspersed with remnants of the original lagoons.

Offshore to the east lie coral reefs. Most of the peninsula has shallow, highly permeable soils and virtually no surface water. However, underground water is relatively abundant. The peninsula is honeycombed with extensive underground cave systems, which are connected periodically to the surface via hundreds of natural sinkholes (*cenotes*). The ancient Maya believed that these *cenotes* led to the underworld.

Diversity of landforms

This sweeping account of Mexico's major relief regions fails to do justice to the extraordinary variety of landforms that can be found in many parts of the country. Superimposed on top of the general relief pattern are innumerable smaller-scale features, where rain, rivers, wind and the sea (and even glaciers) have done their creative work. Plateaus have been dissected to leave mesas, buttes and pinnacles. Changes of base level in many parts of the country have produced river terraces and drowned valleys. Several areas of Mexico are noted for their limestone karst scenery and landforms, including some spectacular cave formations such as stalagmites, rimstone and flowstone. They include San Luis Potosí, Colima, Oaxaca, Chiapas and the Yucatán Peninsula. Varied desert landforms enliven the otherwise monotonous scenery of Mexico's barren northern deserts. Along the coast, sand dunes, salt marshes and mangrove swamps hide behind sand spits, tombolos and sand bars; elsewhere, majestic cliffs tower over protected inlets and offshore islands, or broad sandy beaches give way to dense stands of palm trees. Off the Quintana Roo coast, the northern section of the longest coral reef in the northern hemisphere attracts diving enthusiasts from all over the world.

4

Land of diverse climates

Mexico is a land of sunshine, so talking about the day's weather is not as common as it is in Canada or the USA. Within the tropics, the difference between summer and winter temperatures is relatively small. Indeed, it is often smaller than the diurnal difference between daytime and nighttime temperatures. This means that terms such as summer and winter lose some of their significance. More important in almost all of Mexico are the terms dry season and rainy season.

Mexico's daily weather does not vary with the same rapidity as many places at higher latitudes. Nevertheless, daily weather readings of temperature, humidity, wind, and precipitation allow for weather forecasts to be made. Compiling and averaging weather data over an extended period of time allows longer-term generalizations to be made about an area's climate. In addition to monthly averages of high and low temperatures, wind speeds and direction, humidity and rainfall, any discussion of climate must also consider the probabilities of specific extreme weather events such as hurricanes, floods and droughts.

The major determinants of weather and climate in Mexico are its latitudinal position astride the Tropic of Cancer, its considerable variations of altitude above sea level, its relatively narrow shape which allows oceanic influences to play a part, and continental-scale pressure and wind patterns. Superimposed on the big picture are innumerable local variations in topography and land use that help to create an amazing mosaic of climates.

Mexico has an immense diversity of weather, climate and ecosystems. It is one of five countries in the world that have tropical rainforests, high elevation frigid mountains and dry deserts. On any given day weather conditions vary enormously from one end of the country to the other.

This chapter first looks at the main factors influencing weather and climate in Mexico. We then take a closer look at the national patterns of temperatures and precipitation before examining climatic hazards, climatic regions and climate change.

Latitude and solar energy

Perhaps the most important climatic factor is latitude. It tends to be warmer closer to the equator. In general, the farther from the equator, the lower the sun is in the sky, and the incoming solar energy is spread over a wider area resulting in a lower temperature. About 50% of the solar radiation is absorbed by land and water and re-radiated. Another 20% is absorbed by airborne particles, dust and clouds. The remaining 30% is reflected by clouds, dust particles and the earth itself. Air temperatures depend on the re-radiation of heat from the earth's surface, rather than direct heating by sunlight. Greenhouse gases in the atmosphere trap some of the incoming energy as well as some of the re-radiated energy.

Figure 4.1 shows how the effect of latitude on temperature is most marked in January when temperatures in southern Mexico are much warmer than in northern Mexico. In May (Figure 4.2), all areas are warmer because this is the start of the period when the northern hemisphere receives most solar energy (summer). Most of Mexico experiences maximum temperatures in May, immediately before the start of the rainy season. The effects of latitude are still apparent, even if much less clear.

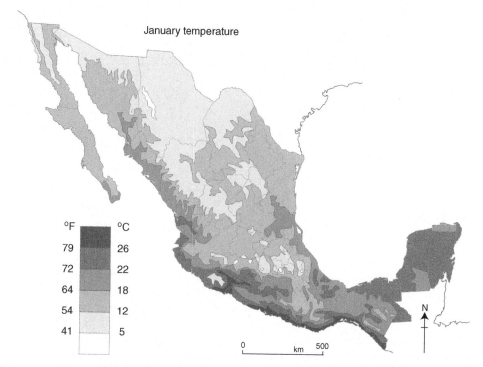

January temperature

°F	°C
79	26
72	22
64	18
54	12
41	5

0   km   500

N

Figure 4.1 Mean January temperatures in Mexico[1]

Latitude is clearly only part of the explanation for differences in temperatures. Mexico and the Sahara Desert are at the same latitude and receive about the same amount of sunlight. Why is Mexico so much cooler? To answer this, we must look at additional factors that affect climate.

Altitude and temperatures

Elevation above sea level plays a very important role in determining temperature. The air at low elevations has greater density and can hold considerably more heat than the thinner air at higher altitudes. For every 1000 m gain in elevation, the temperature declines on average by 6.4°C (3.5°F for every 1000 ft).

Most of Mexico is above 1000 m (about 3300 ft) in elevation; as a result most of Mexico has a more temperate climate than might be expected given its latitude. The effects of altitude are readily apparent in Figures 4.1 and 4.2.

The famous explorer Alexander von Humboldt, one of the founding fathers of physical geography and meteorology, was the first to describe the vertical differentiation of climatic and vegetation zones in Mexico. Writing in 1811, he proposed the terms

tierra caliente, tierra templada, and *tierra fría*, still widely used by non-specialists today.

Tierra caliente (hot land) includes all areas under about 900 m (3000 ft). These areas generally have a mean annual temperature above 25°C (77°F). Their natural vegetation is usually either tropical evergreen or tropical deciduous forest. Farms produce tropical crops such as sugar-cane and bananas.

Tierra templada (temperate land) is the area between 900 and 1800 m (3000 to 6000 ft) where mean annual temperatures are usually between about 18°C and 25°C (64°F to 77°F). The natural vegetation in these zones is temperate forest, such as oak and pine-oak forest. Farms grow crops such as corn (maize), wheat and coffee.

Tierra fría (cold land) is over 1800 m (6000 ft) where mean annual temperatures are in the range 13°–18°C (55°–64°F). At these altitudes pine and pine-fir forests are common. Farm crops include barley and potatoes. On the highest mountain tops, above the *tierra fría* is *tierra helada*, frozen land.

A comparison of relief and temperature maps (Figures 3.1, 4.1 and 4.2) shows that these elevation categories work quite well. The precise elevation of each zone is slightly lower in northern Mexico, to compen-

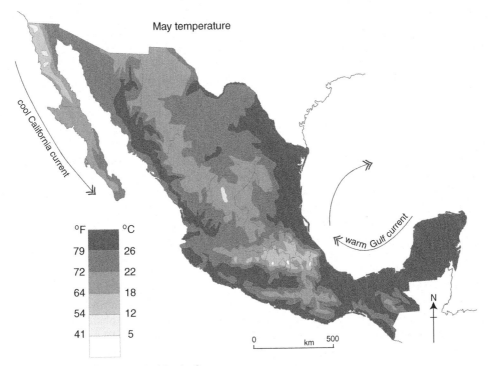

Figure 4.2 Mean May temperatures in Mexico[2]

sate for latitudinal effects, than in southern Mexico. Similarly, the height of any particular zone often differs slightly on either side of a mountain range.

This brief discussion of mean annual temperatures does not tell us anything about the variation of temperatures from season to season. In general, areas nearer the equator have smaller seasonal temperature variations. For example, in the southern cities of Chilpancingo, Oaxaca, Tuxtla Gutiérrez and Chetumal, summer temperatures are only about 3°C (5°F) above winter levels. In contrast, the difference in average summer and winter temperatures in the northern Mexican cities of Hermosillo, Chihuahua and Monterrey is about 15°C (27°F).

Mexicali, one of Mexico's northernmost cities, has an average July temperature of a very hot 33°C (91°F). The average July high is 40°C (104°F) compared to a low of 26°C (79°F). The average in January is only 12°C (54°F). The seasonal variation of 21°C (38°F) is the highest in the country. Contributing to this variation is the fact that cloud cover is significantly greater in winter compared to summer. For most areas in Mexico, cloud cover is more intense in summer than winter, therefore diminishing seasonal temperature variations.

Continentality

Continentality, or distance from a major ocean, also affects climate. Water absorbs and stores solar energy far more effectively than land. The sun's rays penetrate water, heating areas below the surface. The energy stored in the water during the day and during summer is re-radiated, slowly, during the night and winter. On the other hand, the sun's rays do not penetrate land; consequently, the heat remains mostly on the surface, and is quickly re-radiated. In addition, the air in coastal areas tends to be more humid which also moderates diurnal temperature changes. In sum, oceans have a strong tempering effect on air temperatures. They keep summer and daytime temperatures relatively low as the sun's energy is being absorbed by the water, but they also keep winter and night temperatures relatively warm as the absorbed solar energy is slowly released.

As a result of continentality, as well as elevation, inland areas of Mexico experience far higher temperature extremes than coastal areas. The highest reported (but unverified) temperature in Mexico was 59°C (138°F) at the arid inland town of Nazas in western Durango in May 1969. If true, it would be the world record high. The coldest town temperature of –23°C (–9°F) occurred in January 1992 in Villa Ahumada in northern Chihuahua. Both of these extreme temperatures occurred in arid locations, far away from the tempering influence of oceans.

Ocean currents

Ocean currents have a significant effect on climates. Warm ocean currents tend to bring warm and humid air with them to coastal areas. Cold ocean currents are associated with cooler, drier air. In Mexico, the most important ocean current is the cold California Current off the west coast, which has a significant cooling and drying impact on the coast of the Baja Peninsula. The impact of this current can be seen by looking at the summer temperatures of Tijuana, on the coast, and Mexicali, just 160 km (100 mi) inland. When the summer afternoon temperature on the beach in Tijuana is 26°C (79°F), the temperature in Mexicali may be 40°C (104°F). The warm ocean currents on Mexico's south coast and in the Gulf of Mexico raise the temperatures, humidity and rainfall slightly in those areas.

The Hadley cell and prevailing winds

Winds result from differences in air pressure, which are related to variations in the weight of air. Cold air is heavier and sinks; lighter warm air tends to rise. Winds normally flow from high pressure areas to low pressure areas. Sometimes the difference in pressure is slight over vast areas, and the winds are gentle. At other times, the pressure difference is great and distances are short, resulting in high wind velocities.

The driving force behind much of Mexico's weather and climate is the Hadley cell. As we have seen, solar heating is at a maximum near the equator and diminishes towards the poles. The area near the equator is the Intertropical Convergence Zone or ITCZ. The heating of the ITCZ makes the air rise, leaving an area of low pressure on the surface. This low pressure sucks in air along the earth's surface from the subtropical high pressure areas about 30°N and S of the equator creating the trade winds. The trade winds pick up moisture and latent heat over the oceans before converging from either side of the equator in the ITCZ. As the air in the ITCZ rises vertically, its water vapor condenses and rain falls from the towering convective clouds. This is the ascending limb of the Hadley cell. At a height of 10–15 km above the surface, the air, now minus its moisture, returns polewards as high level anti-trade winds. Sunbathers on Mexican beaches who notice two sets of clouds above them at different heights traveling in opposite directions are witnessing the trade winds and anti-trade winds in action.

In the subtropics, this air then descends again towards the surface to complete the cell and initiates the surface trade winds again. The descending air warms up as it sinks; its relative humidity decreases, and so no precipitation occurs; hence these high pressure subtropical areas are arid. The subtropical high is also the source of the so-called westerly winds which flow from the southwest starting at the subtropical high and toward the subpolar low, about 60°N latitude.

The precise direction of the trade winds is complicated by the spinning of the earth. Winds in the northern hemisphere tend to curve to the right as they blow from high towards low pressure areas; in the southern hemisphere, winds curve to the left. This explains why the trade winds, trying to blow directly towards the equator from the subtropical highs become north-east and south-east trade winds respectively.

Local winds

Local winds occur wherever pressure differences are sufficiently large. Mountains can have a pronounced effect. Cold air tends to accumulate over mountains and at night often slides down into valleys, resulting in cool night breezes. During the day, the situation may be reversed, especially near the coast when onshore coastal breezes transfer air from the ocean to the land.

Precipitation

Warm air absorbs water through evaporation from nearby bodies of water and through evapotranspiration from plants. The amount of water the air holds compared to the maximum amount it can hold at that temperature is the relative humidity. If warm moist air rises, it will cool. As it cools, its relative humidity rises. If relative humidity reaches 100% and condensation nuclei (particles such as dust or contaminants) are present, then water vapor will condense out of the air to form clouds. As clouds develop, water molecules coalesce until individual drops are heavy enough to fall out of the cloud as precipitation. Ice crystals fall as snow, water falls as raindrops, frozen ice pellets fall as hail.

For precipitation to occur, the weight of the individual drops must be sufficient for the effects of gravity to overcome the upwards thrust of the surrounding air. In very unstable conditions where air is rising rapidly, individual raindrops must become much larger before they can fall out of the cloud. The largest raindrops will have traveled up and down inside the cloud repeatedly, gaining size, before they finally fall to the ground. The same principle applies to hailstorms which gather an additional layer of ice for every trip they make inside the cloud before falling. In Mexico, most precipitation falls as rain, though snowfalls are not uncommon in parts of northern Mexico or at the highest elevations.

Though Mexico is considered to be relatively arid, the country as a whole receives an average of about 760 mm (30 in) of rain per year. This is a considerable amount of precipitation, almost exactly the same amount as Toronto, and considerably more than the average for Canada as a whole or the USA.

The three basic types of rainfall are all very apparent in Mexico. Convectional rain is associated with hot afternoons. During the morning, warm air near the surface collects great quantities of moisture. As temperatures increase towards mid-day, pockets of moist warm air are sent upwards, quickly leading to condensation and clouds. As the clouds continue to rise, they cool to the point where precipitation becomes inevitable. Afternoon and evening rain showers result, often heavy and accompanied by thunder and lightening. Convectional rain occurs throughout Mexico but is a summer phenomenon since this is the time of year when solar radiation and ground heating is at a maximum. The effects of convectional rain are enhanced by the presence at that time over southern Mexico of the Intertropical Convergence Zone, a broad belt of generally rising air which migrates seasonally either side of the equator.

Orographic rainfall, the second type of rainfall, is associated with mountains. Mountains block the movement of clouds and force them to rise. This has a profound impact on precipitation. As the clouds rise, further condensation occurs and precipitation becomes extremely likely, as they cool to the point where they can no longer hold their moisture. Therefore, it rains a great deal on the windward or wet side of the range. By the time the air passes over the mountain range to the other side, it has lost much of its moisture. As it descends, it warms up and its relative humidity falls, so that there is little chance of any precipitation on the leeward side, known as the rain shadow.

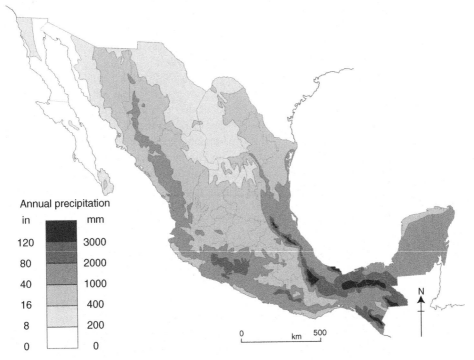

Annual precipitation

in	mm
120	3000
80	2000
40	1000
16	400
8	200
0	0

N

0   km   500

Figure 4.3 Precipitation in Mexico[3]

For example, the summer north-east trade winds blow moist clouds from the Gulf of Mexico towards the Southern Sierra Madre and Chiapas Highlands. The eastern side of these mountains receives heavy rainfall. The mountain slopes in central Veracruz, eastern Oaxaca and parts of Chiapas have about 150 cloudy days and get about 2000 mm (80 in) of rain a year. However, the western slopes get only half as much rain and have only 90 cloudy days a year. Orographic precipitation sets virtually all the rainfall and snowfall records, even more than hurricanes. Tenango, Oaxaca is the rainiest place in Mexico; it receives about 5000 mm (16.4 ft) of rain each year.

The orientation of mountain ranges is therefore critical to understanding precipitation patterns. The differences between windward and leeward sides of a mountain range can be very dramatic. For instance, El Chico and Pachuca in the state of Hidalgo are only 10 km apart but have 1500 and 400 mm of precipitation respectively each year.

The third type of rainfall is called cyclonic or frontal precipitation. This is the form of precipitation brought by the mid-latitude storms known as *nortes*, and the tropical storms that sometimes evolve into hurricanes, which we discuss in more detail below.

Distribution and timing of precipitation

While Mexico taken as a whole gets enough rainfall, the main problem is distribution. In general the north and central plateaus are dry while the southeast receives by far the most rain. Parts of Tabasco, Northern Chiapas and Veracruz get over 4000 mm (160 in) of rain a year. This is a direct effect of the onshore north-east trade winds, which collect moisture as they cross the Gulf of Mexico and then deposit it as they reach land.

Average annual rainfall figures conceal great differences from one year to the next. In general, the variability of rainfall is indirectly proportional to the long-term average. This means that areas with low totals tend to experience high variability, greatly increasing their drought hazard.

Why do parts of northern Mexico receive very little precipitation, making them deserts? The major reason is that the zone between the Tropic of Cancer (latitude 23.5°N) and latitude 30°N is the descending air segment of the Hadley Cell. As we saw earlier, high level anti-trade winds eventually descend towards the surface in the subtropics. The descending air is warming up as it sinks, so its relative humidity

is decreasing and no condensation or precipitation will occur, hence these high pressure subtropical areas are arid—deserts.

The climate of the west coast of Baja is influenced by the cool Californian current, which runs south. The relative humidity of the air above it drops as the current enters warmer waters, so it is not likely to bring rain to the peninsula.

The marked division into a wet and a dry season that characterizes most of Mexico means that most places get almost all their rain between June and October, while January through May are dry months. Because most rainfall is in the summer months, about 71% of rainfall evaporates soon after falling. This figure can be even higher in urban areas. Only about 26% runs off into rivers and lakes, and 3% seeps down to recharge subterranean aquifers.

Except for the extreme north-west corner of Baja California. which has a Mediterranean climate regime where summers are dry and most rain falls in winter, winter months elsewhere in Mexico are dry. Southern and central Mexico have markedly dry winters, receiving less than 5% of their annual precipitation totals in the first three months of the year. The northern half of Mexico and the eastern coastal strip, including the Yucatán peninsula, have slightly more balanced precipitation, receiving between 5 and 18% of annual totals between January and March.

Climatic hazards
Hurricanes

Hurricanes (also called tropical cyclones or typhoons) are powerful tropical storms originating over the ocean that can have devastating consequences when they make landfall. Hurricanes originate on both sides of Mexico, in the Atlantic and in the Pacific. The Pacific Ocean storms, which are generally considered less dangerous, are especially prone to hit the coasts of Baja California and Sonora, but can cause damage anywhere on the Pacific coast. The Atlantic hurricanes cross the Caribbean Sea and are especially destructive.

Hurricanes form over warm ocean waters from July to October. They are violent low-pressure (cyclonic) systems, up to 150 km across, which whip the winds up, often to speeds approaching 300 kph (200 mph) (Table 4.1). The storms spiral counterclockwise, pulling surrounding air into a vortex, composed of a tight wall of cloud around a cloud-free eye. They suck up vast quantities of moist air,

Table 4.1 Recent severe hurricanes affecting Mexico[4]

Year	Storm name	States affected	Strength	Max. wind km/hr
1967	Beulah	Tamaulipas	H5	260
1976	Liza	Baja California Sur, Sinaloa, Sonora	H4	220
1976	Madeline	Guerrero	H4	232
1988	Gilbert	Quintana Roo, Yucatán	H5	270
1989	Kiko	Baja California Sur, Sonora	H3	195
1990	Diana	Veracruz	H2	158
1992	Virgil	Michoacán	H2	175
1993	Calvin	Jalisco	H2	167
1997	Pauline	Oaxaca, Guerrero,	H4	215
1998	Mitch	Chiapas, Quintana Roo, Campeche, Tabasco, Yucatán	H5	285
2002	Isidore	Quintana Roo	H3	205
2002	Kenna	Jalisco, Nayarit	H5	265
2005	Emily	Quintana Roo	H4	240
2005	Wilma	Quintana Roo	H5	250
2006	John	Baja California	H4	215
2006	Lane	Sinaloa	H3	190
2007	Dean	Quintana Roo, Campeche, Veracruz, Hidalgo, Puebla, Querétaro	H5	270 (gusts to 350)
2009	Jimena	Baja California Sur, Sonora	H4	215

which is pushed upward by the wind, where it cools and drops enormous amounts of rain. Atlantic hurricanes move generally westwards, gaining energy from tropical waters; their paths tend to bend more and more to their right as they go, so that some will eventually double back on themselves across Florida.

Besides extremely high winds, hurricanes bring sea surges, very heavy rains and serious flooding. If hurricane warnings are ignored and people do not evacuate their homes to find emergency shelters, the loss of life can be considerable.

Even with preparations, property damage from a direct hit invariably runs into millions of dollars. Further damage results from tidal waves striking the coast and flooding, which can extend for hundreds of kilometers inland, destroying highways and rail lines. Port facilities often bear the brunt of the storms as they rip through breakwaters and decimate protective mangrove swamps and palm groves. The single state which suffers from most hurricanes is Quintana Roo.

Northers

Mid-latitude storms known as *nortes* (northers) disturb the normal weather patterns up to 20 times a year during winter, from November to March. They occur when northern polar air moves south into northern and central Mexico. They bring low pressure (cyclonic) conditions, heralded by the arrival of a cold front. The polar air displaces the warmer surface air, forcing it to rise as the cool air pushes its way underneath. At the surface, a sudden drop in temperature and the advent of cold winds marks the passage of the front, followed by several days of overcast skies with light rains or drizzle, onomatopoeically called *chipichipis* in some areas. Rains from *nortes* are heavier on the northern or eastern sides of mountains where the cool air is forced to rise. As the front passes, the temperature can drop by 5–8°C (9–14°F) in a few hours. From an agricultural perspective these rains are a welcome sight for farmers, helping to improve grazing land and reduce the chances of wind-blown soil erosion. However, the winds can play havoc with shipping in the Gulf of Mexico and result in ports being temporarily closed. Veracruz and Tampico are regularly affected.

La Niña and El Niño

These are major periodic disturbances to the normal oceanic and atmospheric circulation patterns over the Pacific Ocean which have widespread effects around the world. The normal circulation in the equatorial Pacific (the Walker circulation cell) results from a low pressure area over the western Pacific (due to warm surface ocean temperatures) and a high pressure area over the eastern Pacific (due to the upwelling of cold ocean water off the coast of Ecuador). Surface trade winds blow from east to west, while high altitude air flow is from west to east.

A La Niña event is an intensification of the normal Walker cell. This results in warmer and drier conditions than normal.

However, during an El Niño Southern Oscillation (ENSO) event, the Walker circulation pattern is essentially reversed. Early in the year, warm ocean water extends much further east, causing warm moist air to rise off the coast of South and Central America, bringing heavy rainfall to areas along the west coast of Mexico. The El Niño in 1998 raised the temperature of water off Mexico's Pacific coast by some 3° to 5°C (6° to 9°F) and also increased the humidity considerably. Historically, ENSO events have occurred every four to seven years, but their frequency may now be increasing.

The effects of an ENSO event are also felt on the Gulf coast. The low pressure area resulting from the air rising off the western coast causes air from further east to be dragged across Mexico. This means that more cold fronts or *nortes* enter north and central Mexico. Winter precipitation in these areas increases significantly, especially in the north, and

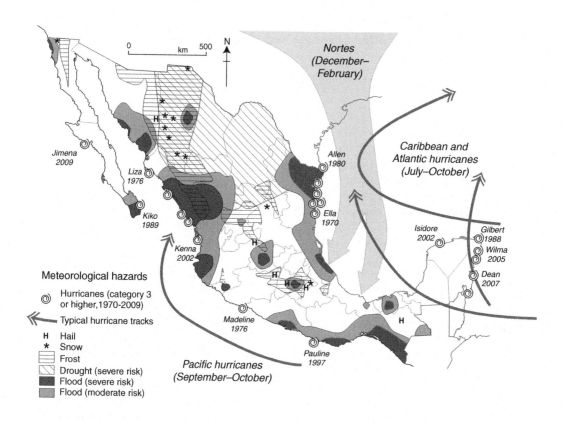

Figure 4.4 Climatic hazards[5]

temperatures are much cooler than usual. Flooding can result in coastal areas. ENSO effects are also felt in other parts of the world.

In Mexico, ENSO events not only affect winter precipitation but also summer precipitation, which is more critical for farmers. This is because they push the equatorial Intertropical Convergence Zone (ITCZ), where the north-east and south-east trade winds meet, further south. This reduces the convective activity and rainfall in Mexico's central highlands. Furthermore, this may reduce cloud cover and therefore increase solar radiation and evapotranspiration, making the ground even drier.[6]

In summary, subsistence corn (maize) farmers find that their cooler, wetter winter than normal is immediately followed by a hotter and drier summer growing season. This can have disastrous consequences for their food security. The rapid onset of changed conditions does not allow much time for adequate adjustments to be made to their choice of crops or farming methods.

Historical analysis combined with greater climatological understanding shows that many of the worst droughts and floods in Mexico have been associated with either ENSO events or with the related Pacific-North American Oscillation. Perhaps 65% of the variability of Mexican climate results from changes in these large-scale circulations.[7]

Figure 4.4 shows the location of various climatic hazards, including droughts and floods which are discussed further in the next chapter.

Climatic regions

Climatologists have developed several scientific systems to classify climates. The system developed by Wladimir Köppen in the early 20th century is one of the earliest and best known. The Köppen climate classification system assumes that climate is best reflected in native vegetation and can be accurately classified using seasonal variations in temperatures and precipitation. Mexican climatologists, including Enriqueta García, have proposed minor modifications to the Köppen system to make it more appropriate for Mexico. The following paragraphs reflect García's revised Köppen system.[8]

Given that Mexico has many mountains with rapid changes in elevation, temperature and rainfall, applying the Köppen system, even as modified by García, to Mexico can become extremely complicated. A relatively small area of Mexico may include several Köppen climate categories. Aggregating these areas provides a less complicated, more understandable, picture of Mexico's climates (Figure 4.5).

Two tropical climates

Mexico has two tropical climates which have average temperatures of over 18°C (64°F) for all twelve months of the year.

The first, tropical wet (Af in the Köppen system, see Figure 4.3), has at least 60 mm (2.4 in) of rain in every month of the year. This is the climate of the Amazon and Indonesian rainforests. In Mexico this is the climate of the Gulf Coast Plain in southern Veracruz and Tabasco (classic *tierra caliente* areas). It also occurs in the Oaxaca and Chiapas highlands (Figure 4.5). The rains fall all year, varying from about 120–150 mm (4–5 in) in April to 380 mm (15 in) in September.

The tropical wet-and-dry (Aw) category (Figure 4.6 shows the climate graph for Cancún) has a pronounced dry season. The dry winter months typically get less than 40 mm (1 in) of rain, compared to over 150 mm (6 in) in each of the summer months. Parts of West Africa, Brazil and India have a similar climate. Much of coastal Mexico, stretching from Nayarit along the Pacific coast all the way to Guatemala, is in this category. It also covers many inland areas along the Pacific coast. Central and northern Veracruz and most of the Yucatán Peninsula also have this tropical climate with summer rains.

Two dry climates

Areas with an arid (desert) climate (BW) usually receive less than 250 mm (10 in) of rain a year (Figure 4.6 has the climate graph for Ciudad Juárez). This is the climate of the Sahara Desert and Central Australia. In Mexico dry desert areas include most of Baja California, western Sonora, and the northern section of the Central Plateau. These areas can experience frost and freezing during the winter.

Areas with the second type of arid climate, semi-arid (dry steppe) (BS), receive 250–750 mm (10–30 in) of rain a year. This is the climate of the African savanna lands and much of central Asia.

In Mexico, this climate region includes most of the Central Plateau as well as western sections of the Western Sierra Madre, northern Yucatán and scattered inland areas as far south as Oaxaca. The rains in this region fall mostly in the summer, and localized heavy thunderstorms are quite common.

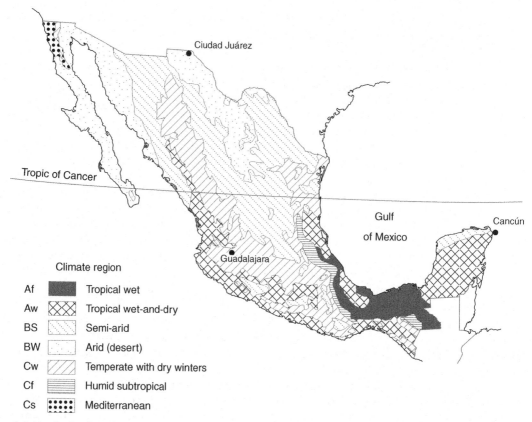

Figure 4.5 Mexico's climatic regions⁹

Climate region

Af		Tropical wet
Aw		Tropical wet-and-dry
BS		Semi-arid
BW		Arid (desert)
Cw		Temperate with dry winters
Cf		Humid subtropical
Cs		Mediterranean

The southern parts of this climatic region are warmer than the northern parts.

Three temperate zones

Temperate climates typically have average temperatures above 10°C (50°F) in their warmest months, and a coldest month average between 3°C and 18°C (27–64°F). Moisture characteristics distinguish between the three temperate climates.

The temperate with dry winters climate (Cw) is characterized by mild temperatures, low humidity, and summer rainfall ranging from about 600 to 1200mm (25–45 in) per year (climate graph for Guadalajara is in Figure 4.6). This is classic *tierra templada* country. The low nighttime temperatures in winter are typically around 5°C (41°F). Of course, higher elevations have lower temperatures with occasional frost. The highest temperatures usually reach about 35°C (95°F), though temperatures may reach as high as 40°C (104°F). This climate is similar to that of the Kenyan Highlands. In Mexico, this climate includes parts of Nuevo León and Tamaulipas,

most of the Western Sierra Madre and many mountainous areas in western, central and southern Mexico. Most of the Volcanic Axis is in this temperate with dry winters zone. Here, the major control as far as temperatures are concerned is altitude, which directly affects precise rainfall amounts and seasonality, resulting in a mosaic of microclimates and natural vegetation regions (see next chapter).

Compared with the temperate with dry winters climate, the humid subtropical (Cf) zone gets more rainfall, is more humid and gets rain throughout the year. The only areas of Mexico with this climate are the eastern slopes of the Eastern Sierra Madre and some parts of the southern mountain systems.

The Mediterranean climate (Cs) is the mild climate associated with Europe's Mediterranean coast as well as the California coast. The area around Tijuana is the only part of Mexico with this type of climate. This area is relatively arid and gets less than 400 mm (15 in) of rain a year; it is unique in Mexico, being the only place that is dry in summer and gets rain only in winter.

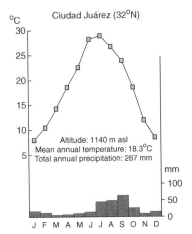
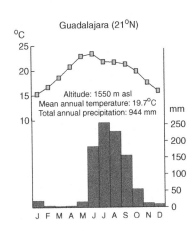
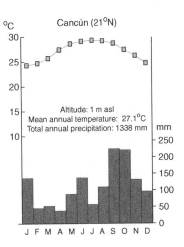

Figure 4.6 Climate graphs for three cities[10]

Climate change in cities

As large urban areas grow in size, they change their local climate in various ways. The best known effect is that called the urban heat island: the air above cities is significantly warmer than the surrounding air in suburban and rural areas. People, homes, vehicles and factories all emit heat which becomes trapped immediately above the city. The difference in temperature is most noticeable just before sunrise. The irregular built-up surfaces of cities absorb and trap more heat than vegetated areas.

Wind speeds in cities tend to be lower than in their rural outskirts. Precipitation tends to be slightly higher, as a result of the additional heat energy, which causes mid-afternoon instability, and because city air has higher concentrations of particulates (dust, smog, contaminants) from vehicles and factories.

Mexican cities are no exception. The urban heat island differential has risen by an average of 0.44°C per decade for large cities (population over one million), and by 0.37°C per decade for mid-sized cities (population between 150,000 and 1,000,000). These rates are clearly greater than the background effect of global warming, variously estimated at between 0.07 and 0.20°C a decade.

There is no doubt that accelerated urbanization has warmed and is continuing to warm urban air, affecting the comfort levels of millions of people. The cities where urban temperatures have risen most rapidly are Torreón, which warmed at a rate of 1.2°C per decade from 1952–1998 and Guadalajara, where temperatures rose by 0.74°C a decade from 1920–1997.[11]

The case of Mexico City shows an additional complication. At the end of the 19th century, comparing minimum temperatures, Mexico City (population then 400,000) was about 1.5°C warmer than surrounding areas. This difference had risen dramatically to about 9°C (16°F) by the 1980s.

Urbanization has certainly played a part, and its effects have perhaps been exacerbated by the city's unfortunate position in a basin, which traps air, heat and contamination. However, climate modeling suggests that the loss of lakes in the Valley of Mexico, including the draining of most of Lake Texcoco, has played at least as large a part in Mexico City's increased temperatures as the expansion of its urban area.[12]

In addition, the incidence of intense rain showers (those where more than 20 mm (0.8 in) falls per hour) in Mexico City has also risen steadily, from four a decade in the 1940s to twenty a decade in 1980s. There is, however, no convincing evidence that wet season rainfall totals have increased, despite the combination of increased temperatures and instability, and the higher number of particulates in the air from dust, vehicle exhausts and factories. Away from the edge of the city, precipitation appears to have declined. In summary, the expansion of Mexico City appears to have led to warmer, drier conditions in the Valley of Mexico.[13]

Urban areas also have distinctive effects on hydrology. The roads and buildings of cities form impermeable surfaces which reduce infiltration almost to zero and greatly increase surface runoff. The lag time between a rainstorm and peak discharge in stream channels is much less in urban areas than in their rural surroundings. This makes the likelihood of flooding (see chapter 23) much greater in urban areas. In most cities, surface runoff is channeled rapidly into gutters and drains (a form of high speed throughflow) in an effort to reduce flood risk.

Global climate change

The study of historical climatic changes in Mexico has produced some surprises. For instance, it is now believed by many archaeologists that slow changes of climate, to which local populations were unable to respond sufficiently rapidly, may have been at least partially responsible for the collapse of several ancient civilizations including the Teotihuacanos in central Mexico and the classic-period Maya in southern Mexico.

Climatic change has also played an important role in food availability for hundreds of years. It was at least partially responsible for the severity of droughts and floods, both of which caused prolonged periods of food scarcity on numerous occasions during colonial times.[14]

Climate change is here to stay, even if its effects are far from clear. It appears likely that global warming will increase the frequency of El Niño Southern Oscillation events as well as their duration. These changes will almost certainly have profound repercussions on the lives of many subsistence farmers, possibly leading to a drop in production for rainfed corn (maize) of between 20 and 60% if no adaptive actions are undertaken in advance.[15] In the central part of Veracruz, the frequency of extreme temperature and precipitation events has already increased, with serious implications for the area's water balance.[16]

Other concerns are sea level change and possible loss or salinization of low lying coastal areas, effects on soils, an increase in endangered species because of habitat change, the degree of resilience of major ecosystems, impacts on water availability and increased incidence of droughts, as well as the implementation, cost and effectiveness of potential remediation measures.

5

Ecosystems and biodiversity

Mexico's large area (about 2,000,000 km^2), its position astride the Tropic of Cancer and its geological history as a land bridge between continents, greatly enriches the diversity of species found within it. Northern Mexico falls in the Nearctic biogeographical region while southern Mexico is in the Neotropical region (Figure 5.1). Though some overlap of species occurs near the divide, each of these major ecozones has distinctive flora and fauna which developed in relative isolation over a long period of time.

Mexico has representative areas of virtually all the world's biomes. It is one of the most mega-diverse countries of the world, home to more than 10% of all the species on earth. Mexico's biodiversity is highest in its tropical southern areas including the coral reefs off the Quintana Roo coastline. Mexico has 30,000 different species of flora (many not yet formally identified), compared to 18,000 species in the USA and 12,000 species in Europe. Only Brazil, Colombia and possibly China have more. Some 9300 of these flowering plants (3.7% of the world total) exist only in Mexico.

Moreover, Mexico is first in the world for reptile species (707 in total, 368 of them unique to Mexico), second for mammals (491 species, including 136 found only in Mexico) and fourth for amphibians (292, of which 174 are endemic to Mexico). Mexico is also home to more than 2500 species of spiders (70% of them endemic) and 1100 species of birds.[1]

An ecosystem is the community of plants, animals and other living organisms living in an area, together with their interactions with each other and with their associated non-living (abiotic) components such as soil. In general, ecosystems tend to align roughly with climatic regions. But other things are important also, and considerable local variations can occur. In certain situations, precipitation may be extremely scarce, but vegetation can be lush if there is some other source of water, such as a desert oasis or broad river delta.

There are complex interrelationships between soils and ecosystems. The development and maintenance of soils are a function of numerous factors including: mechanical and chemical weathering of bedrock; decaying vegetation; the action of worms, algae and insects; temperature and moisture conditions; slope gradients and drainage; time for these processes to operate; and the influence of man and animals.

The pattern of ecosystems in Mexico is complicated by soil types, rugged topography and rapid changes in elevation. Mexico is one of the richest countries in the world in terms of ecosystem diversity. To avoid undue complexity, we will limit our discussion to five basic ecosystems: tropical evergreen forests, tropical deciduous forests, temperate forests, grasslands and, lastly, deserts and semi-arid scrubland. The boundaries between these ecosystems are not clear cut; the characteristics of two or more ecosystems may co-exist in the same relatively small area.

As we discuss the ecosystems shown in Figure 5.1, it is well worth comparing their distribution to the climate regions shown in Figure 4.5.

Soils

Soil science is a very specialist subject, but the following types of soil (presented in alphabetical order) all play a significant role in Mexico[2]:

Andosols have a dark upper horizon, loose texture, and are well drained soils which develop in areas of recent volcanic activity such as the Volcanic Axis. They are commonly found associated with pine-oak forests and are very susceptible to erosion.

Arenosols develop on sandy substrates and are widespread on the Baja California peninsula.

Calcisols (previously classified as xerosols) develop in the arid and semi-arid scrubland regions of northern Mexico. Their upper horizons are very poor in humus, and they are sometimes saline and often underlain by calcareous hardpans. They have a limited agricultural potential but can be productive if irrigated.

Fluvisols are very fertile soils developed on alluvial deposits. Gleysols are common in the Tabasco marshlands, in the areas where tropical evergreen forests are found. These soils are regularly waterlogged and are mottled blue and grey in color, though they may turn reddish when dry. Gleysols can be useful for crops that have heavy water demands; they are rarely susceptible to erosion.

Leptosols are poorly developed shallow soils, less than 30 cm deep, which are often subject to erosion. The upper layers have abundant humus and can be quite fertile. They include rendzic leptosols (formerly known as rendzinas) which develop on limestone. They are associated with the tropical evergreen forests of the Yucatán Peninsula and were the soils on which the ancient Maya developed their intensive agricultural systems.

Phaeozems are commonly found under pine-oak forests as well as under tropical deciduous and thorn forests. They have a dark-colored upper horizon, rich in organic matter and have a smooth texture. They are very useful for agriculture, but erosion can be a problem on steeper slopes.

Regosols are poorly developed soils found in areas like the Baja California desert and in some tropical deciduous and thorn forest regions where the parent material is largely unconsolidated. They are shallow with indistinct horizons and are usually light in color.

Vertisols form on clay-rich parent material in regions which have a marked dry season. Characterized by wide, deep cracks during the dry season, they occur in some sections along the Pacific Coastal Plain and also on the Northern Gulf Plain. Vertisols are black or grey in color, or occasionally reddish-brown. They are usually fertile and underlie many of Mexico's most productive sugar cane fields and citrus orchards.

Tropical evergreen forests

Tropical evergreen forests include a very wide diversity of species. Mature forests typically have well in excess of 100 different tree species per hectare. In areas with a marked winter dry season, trees range up to about 35 m (110 ft) in height and up to half the species may be deciduous, losing their leaves in the short dry season. In areas with year-round rains, broadleaf evergreen rainforest trees predominate and form a dense green canopy up to 50 m (160 ft) above the jungle floor. Below the canopy are shorter broadleaf plants and palms that form an intermediate level of treetops. Tree ferns, vines and epiphytes, including orchids, are abundant. Except in disturbed areas, shrubs and grasses are of minimal importance because little sunlight reaches the ground. In Mexico, these forests often include economically important trees such as mahogany, tropical cedar, rosewood, copal, silk-cotton and chicle, the original source for chewing gum. Many of these plants have characteristic buttress trunks, giving them stability in areas where the soils are generally fairly shallow.

Soils in these regions are not as fertile as the exuberant vegetation might suggest; nutrients are recycled rapidly in the hot, damp conditions, and relatively little organic material accumulates in the soil. Mexico's rainforests contain a wide range of fauna including howler and spider monkeys, jaguars, ocelots, tapirs, anteaters, deer, wild pigs and hundreds of birds and reptiles.

Tropical forests predominate in a broad band from northern Veracruz to southeastern Chiapas and Quintana Roo (Figure 5.1). They are also found

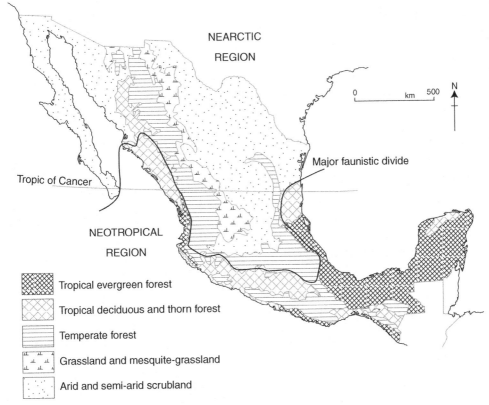

Figure 5.1 Mexico's principal natural ecosystems[3]

along the Pacific coast in Nayarit, Jalisco, Guerrero, Oaxaca and Chiapas. In many coastal locations, rainforests give way to swamps and mangrove thickets.

Tropical deciduous forests and thorn forests

These overlapping ecosystems predominate in drier, cooler areas than the tropical forests discussed above. Some areas may include groves of trees, but not nearly as dense or species-diverse as in tropical forests. Other areas are characterized by scattered trees and occasional cacti, interspersed with open areas of grasses and shrubs, many with thorns.

The trees generally are four to eight meters tall (13–26 ft) with some ranging up to 15 m (50 ft). Unlike tropical evergreen forests, these ecosystems usually only have a single arboreal stratum, containing hardwood trees like mesquite and oaks. These ecosystems have limited value for forestry but are important areas for agriculture and the production of several of the 200-plus species of agave.

Tropical deciduous forests predominate on the western side of the Western Sierra Madre in Sinaloa and eastern Sonora as well as in the Balsas basin

and along the nearby Pacific coast. Parts of Oaxaca, Chiapas, northern Yucatán, eastern San Luis Potosi and southern Tamaulipas also fall into this category.

Temperate forests

Temperate forests are found in areas that are generally drier, cooler and at higher elevation than tropical deciduous forests. These forests tend to be relatively open with grasses and shrubs between the trees. Oaks are abundant up to about 1500 m (5000 ft). Pines appear at about 1000 m (3300 ft) but are most abundant at elevations above 2000 m (6600 ft); individual trees can reach more than 30 m (110 ft) in height. Firs become dominant at about 2400 m. Forests of pine and fir exist up to the timberline, which is usually at about 4000 m (13,000 ft).

More than 48 distinct species of pine tree have been recognized in Mexico, more than in any other country. Hardy grasses and stunted woody plants grow on the ground of these mountain forests. Soils are generally quite good. Temperate forest ecosystems are found in virtually all the mountain areas of

Mexico from the USA border all the way to Guatemala (Figure 5.1).

Most of the Volcanic Axis is shown on the map as lying within the temperate forest region. As noted previously, however, the variations of altitude within the Volcanic Axis result in a veritable mosaic of natural vegetation regions. Gradual transitions occur within the temperate forests of the Volcanic Axis from pine-oak forests to pine-fir forests and in favored places to cloud forests, before the tree line (and *tierra helada*) is reached. Whether fire, in the long term, destroys or replenishes these pine-oak forests is hotly disputed by botanists.

Intensive exploitation of these forests decimated them during colonial times. Pine trees, in particular, proved to be especially versatile, used for everything from charcoal production, for smelting mineral ores, pit props, ship-building and pulp to furniture-making. It is difficult to imagine, when viewing the landscapes of central Mexico today, that virtually everywhere was still forested when the Spanish conquistadors arrived in the 16th century. Today, the Volcanic Axis has comparatively little natural vegetation left. Long before the Spanish arrived, the broad intermontane valleys and the excellent water supply of central Mexico became the focus for large-scale urbanized settlements. The ancient cities of Tula, Teotihuacan and the Aztec capital Tenochtitlan were each pre-eminent in their day. This ecosystem's dominance in terms of population distribution has continued to the present day, as shown by the clustering within it of many of the country's largest cities, including Mexico City, Guadalajara, Toluca, Puebla and Morelia.

Table 5.1 Selected UNESCO Biosphere Reserves

Biosphere Reserve	State/s	Importance
El Triunfo	Chiapas	mountainous evergreen cloud forest; a primary Pleistocene refuge for numerous endemic plants and animals.
Cuatrociénegas	Coahuila	oasis with 500 pools preserving species found only in the Chihuahua desert.
Mapimí	Durango, Chihuahua and Coahuila	fragile warm desert and semi desert ecosystems.
La Michilía	Durango	mountainous pine-oak forest; black bears and wolves.
Chamela Cuixmala	Jalisco	Pacific coast dry tropical forest with iguanas and crocodiles.
Sierra de Manantlán	Jalisco and Colima	transition of Nearctic and Neotropical biological realms; wild perennial corn.
Monarch butterfly migration sites	Michoacán and State of Mexico	unique annual butterfly migration linking Mexico to Canada and the USA; ecotourism.
Huatulco	Oaxaca	coastal reserve for endangered sea turtles and dolphins.
Banco Chinchorro	Quintana Roo	sea grass beds, mangroves, sandy beaches and coral reefs; more than 95 species of coral.
Sian Ka'an	Quintana Roo	coastal limestone plain, and extensive barrier reef system, with more than 4000 plant species.
Laguna Madre and Río Bravo Delta	Tamaulipas	migratory bird haven on coastal wetlands.
Los Tuxtlas	Veracruz	jungle-covered volcanic region, with pre Hispanic sites.
Calakmul	Yucatán	largest forest reserve in Mexico; tropical rainforest with important Mayan sites; ecotourism.
Ría Celestún	Yucatán and Campeche	wetlands and drowned river valley (ría) with diverse fauna and flora.
Ría Lagartos	Yucatán	coastal estuary; diverse birdlife with over 18,000 pink flamingos.

Grasslands and mesquite-grasslands

Open savannas or grasslands have a mixture of grass and flower species with relatively few scattered shrubs and trees. In some areas, mesquite trees are prominent, giving rise to the subcategory of mesquite-grasslands. This ecosystem also includes the higher altitude subalpine grasslands which occur on the highest mountains above the tree line. These grassland areas tend to have quite fertile brown and red-brown soils. Cattle ranching and farming are widely practiced in grassland areas, though they are prone to drought and some areas have been severely overgrazed, leading to soil erosion. Some ecologists consider that most grasslands are unlikely to be truly natural and that they probably represent secondary vegetation following continual disturbance by human activity. The area in this zone stretches in a band east of the Western Sierra Madre from Ciudad Juárez as far south as Aguascalientes.

Desert and semi-arid scrubland

This ecosystem includes arid desert and semiarid areas. The transition from desert vegetation to semiarid scrubland is relatively gradual. Drought-resistant woody plants, cacti, yuccas, agaves and thorny shrubs may occur in either semiarid or arid areas. The species in these areas have a very high degree of endemism. Mexico has the world's richest assortment of cacti with over 900 species, 79% of them endemic. Ground cover and grasses are more abundant in the semiarid areas. Most of these areas have poor, nutrient-deficient soils, and impenetrable hardpans such as calcretes are commonly found just beneath the surface. However, agriculture (commonly cotton, wheat and soya) is possible where irrigation is available. In terms of area, this is Mexico's largest ecosystem. Desert ecosystems predominate in Baja California and Sonora, one of the world's greatest cactus gardens. Semiarid vegetation is dominant in most of the Central Plateau as well as northern Nuevo León and Tamaulipas (Figure 5.1).

Modifications to natural ecosystems

As already noted, Mexico's natural ecosystems are under great pressure.

Soil degradation (physical removal by erosion, or loss of fertility due to changes in soil chemistry) is a particularly serious environmental problem. Several states—Aguascalientes, Colima, Durango, Guanajuato, Guerrero, Jalisco, Mexico and Michoacán—have soil degradation affecting more than 20% of their total area.[4] The primary causes of soil degradation are overgrazing, inappropriate farming, salinization and deforestation.

Over half of Mexico's total land area is used as pastureland for livestock, primarily cattle. Though the total number of cattle has declined by about 10% since 1980, overgrazing is still having a detrimental impact on soils and leading to erosion, particularly in the states of Mexico, Morelos, Querétaro, Guanajuato, Jalisco and Sinaloa.[7]

Chemical soil degradation, where loss of organic material and minerals reduces soil fertility, affects 18% of Mexico, with rates varying from 55% of all land in the state of Yucatán, and over 30% in Chiapas, Veracruz and Tabasco, to less than 3.5% of Baja California, Coahuila and Sonora.[8] The natural minerals and salts in irrigation water can accumulate in the

Native and non-native crops and animals

Dozens of food crops are native to Mexico, including tobacco, corn (maize), squash, avocados, guavas, cacao, peanuts, vanilla, tomatoes, chile peppers and papayas. In addition, two native dyes became major items of trade during colonial times: cochineal (scarlet) derived from insects, and indigo (blue-purple) derived from a plant.

A plethora of ornamental plants including all dahlias and most cacti originate from Mexico. Before the Spanish arrived, there were very few domesticated animals in Mexico, the main exceptions being dogs and (in the north) turkeys.

After the Conquest, Spanish settlers introduced numerous Old World species into the New World. The most pernicious introductions were human-borne diseases, which led to the rapid and tragic decimation of the indigenous population. However, most of the introductions were deliberate, made with the intention of increasing the diversity of available food and resources. Among the non-native (exotic) plants and animals introduced were sheep, pigs, chickens, goats, cattle, wheat, barley, figs, grapes, olives, peaches, quinces, pomegranates, cabbages, lettuces and radishes, as well as many flowers, weeds and rodents.

The value of rainforests[5]

One study found that native Indian groups inhabiting the tropical rainforest had uses for more than 1300 different plants. The largest category, those used for medicinal purposes, included 780 species. Also significant were the number of plants considered edible (360), useful in construction (175), for fuel (93), as a source of honey (84), forage (73), crafts (59), poison (52), ornamental purposes (51), tools (51) and ceremonial use (50). In addition, plants were employed for dyes, shade, stimulants, fertilizer, insecticides, perfume, latex and soap.

It is widely believed that if we could put a true economic value on all the benefits of rainforests, their continued destruction would be much less likely. These benefits include not only the uses attributed to their plants and animals, but also their less tangible aesthetic and educational values and their role as a source of freshwater and in carbon sequestration. In 2003, Formula One, the motor racing organization, announced it had signed an agreement with Los Altos, a small village in Chiapas, to pay the villagers to preserve the surrounding forest to capture an amount of carbon equivalent to the carbon emissions produced by Formula One events worldwide. The villagers will receive $66,000 for preserving an area of forest capable of capturing 5500 tons of carbon a year.[6]

Increasingly, forest management seeks not only to protect carefully selected old-growth areas, but also to encourage local people to manage their forests from a multiple use perspective while promoting the growth of forest plantations elsewhere for specific purposes. (See chapter 15 for an example of community-based sustainable forestry.)

soil as the water evaporates causing soil salinization, which reduces soil productivity. Though it impacts only 0.6% of Mexico, salinization occurs in some of the most productive, irrigated, agricultural areas, especially in the states of Sinaloa (3.6%), Guanajuato (3.3%), Tamaulipas (1.9%), Sonora (1.7%) and Baja California (1.4%).[9]

However, soil erosion is not necessarily all bad news. Pre-Columbian Mixtec Indians in Oaxaca's Nochixtlán Valley, where more than five meters of soil have been stripped from hillsides in the past 400 years, appear to have deliberately encouraged soil erosion in order to create new agricultural land. Over a 1000-year period they doubled the width of the valley floor to about 3000 m, while also infilling some of the tributary valleys with terraces. They regarded soil erosion not as a hazard to be prevented, but as an opportunity to be seized.[10]

Deforestation has been on-going for centuries. About 30% of the original temperate forests and 45% of the original tropical forests are now gone.[11] In 2005, 33% of Mexico was forested: 341,415 km² of temperate forest and 313,635 km² of tropical forest. However, in the decade between 1993 and 2002, Mexico lost about 3594 km² of temperate forest and 1100 km² of tropical forest.[12] On the bright side, in 2004 about 200 million trees were planted, reforesting almost 2000 km².

The principal reasons for the loss of natural ecosystems and biodiversity are habitat alteration (deforestation for agriculture, forestry plantations and settlements), overexploitation (land degradation) and contamination (acid rainfall and oil extraction). Changes have also occurred due to on-going climate change, the introduction of new species (especially cattle, sheep, weeds and certain fish) and man-made or natural hazards, such as fires, volcanic eruptions and tropical hurricanes. Habitat change has been happening for hundreds of years and will no doubt continue long into the future.

In an effort to safeguard its biodiversity and natural ecosystems, Mexico has established over 150 nature reserves and parks, including more than 30 UNESCO-designated Biosphere Reserves (Table 5.1), protecting 9.5% of its land area, though not all the reserves are rigorously managed. In addition, Mexico has granted protected status to 19.7% of its 209,000 km² of territorial waters.

6

Water availability, rivers and aquifers

Water is one of Mexico's most vital natural resources. Mexico's water resources include its east and west coastlines as well as its interior freshwater rivers, lakes and aquifers. Mexico's long seacoast strongly affects its climate and is basic to its shipping, fishing and tourism industries. Freshwater resources are essential to agriculture, industry and electricity generation as well as household and commercial activities. Furthermore, coastal and interior water resources are essential to Mexico's ecology and natural environment.

Coastal resources

Mexico's 11,122-km coastline is the longest in Latin America. About two-thirds of the coastline is on the Pacific Ocean and the remaining third is on Gulf of Mexico and the Caribbean Sea.

A long coastline facilitates shipping if adequate harbors are available. Unfortunately, there are relatively few good natural harbors in Mexico. Along the Gulf coast, only the Laguna de Tamiahua, south of Tampico, and some small islands at Veracruz provide adequate natural harborage. On the west coast where the mountains plunge into the Pacific Ocean, there are better natural harbors such as those at Acapulco, Manzanillo, Topolobampo and Ensenada. Some potentially good west coast natural harbors, such as Magdalena Bay and La Paz in Baja California Sur, are quite isolated and therefore inconvenient for large scale shipping. Because of its lack of good natural harbors, Mexico has had to construct and dredge numerous harbors such as those at Lázaro Cardenas and Mazatlán. The five largest ports—Tampico and Veracruz on the Gulf as well as Guaymas, Mazatlán and Manzanillo on the Pacific—handle about 80% of Mexico's ocean freight.

Mexico's long coastline supports an enormous and rapidly growing tourism industry (see chapter 19). The biggest coastal tourist destination is the Maya Riviera extending south from Cancún almost all the way to the border with Belize. Pacific resorts include Acapulco, which has been popular for many decades, as well as rapidly growing newer resorts such as the southern tip of the Baja California peninsula around Cabo San Lucas, Mazatlán, Puerto Vallarta, Zihuatanejo-Ixtapa and Huatulco.

Mexico's coasts are also valuable for fishing (see chapter 15). The cold California Current carries plankton and other nutrients southwards along the western side of the Baja California Peninsula. These nutrients provide abundant food for marine life. In addition, the warmer water of the Gulf of California is rich with nutrients and marine life. Mexico's four northwest coastal states produce almost 60% of Mexico's total fish catch with Sonora alone contributing about 25%. The most important commercial fish in these states are shrimp, tuna and sardines. States along the Gulf of Mexico fish primarily for shrimp, carp and oysters. The seasonal migration of whales along the Pacific coast is a valuable resource for tourism.

Freshwater availability in Mexico

Mexico's freshwater resources are a function of rainfall, sun intensity and topography as well as vegetation and soil conditions. Though parts of northern Mexico are arid, the country as a whole receives an average of 760 mm of precipitation a year (slightly over 30 in).[1] This is a considerable amount, more than that received by either Canada or the USA (Table 6.1).

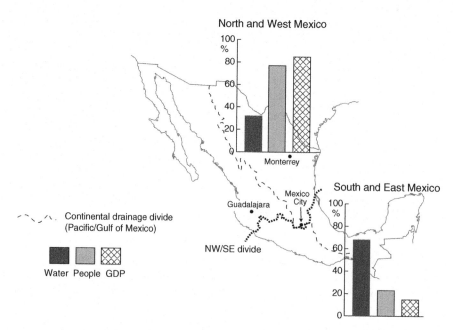

Figure 6.1 Mexico's north–south divide: water, people and GDP

It is customary to distinguish between economic water scarcity and physical water scarcity. Economic water scarcity exists when people do not have the necessary economic means to access an adequate supply of water. This is the case for much of sub-Saharan Africa, but economic water scarcity is rarely found in Mexico. Physical water scarcity exists where physical access to water is limited and when demand outstrips the natural supply. Northern Mexico suffers from physical water scarcity. Physical scarcity can result directly from human activity. For example, overuse of water in the Colorado River basin in the USA means that very little water now reaches the increasingly saline delta area in Mexico.

While Mexico as a whole gets enough rainfall, the main problem is geographical distribution. Relatively sparsely populated southern Mexico gets by far the most rain and therefore has the greatest water availability. The north, particularly the northwest, is very dry. Temporal distribution and variability exacerbate the problem; 77% of total rainfall occurs between June and October. Rainfall in heavily populated central Mexico is about the national average (772 mm); however, this region is quite dry between November and May. Regions with lower rainfall totals tend to experience higher year-on-year variability.

It is worth noting that 73% of Mexico's rainfall either evaporates directly or evapotranspirates through plants. About 25% runs off into rivers and lakes. Only roughly 2% seeps down to recharge subterranean aquifers.[2]

The spatial distribution of population and economic activity exacerbates problems of rainfall distribution. In short, too many people live in areas where there is too little water. South and southeastern Mexico (Figure 6.1) receive 68% of the rainfall but have only 23% of the population and produce only 15% of the gross domestic product. On other hand, the rest of Mexico receives only 32% of the rainfall but has 77% of the population and 85% of economic production. The problem is getting worse because the most rapid population and economic growth is in the north, the driest part of the country.

For the country as a whole, on average there are roughly 4300 m³ of runoff per person. (Table 6.1) In terms of per person water availability, the Lerma basin between Mexico City and Guadalajara (Figure 6.3) has only about one-third of the national average while the very heavily populated Valley of Mexico, containing the Mexico City Metropolitan Area, has only one-thirtieth of the national average.[4] On the other hand, the basins in the southeast receive many times the national average.

Availability of water per person is a function of population size and the total amount of water available. Though Mexico gets more rain than the USA

Table 6.1 Water in Mexico compared to other countries[3]

	Canada	Brazil	USA	Mexico
Average precipitation (mm/yr)	537	1 782	715	760
Available water (m3/person/yr)	84 500	37 300	7 100	4 300
Water consumed (m3/person/yr)	1 472	336	1 647	759
Agricultural land total (millions of hectares)	67.6	66.6	175.5	27.3
Irrigated land	0.8	2.9	21.4	6.5
% irrigated	1.2	4.4	12.2	23.8
Water footprint (m3/person/yr)	2 049	1 381	2 483	1 441

or Canada, the availability of water per person in Mexico is only one-twentieth that of Canada and slightly more than half that of the USA because Mexico's population density is far higher. In other words, though each square kilometer in Mexico receives more rain on average, that rain must be divided among more people. Of 177 countries analyzed by the FAO, Mexico ranked 90th in terms of water availability per person.[6] However, if Mexico is divided into two zones, the south would rank 51st and the north would rank 131st.

Mexico's per person consumption of water is about half that of Canada (Figure 6.2) but with proportionately more allocated to agriculture. Nationally, about 75% of water consumption is used in agriculture while settlements and industry use about 17% and 8% respectively.

Rivers

Mexico does not have a large, important navigable river such as the St. Lawrence, Mississippi or Rhine. Rivers had only a minor influence on the pattern of Mexico's historical development. In contrast, the

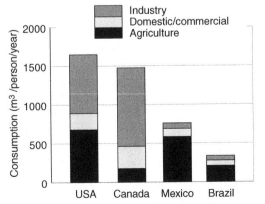

Figure 6.2 Consumption of water[5]

pattern of development of the USA was strongly influenced by such large navigable rivers as the Hudson, Ohio, Mississippi and Missouri.

In looking at the size and importance of rivers there are three interrelated dimensions of particular interest: the river's length, the size of its basin or drainage area, and the amount of water that it carries (discharge) which can vary enormously from season to season as well as from year to year. Most atlases and almanacs list river sizes only by length. The Nile is the world's longest river, but the amount of water entering the sea from the Amazon River is about 10,000 times greater than that from the Nile.

Table 6.2 and Figure 6.3 show the locations and basic characteristics of Mexico's major rivers. The total amount of water that annually flows in Mexican rivers is roughly 410 km[3], about 25% more than the St. Lawrence River. It is about 25% less than the flow in the Mississippi River which has a drainage basin 65% larger than all of Mexico. Consistent with rainfall patterns, the largest river flows are in the sparsely populated south.

Since Mexican rivers are used very little for transport, river length is not particularly relevant except in so far as it relates to levels of pollution or reliability of flow. The two rivers in Mexico that are the longest and have the largest drainage basins start in the US state of Colorado.

The first is the Río Bravo, known as the Río Grande north of the border, which is the longest at about 3000 km (1900 mi). It forms the border between Mexico and the USA for about 2000 km (1250 mi). It is considered Mexico's longest river. Though it drains about a quarter of Mexico's total area, its drainage basin is arid and its total flow is less than 2% of Mexico's total. The other is the Colorado River (Río Colorado), which flows almost entirely in

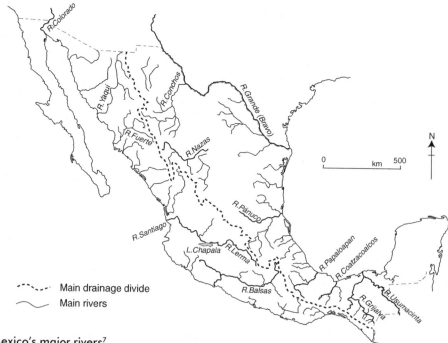

Figure 6.3 Mexico's major rivers[7]

the USA. These two very long rivers contribute very little to Mexico's water resource.

The Río Colorado formed a vast delta in the otherwise arid Sonoran desert in northern Mexico where it enters the Sea of Cortés (Figure 6.4). The delta wetlands created ideal conditions for a rich variety of wildlife. The river enters Mexico at the Southerly International Boundary where a gauging station records the river's discharge (Figure 6.5). This river is one of the most altered river systems in the world. The amount of water reaching Mexico has declined dramatically as a result of the Hoover and Glen Canyon dams and other diversions of Colorado River water in the USA. The few years of higher flows in the 1980s coincide with flood releases from US dams when they had been filled by heavy rains.

The river's drastically reduced annual discharge violates a 1944 treaty under which the USA guaranteed that at least 1750 million cubic meters would enter Mexico each year via the Morelos diversionary dam in the Mexicali Valley. The Río Colorado wetlands have been reduced to about 5% of their original extent, and the potential water supply for the rapidly-growing urban centers of Mexicali, Tijuana, Tecate and Rosarito has been compromised.

Mexico's six largest rivers account for over 60% of Mexico's total river discharge. Interestingly, the Mexican river with the greatest flow, the Grijalva–

Usumacinta, does not start in Mexico either. The river has a double name because it is actually a double river, with two branches of similar length that both start, about 120 km (75 mi) apart, in Guatemala. Each branch flows about 750 km (465 mi) through Chiapas before they unite in Tabasco about 25 km from the Gulf of Mexico. The Usumacinta forms the border between Mexico and Guatemala as well as the border between the states of Campeche and Tabasco. Each of the two branches has a flow of about 14% of Mexico's total. The flow of the combined Grijalva–Usumacinta River is about twice that of the Missouri River in the USA. They drain areas in Guatemala and the states of Chiapas, Tabasco and western Campeche which annually receive over 2500 mm (100 in) of rain.

There are several other important Mexican rivers. The Lerma River starts in the State of Mexico and flows westward into Lake Chapala and continues to the Pacific Ocean with the name Santiago. The Lerma–Santiago River system is about 1280 km (800 mi) long and thus is the second longest after the Río Grande. It is the longest river entirely in Mexico. It drains about 6% of Mexico. The Lerma–Santiago, which flows through several states, is one of the economically most important rivers in Mexico because it feeds some of the country's prime agricultural areas as well as the two largest metropolitan areas:

Table 6.2 Mexico's major rivers[8]

River	Source	Outflow	Basin area km² x 10³	Length km	Discharge m³ x 10⁹	Discharge % of total
Colorado						
(a) pre Hoover Dam (1934)	Colorado, USA	G. of California	615	2730	20	4.9
(b) post 1934			615	2730	2	0.5
Río Bravo (Río Grande)	Colorado, USA	Gulf of Mexico	840	3000	7	1.7
Lerma–Santiago	State of Mexico	Pacific Ocean	124	1280	8	2.0
Balsas	Tlaxcala	Pacific Ocean	117	770	24	5.9
Grijalva–Usumacinta	Guatemala	Gulf of Mexico	84	766	116	28.3
Papaloapan	Oaxaca	Gulf of Mexico	47	540	45	11.0
Pánuco–Tamesi–Moctezuma	Puebla, Hidalgo, San Luis Potosí	Gulf of Mexico	85	680	19	4.6
Coatzacoalcos	Oaxaca	Gulf of Mexico	17	332	34	8.3
Fuerte	Chihuahua	Pacific Ocean	34	540	5	1.2
Yaqui	Sonora	G. of California	73	740	4	1.0

Mexico City and Guadalajara. However, its flow is quite small, only about 2% of the national total.

The Balsas River, which enters the Pacific well to the south of the mouth of the Lerma–Santiago, is the third longest at 840 km (520 mi) and has the third largest basin. Though its flow is about three times that of the Lerma–Santiago and offers white-water rafting opportunities, it is not as important economically.

Three major rivers flow into the Gulf of Mexico through the state of Veracruz. The Rivers Papaloapan and Coatzacoalcos start in Oaxaca and flow through southern Veracruz. Their combined flow is nearly 20% of the national total. The Pánuco–Tamesi–Moctezuma River system starts in the State of Mexico and carries nearly 5% to the Gulf of Mexico at Tampico.

There are numerous rather long rivers that flow west to the Pacific from the Western Sierra Madre, but these have relatively little water. There are also several rather long rivers such as the Nazas that flow into landlocked basins and either die or feed small drying lakes. The marked contrast in most of Mexico between a winter dry season and summer rainy season means than many streams do not flow year round but are intermittent. Their steep-sided wadi-like valleys, dry most of the year, may only carry a significant quantity of water occasionally, following heavy and prolonged rain perhaps many kilometers away. These

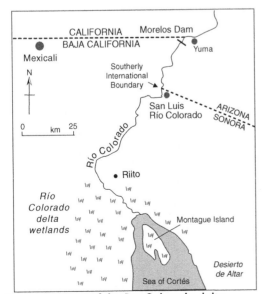

Figure 6.4 Map of the Río Colorado delta

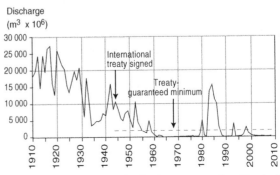

Figure 6.5 Río Colorado discharge entering Mexico[9]

channels may fill within hours during low frequency but high magnitude flash flooding events.

Drainage patterns influence how rapidly water is transferred through a river basin and therefore affect the degree of variability of a river's discharge. With a dendritic (tree-like) pattern, typical of drainage basins that are roughly circular in shape, peak water discharges tend to be much higher than with drainage patterns comprised mainly of parallel rivers in elongated basins.

Mexico has examples of almost every conceivable kind of drainage pattern. The numerous branching tributaries of many larger rivers form classic dendritic patterns. Parallel drainage patterns are found on many parts of the steep western side of the Western Sierra Madre. Radial drainage is common on volcanic cones. Endoreic drainage exists in the closed basins of semi-arid northern Mexico. A confusing network of distributaries and braided channels characterizes the Grijalva basin in Tabasco. Karstic patterns with sinkholes and subterranean channels can be found in the Yucatán Peninsula.

Almost half of the water in Mexican rivers is used for productive purposes, primarily for hydroelectric power. Mexico's dams have an installed capacity of about 11 gigawatts of electricity, roughly one fifth of the country's total generating capacity; they don't operate at full capacity, so they only generate about one eighth of the nation's electricity. While only about a fifth of the total river water is consumed for other productive purposes, this proportion is far higher for rivers in the drier northern part of Mexico.

Lakes and reservoirs

Mexico's natural lakes are small in total volume and relatively few in number as a result of its mountainous terrain and very diverse rainfall pattern. The great internal basin between the Western and Eastern Sierra Madres would form a gigantic lake if rainfall was more abundant. However, with scarce rainfall and a dry climate, the little rain that does fall tends to evaporate quickly. Consequentially, there are virtually no natural lakes in the great Mapimí basin of northern Mexico.

Where rainfall is very abundant, in the south, the terrain is quite steeply sloped. The rainfall rushes down these slopes to the sea. Mexico's natural lakes are small in comparison to man-made reservoirs that have formed behind dams. Of Mexico's fifty largest internal bodies of water, in terms of volume, only three are natural lakes. The volume of water in Mexico's natural and man-made lakes varies enormously

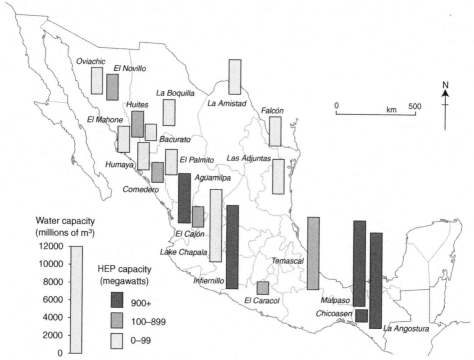

Figure 6.6 Lake Chapala and Mexico's largest reservoirs[10]

The Enchanted Lake[11]

The beautiful crater lake of La Laguna Encantada (The Enchanted Lake) in Veracruz rises every dry season but falls again during the rainy season. This lake is near Catemaco (better known for its witches) in the Tuxtlas region of the state of Veracruz. Did one of the witches cast a spell on the lake, making its level change out of synchronization with all the other lakes in the country?

The lake has a circumference of about 1500 m (slightly under one mile) and nestles on the southern flank of the 1400-m-high San Martín Volcano.

The basaltic lavas and layers of ash forming the volcano are highly permeable and porous. As a result, despite the heavy rainfall, there are no permanent streams flowing down its upper slopes.

Some distance away from the volcano, though, there are several good-sized lakes including Cate-maco and Laguna Encantada. Catemaco is large enough to capture plenty of rainfall to maintain its level. Laguna Encantada's much smaller basin, however, does not receive enough rain to keep its level high.

Instead, most of La Laguna Encantada's water supply comes from underground. Water that falls on the slopes of the San Martín volcano during the rainy season soaks into the ground and then percolates so slowly towards the lake that it takes six months (or perhaps 18 months?) to reach it.

The result? The lake is unable to sustain its level during the rainy season, but the underground water reaching it every dry season is more than sufficient to replenish its level. Maybe the witches of Catemaco have something to do with it, but hydrology also plays a part!

from season to season and even more from year to year. The capacities shown in Table 6.3 are maximum values; in virtually all cases the amount of water actually present at any given time is far less.

Lake Chapala, straddling the boundary between the states of Jalisco and Michoacán, is the largest natural lake. It is surpassed in volume of water by four or five man-made lakes (Figure 6.6). In 2008, Lake Chapala appeared virtually full but still contained only about half of its "official" capacity (see chapter 7 and Figure 7.1). The amount of water in the second largest natural lake, Cuitzeo, in Michoacán, is surpassed by more than twenty-five man-made reservoirs. The third largest natural lake, Pátzcuaro, also in Michoacán, is surpassed by over thirty reservoirs.

Mexico's dams and reservoirs serve many valuable functions. The amount of power that can be generated is a function of the amount of water streaming through the generators and its pressure, which is related to the height of the dam. Just over half of hydroelectric power is generated by dams on rivers which start in southern mountain ranges and flow into the southern portion of the Gulf of Mexico (Figures 6.6 and 16.2). Most of the rest comes from dams on rivers along the Pacific coast from the Balsas basin all the way north to Sonora.

Virtually all Mexican dams, except those in the rainiest southern areas, provide water for irrigated agriculture. This is particularly true in arid northern Mexico. Mexico ranks sixth in the world with about 63,000 km³ of irrigated agriculture. It is well behind India (558,000), China (546,000), the USA (224,000), Pakistan (182,000) and Iran (76,500). About 23% of Mexico's cultivated area is irrigated, compared to 99.9% in Egypt, 82% in Pakistan, 47% in China and only 12% in the USA.

Dams also protect against floods, especially in the drier northern areas which are very susceptible to floods from rare but torrential downpours. In addition, dams provide a source of water for urban populations, especially in the largest metropolitan areas. Finally, the reservoirs behind dams throughout Mexico are an important recreational resource.

On the other hand, the construction of dams can also have negative effects, including habitat loss, the need to relocate existing residents away from the reservoir site, adverse changes in river flows downstream of the dam and sediment accumulation behind the dam which reduces the reservoir capacity.

Mexico's freshwater aquifers

Mexico's groundwater aquifers are a very important resource. About 64% of public water supplies come from wells sunk into aquifers. Mexico City, Monterrey and several other metropolitan areas rely heavily on aquifers. Aquifers also provide about a third of all the water for agriculture and livestock.

The largest aquifer resource in terms of renewable water availability is in the Yucatán Peninsula, with about a third of the national total. A large portion of the rainfall in the Yucatán seeps into its aquifers; there are virtually no rivers to carry rainwater to the ocean. The states of Chiapas and Tabasco, where rainfall is the heaviest, account for about a quarter of Mexico's aquifer resource. The next largest sources are the Balsas and Lerma–Santiago basins but each holds under a tenth of the national total.

According to the National Water Commission, 104 of the country's 653 identified aquifers are over-exploited in that more water is withdrawn each year than is naturally replaced.[12] The velocity of water movements underground can be astonishingly slow; it may take rainwater water tens or even hundreds of years to reach the aquifer it is replenishing. (For a curious case of replenishment rates, see The Enchanted Lake box). The number of overused aquifers has increased rapidly in recent decades from 32 in 1972, to 80 in 1985, and 104 in 2004. When coastal aquifers are over-exploited, seawater seeps in to replenish the aquifer, and eventually the aquifer can become too salty to be used for irrigation. Salt-water intrusion is a significant problem for 17 aquifers located in Baja California, Baja California Sur, Colima, Sonora and Veracruz (Figure 6.7).

Nearly 60% of the total groundwater extracted is withdrawn from overexploited aquifers. As expected, the over-exploited aquifers (Figure 6.7) are in the heaviest populated and the most arid areas. Total water extraction exceeds recharge in Mexico City, Monterrey and other large northern metropolitan areas as well as irrigated areas of Sonora, the central northern plateau, the Lerma basin and Baja California.

Mexico City, which 500 hundred years ago was a city of marvelous canals, currently has a serious water problem. More than 60% of its water comes from the exploitation of deep wells sunk into its subterranean aquifers. Rainfall is only able to recharge about 1/3rd of the water extracted each year. Thus, the aquifers are losing water rapidly and receding farther and farther from ground level. This "mining of water" from the aquifer has resulted in severe subsidence problems in Mexico City. The wells must be sunk deeper every year and more energy must be used to pump the needed water to the surface. Mexico City's water issues are analysed more thoroughly in chapter 23.

There are also significant water problems in many other areas of the country. For example, Monterrey is in a closed basin without an adequate flow of river water. To get the water it needs for its residents and industries, Monterrey is also unsustainably "mining" its aquifer.

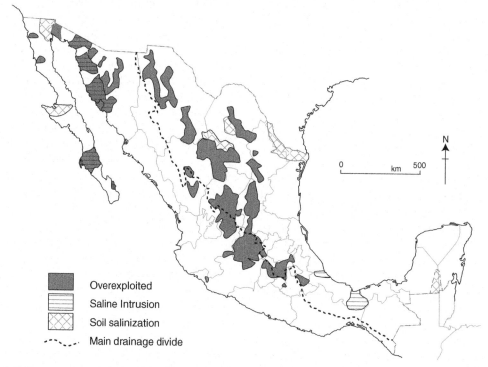

Figure 6.7 Overexploited aquifers and areas of salinization[13]

7

Water issues and hazards

Water is a major issue in Mexico as well as many other parts of the world. The issue has two basic components: water quantity and water quality. As discussed previously, Mexico's water quantity issues are associated with the spatial and temporal distribution of available water.

A commonly used measure of "severe water stress" is areas where water consumption exceeds 40% of the water naturally available.[1] According to this measure, 44% of Mexico is severely water stressed, compared to 88% in Egypt, 80% in India, 45% in China, 32% in the USA and only 1% in Canada.

The most severely water stressed area is the Valley of Mexico which consumes about 120% of naturally available water. It does this by pumping massive amounts of water from surrounding basins.

Northern Mexico is also an area of very extreme water stress. Baja California and Sonora (Figure 6.3) are very severely stressed. Of naturally available water, they consume 86% and 79% respectively. The Río Grande basin and the internal Mapimí basin have very high stress measures of 66% and 55% respectively. The Lerma–Santiago and Balsas basins are approaching severe stress levels with measures of 38% and 37% respectively.

The efficiency of water use is an important factor contributing to water stress. Traditional inefficient irrigation methods are used in over 80% of Mexico's irrigated land area. These methods usually result in water losses of between 40% and 60%. In addition, losses from public urban water supply systems range from 30% to 50%. While some losses are inevitable, improved water use efficiency would go a long way to alleviate water stress.

Water footprint is a measure of the total volume of water used to produce all the goods and services consumed per person in a country each year.[2] It includes all water used inside the country (agricultural, industrial, domestic, and commercial) as well as all the water used in producing imports. Mexico's water footprint is 1441 m^3 per person per year, compared to 2483 for the USA, 1381 for Brazil and 702 for China. That Mexico's staple food is corn greatly reduces its water footprint. A total of 909 liters of water are needed to produce each kilogram of corn, compared to 1334 for wheat, 2291 for rice, 3918 for chicken and 15,497 for beef. Beef is so high because it includes the water needed for cattle and for processing the beef as well as all the water needed to grow the feed eaten by cattle.

Water quality

Water quality is just as important as water quantity. Water pollution occurs when water composition has been modified by natural forces or human activity to the point where it is not suitable for a specified purpose. Water pollution is a relative term. Water that is acceptable for irrigating crops might not be good enough for household use; water that is fine for showering or washing clothes might not be acceptable for drinking.

The amount of organic wastes that can be decomposed in water depends on the level of dissolved oxygen in the water. Biological oxygen demand (BOD) is the commonly used measure of the amount of organic waste introduced to a body of water. If the amount of BOD exceeds the water's oxygen level for

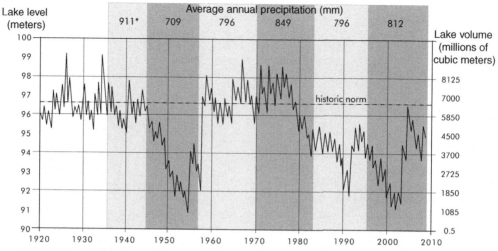

Notes: Lake level: lake surface level in meters (level 100 coincides with an elevation of 1526.8 meters above sea level;
at level 90 the lake is essentially empty.)
Precipitation: average of four weather stations: Chapala, Jamay, Jocotepec and Tuxcueca.
*precipitation value for 1936-45 is based on Chapala weather station only.

Figure 7.1 The level of Lake Chapala, 1920–2008

extended periods of time, the water becomes septic and most forms of aquatic life are killed. Fecal coliform counts are a measure of human-generated waste.

The use of fertilizers greatly increases the amounts of nitrates and phosphates in receiving water. The overabundance of these nutrients in water stimulates an explosion of some algae. This leads to a secondary explosion of oxygen-consuming bacteria which feed on the algae. This drastically reduces the water's oxygen level, killing fish and plants. This process, known as eutrophication, can effectively kill the body of water. Fertilizer pollution is widespread in Mexico particularly in the wide agricultural band stretching from Jalisco to Veracruz. At present there are no laws or regulations governing the discharge of agricultural wastes.

Industries use a relatively small amount of water, but their combined water pollution discharges are three times greater than those from all domestic users nationwide. Industrial discharges contain an enormous range of biological and chemical pollutants; some, like mercury, arsenic, certain acids and polychlorinated biphenyls (PCBs), are highly toxic. Industries producing the most water pollutants include agro-processing (especially sugar), chemicals, mineral processing and petroleum. Industries tend

to be geographically more concentrated than the general population; therefore, the rivers receiving their wastewater can become extremely polluted. While industrial waste treatment has improved considerably in recent decades, there are still serious local industrial pollution problems.

While Mexico's overall water quantity available per person is adequate, the quality of its surface water is rather poor. The United Nations Environment Program's 2008 Environmental Performance Index of water quality gave Mexico a score of 51.7 (ranking it 106th out of 122 countries), well behind Canada (87.6), Argentina (76.4), the USA (69.7), India (67.7), and China 60.7) but ahead of Russia (48.3), Israel (42.4) and Saudi Arabia (21.5).[3] Contributing to the water quality problem is the fact that virtually all Mexico's rivers receive untreated or poorly treated wastewater discharges from municipal and industrial sources. In general, this is not a problem in the south where river flows are massive and population is sparse. However, the problem is serious in most of the rest of the country where flows are smaller and wastewater discharges are much larger.

Mexico has made good progress in providing sewerage for its people. Between 1990 and 2004, the percentage of the population with sewerage systems increased from 61% to 78%. This is an impressive

The fluctuating level of Lake Chapala

Communities on the northern shore of Lake Chapala, Mexico's largest natural lake, have been an important destination for tourists as well as international retirees, mostly from the USA and Canada, for more than a century. The lake experiences enormous fluctuations in level and size (Figure 7.1). In general, evaporation and other uses lower the lake's level by about one meter (39 in) most years. Rainwater and runoff from the River Lerma basin normally replenishes this water. Superimposed on the cyclical annual fluctuations on the graph are two lengthy periods of low water levels. The first began in about 1945, and coincided with several years of unusually low rainfall totals throughout western Mexico. When normal rainfall patterns resumed at the end of the 1950s, the lake rapidly recovered.

The second period of low lake levels began in about 1980. The lake level fell about 2.5 m, and then oscillated (about level 94.5) for several years, before plummeting another 2.5 m to level 92.0 Heavy rains in 2003-4 helped the lake recover. The available evidence suggests that rainfall amounts since 1980 have been either at or above long-term averages, so this second period of low lake levels must have resulted from human activity. Between 1994 and 2002, much of the River Lerma's water was captured in upstream dams and used for irrigation. These dams can hold roughly half the lake's volume of water. This provoked a fall in lake level of about 3.3 m (almost 11 ft); the lake's volume declined by over 70%. The abundant rains since 2003 have recharged the lake, almost quadrupling its volume (from 1.1 to 4.1 billion m³) and increasing its surface area by about 40%. The lake is shallow, only four to six m (13-20 ft) in depth. While it is the largest lake in terms of surface area, several artificial lakes behind dams are deeper and have a far greater storage capacity.

level given that roughly 25% of the population is considered rural. Sewerage provision varies from under 60% in Oaxaca, Guerrero, Chiapas, Campeche and Yucatán to over 90% in Baja California, Jalisco, Colima, Aquascalientes, Nuevo León and Mexico City. On the other hand, less than a third of the wastewater collected is treated. Over two-thirds of the collected raw sewage is dumped untreated, mostly into rivers though some is discharged into lakes or directly into the ocean.

The Lerma River and some of its tributaries are among the most polluted rivers in Mexico. They carry relatively little flow and receive large amounts of agricultural runoff containing fertilizers and pesticides as well as major quantities of municipal and industrial wastewater from large industrial cities such as Toluca, León, Celaya, Salamanca, Irapuato and Silao. The Lerma River flows into Lake Chapala (see box).

Another heavily polluted river system is the Tula–Moctezuma which runs through Hidalgo and eventually joins the Pánuco River in northern Veracruz. The Mezquital Valley in Hidalgo, 60 km north of Mexico City, owes its importance as an agricultural area to irrigation with municipal and industrial wastewater pumped in from the Mexico City Metropolitan Area (see map, Figure 23.1). The wastewater adds nutrients to the soil and increases yields but causes some long-term environmental impacts. The wastewater eventually flows into the Tula–Moctezuma–Pánuco River system. The Coatzacoalcos River is also heavily polluted from petroleum industry discharges (see chapter 30).

The National Water Commission (Conagua) uses two measures to assess the quality of bodies of water: biological oxygen demand (BOD) and chemical oxygen demand (COD).[4] BOD, described above, is affected by all types of organic discharges such as human, animal and crop wastes. COD is caused by chemical wastes primarily from agricultural fertilizers and pesticides as well as from industrial discharges. According to a Conagua study of about 400 sites in 2007, in terms of BOD, 5% were classified as "highly contaminated" (BOC > 120 mg/l), and 9% were labelled as "contaminated" (BOD > 30 mg/l). The situation is worse with respect to COD: 10% were "highly contaminated" (COD > 200), and 22% were "contaminated" (COD > 40). The highest levels of contamination were found in the Valley of Mexico, the Lerma–Chapala basin, the Northwest and the Balsas basin.

Coastal waters are also regularly monitored for contamination. The percentage of Mexico's resort beaches that met national water quality norms rose from 93.7% in 2003 (when 226 beaches in 35 destinations were tested) to 98.4% in 2007 (276 beaches in 46 destinations).[5] Seawater at all coastal resorts is now well within the national standard except for Ixtapa-Zihuatanejo on the Guerrero coast.

Droughts and floods

Figure 4.4 in a previous chapter shows areas where the risk of drought or flooding is categorized as severe. Drought risk is greatest in north-central Mexico. While the precise definition varies, a drought is defined as a period of time, usually months rather than days, when the precipitation received is well below the long-term average for that location. As a result, droughts are not directly linked to aridity; even a normally wet region could experience a drought if its rainy season fails to bring as much water as usual.

The area of severe drought risk coincides with areas receiving from 200 mm (8 in) to about 800 mm (31 in) of precipitation a year (Figure 4.3). One of the reasons for this is the variability of rainfall in these areas. Precipitation in some periods exceeds the long-term average, allowing farmers the opportunity to make a profit, but in other periods rainfall is below the average, making success difficult. Faced with the prospect of a drought, farmers may be able to adjust either their crops (or livestock) or their precise farming techniques. Their success at adapting to drought conditions will depend, among other factors, on their reserves of stored water and on the minimum lead-time required to make such adjustments.

Central Mexico experienced its worst drought for nearly 70 years in 2009 due to a combination of low rainfall, climate change and the start of an El Niño event.[6] The 20 million residents of Mexico City endured months of water rationing in the first half of 2009. Reservoirs in the Cutzamala system, a major source for the city's water, were at a record low in September 2009, suggesting further rationing in 2010.

Most areas where the flood risk is classified as severe are on the coast. Serious floods are particularly likely where there are extensive coastal lowlands, such as in Tamaulipas, Sinaloa, Veracruz and Tabasco (see

The Tabasco floods of 2007[7]

The small, oil-rich state of Tabasco, one of Mexico's wettest states, is regularly subjected to serious flooding. Much of the state is a wide coastal plain of sediments brought by rivers from the mountains of Chiapas and Guatemala. Two major rivers—the Grijalva and the Usumacinta—converge in the Pantanos de Centla wetlands. These rivers have meandering, braided channels and highly variable flows, partly because of hydropower dams far upstream.

The state's high incidence of floods has been exacerbated by subsidence and deforestation due to oil and gas extraction which has led to excessive silting of river channels. Looking to the future, rising sea levels will only increase this area's vulnerability to flooding.

Several days of heavy rainfall due to a low pressure system led in late October and early November 2007 to massive floods, called by President Felipe Calderón "one of the worst natural disasters in the history of the country." About 80% of Tabasco was under water at one point. Tabasco produces 80% of Mexico's total cacao and 40% of its bananas;

the losses of farm harvests alone were estimated at $480 million. The floods disrupted the lives of more than a million residents, and 20,000 people were forced to seek emergency shelter. The state capital Villahermosa, located near the junction of three branches of the Grijalva River, was particularly badly hit.

It has been claimed that the 2007 floods would have been much less serious if funds allocated for hydrologic infrastructure improvements had not been misappropriated. A new Tabasco Hydrological Plan was announced in 2008. The $850 million plan will ensure the integrated management of six river basins and major improvements to the systems for storm tracking, weather forecasting and disaster prediction. Several rivers will be dredged and the coast will be reinforced with breakwaters and sea walls.

Unfortunately, the plan could not be implemented in time to prevent serious damages from the next big Tabasco flood in early November 2009 which inundated the homes of more than 200,000 people.

box). Coastal flood risk is also associated with likely hurricane tracks; this helps to explain the flood risk in southern Chiapas and on the southern tip of the Baja California Peninsula.

However, flood risk is also high in several small areas of the interior, including Mexico City (urban floods due to torrential convectional rainstorms) and the Lerma Valley in Guanajuato (river floods). The most surprising area to have a high flood risk is in central Chihuahua, where the same small area is not only likely to suffer from floods, but also has a severe risk of droughts. Where precipitation totals are relatively low, the annual variability is much higher. This area rarely receives its annual average in a single year; it is far more likely to receive an amount either well in excess of the average or well below the average. Chihuahua frequently suffered from droughts and harvest failures throughout colonial times, reporting droughts in more than 40 years of the 130 years between 1690 and 1820.[8]

The risk of flooding is particularly pronounced in cities because of the specific characteristics of urban hydrology such as low infiltration rates and high runoff (see chapter 4). In addition, in some urban areas such as Mexico City the flood risk is further exacerbated by subsidence due to excessive groundwater extraction. Pumping from the aquifers causes the land surface above to sink. The surface topography changes and, following torrential rain, the water runoff patterns are changed as the water accumulates in the low areas. Mexico City has a long history of floods (chapter 23).

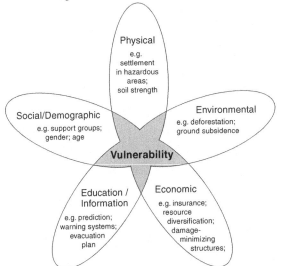

Figure 7.2 Factors affecting vulnerability

Vulnerability

The statistical risk of an event of a particular magnitude occurring may be the same for all groups within a society, but the extent to which these groups all suffer the same consequences depends on the level of vulnerability of each group. What makes some people more vulnerable to climatic and other hazards than others?

Figure 7.2 shows some of the factors that affect the vulnerability of an individual or of a group within society to hazardous events. For instance, groups able to purchase (and claim) insurance against catastrophic loss will be able to rebound from the disaster much more rapidly than groups unable to afford insurance. The very young and the very old tend to be more vulnerable than the active working-age population simply because they are less mobile and less able to uproot their families and relocate.

Numerous studies of drought-affected areas and areas subject to periodic hazard events have found that most people consistently underestimate the statistical probability of a hazard event of any particular size occurring. This underestimation is much smaller among people who have previously personally suffered a major event and proportionately greater among those who have not personally experienced such an event. This overconfidence leads people to undertake such risky strategies as building on river flood plains or coastlines subject to erosion or on the shores of lakes known to have variable levels even though the risks are high that the river eventually floods, the cliffs erode or the lake rises. While it is impossible to avoid all risks, and many sectors of society do not have the means to relocate to safer locations even if they wanted to, it seems that many people actively court risk in the mistaken notion that "it won't affect me" or "it can't happen again".

Water in Mexico's future

If current trends continue unabated into the future, Mexico will face some very serious water problems. Progress is being made on water use efficiency and wastewater treatment. However, this progress does not appear to be accelerating as fast as the currrent water problems.

The over-exploitation of water aquifers is a particularly severe problem. As Mexico City and other metropolitan areas continue to "mine" their aquifers to meet their water needs, they will have to keep drilling deeper wells and using more electricity to power the pumps. If this continues indefinitely, eventually they will completely exhaust their aquifers.

Irrigated agricultural areas in the arid north could face the same fate. The problem continues to grow because in some areas the permits for water extraction issued by the government enable users to withdraw more water from aquifers than can be recharged naturally. There is little incentive for efficient water use; the government does not charge agricultural users for the water they use. In short, the government is giving away water, a nationally owned resource, in the most arid areas of the country.

The situation could become even worse with global climate change. The National Ecology Institute of the National University of Mexico carried out a study in 1999 on the impacts of future climate change.[9] Though this study is dated, particularly for climate change research, its results are worth considering. According to the study, Mexico will experience less or normal precipitation during the rainy summer season. Precipitation might increase during the dry winter months; this could potentially alleviate water shortages during the winter.

The report also predicted climate change for specific regions and identified the most vulnerable. The study predicted decreased rainfall and increased temperature in the Lerma-Santiago basin. This coupled with the expected increase in population and industrial development could lead to very severe water shortages.

Increased vulnerability to drought and desertification are predicted for northern areas of central Mexico. Agriculture in northern Mexico which largely depends on over-exploited aquifers could be severely impacted by drought.

Global sea rise could inundate parts of Tabasco within 40 km (25 mi) of the existing coast. Of course, studies of specific global climate change impacts are still rather speculative and should be treated with caution.

The Government of Mexico is taking steps to address water issues. It has developed a plan for future water use that incorporates legal and regulatory changes, water pollution improvements and economic reforms focused on establishing and collecting appropriate fees and fines.[10] The plan calls for active participation by stakeholders including the general public, agricultural and industrial users as well as nongovernmental organizations.

The plan also promotes aggressive research and technological change designed to improve the efficiency of water use. In recent years, water use efficiency has increased significantly, but far greater efficiencies will have to be achieved in the future to avoid serious water crises.

The plan is impressive but will require government investment of about $2.6 billion a year which is twice the current amount. Serious future water crises can be avoided if these investments are made, new regulations and economic incentives are put in place and new technologies are implemented. However, the unknown impacts of global climate change could jeopardize this scenario.

8

Population decline, followed by population explosion

In the 400 years between the Spanish conquest in 1521 and the 1921 census, Mexico's population changed very dramatically. After an unprecedented crash during the first hundred years, the population very slowly recovered during the subsequent three hundred years prior to growing at an exponential rate during the second half of the twentieth century.

A sudden population decline

How many people lived here before the Europeans arrived in 1519? Nobody really knows. Unfortunately, we do not have solid data on the 15th century population living in the area that is now Mexico. Estimates range from 6 million to 25 million.[1] During the 15th century the majority of the population was living in the central highlands, while a sizeable number lived on the Yucatán Peninsula. The coastal areas attracted some small settlements. Very few people lived in the arid northern regions.

Hernán Cortés and his band of Spanish conquistadors arrived in Mexico in 1519. The conquistadors defeated the Aztecs and took control of Tenochtitlan in 1521. In the following decades, the Spanish quickly colonized most of the rest of Mexico. The spread of Spanish colonial rule and administration during the remainder of the 16th century had disastrous and unexpected social impacts on the indigenous societies.

The indigenous population was decimated during the first 100 years after the Spanish conquest. The population of Mexico crashed to about 1.6 million, mostly as a result of smallpox and other European diseases such as measles, influenza, typhus and bu-

bonic plague.[2] Social and economic disruption and chaos also contributed significantly to the decline. Mexico's population dropped by between 75% and 90% (Table 8.1). This represents one of the largest and most dramatic population declines in all of human history.

Table 8.1 Population growth, 1520–2010[3]

Year or period	End of period population (millions)	Average growth rate for period (%/year)
1520	(?) 15.0	na
1520–1619	1.6	–2.2
1620–1699	2.0	0.3
1700–1799	4.6	0.8
1800–1899	13.6	1.1
1900–1909	15.2	1.1
1910–1920	14.3	–0.6
1921–1929	16.7	1.7
1930–1939	19.7	1.7
1940–1949	25.8	2.7
1950–1959	34.9	3.1
1960–1969	48.2	3.3
1970–1979	66.8	3.3
1980–1989	81.2	2.0
1900–1999	97.5	1.8
2000–2005	103.3	1.5
2010 (est)	112.3	1.3

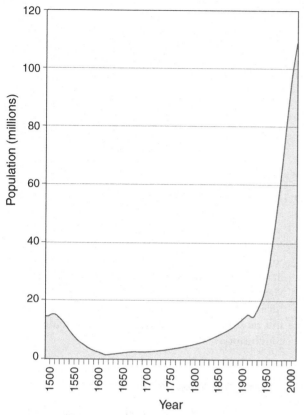

Figure 8.1 Population growth, 1520–2010[4]

What if the Mexican population had not crashed in the 16th century as a result of the conquest and European diseases? Assuming a population of 15 million in 1521, if it had grown at the rather slow rate of 1.0% per year it would have reached almost one billion by 1921 and exceeded 1.9 billion by 2009!

A gradual recovery

From a low point of 1.6 million in about 1620, the Mexican population made a very slow and gradual comeback (Figure 8.1). Growing at a snail's pace of less than 0.3% per year, the population reached about 2 million by the year 1700. During the next century growth increased a little as the surviving indigenous population gained some immunity to the European diseases. Between 1700 and 1800 the population growth rate was only about 0.8% per year. This slow rate was over twice that during the previous century. By the year 1800 the population reached about 4 million. Up until a decade before, Mexico's population had always surpassed that of the USA.

During the 19th century the population growth rate continued to increase, slowly at first but then more quickly. From 1800 to 1910, it grew by about 1.1% per year pushing the total population up to 13.6 million by 1900 and 15.2 million by 1910, the year in which the Mexican Revolution broke out.

Uncertainties of population numbers

The population of a given area is a very important number but is not easy to determine very precisely. Though a great deal of effort goes into determining accurate population figures, the numbers always contain some errors. Every five or ten years most countries conduct a census in an attempt to count every person, usually by going door to door. While censuses arrive at official population figures, they often undercount because many people do not have permanent addresses, are homeless, avoid being counted, etc. Efforts to correct for undercounting can result in over counting.

Between census years, demographers estimate population numbers using average birth and death rates as well as net migration. Birth rates may be applied to the total population or to specific cohorts of women such as those aged 15–20, 20–25, etc. Likewise, use of death rates might apply to the total population or to distinct male and female cohorts. In many cases, such as Mexico, migration is the most problematic component of population estimates. Data on movements within countries between censuses are rarely recorded and a great deal of international migration such as that between Mexico and the USA is not documented.

For longer term population forecasting, demographers must first use trend analyses to estimate future birth, death and net migration rates, and then use these to forecast population levels for years into the future. Obviously, each of these components can introduce errors which are then compounded. Despite all the opportunities for errors, in general demographers do an excellent job forecasting population numbers.

The Revolution and its immediate aftermath had very significant impacts on Mexican families and population growth during the decade between 1910 and 1920. By the 1921 census the population had declined by almost 6% to about 14.3 million.

The late 20th century population explosion

After the Mexican Revolution population growth picked up considerably. It grew by about 1.7% per year between 1921 and 1940, pushing the total population up to 19.7 million by 1940 (Table 8.1). The rate of growth continued to rise, and during the second half of the 20th century Mexico's population exploded. The 1950 population of 25.8 million almost doubled to 48.2 million by 1970. During the next thirty years it more than doubled again, increasing to 103.3 million by 2005. At the average growth rate recorded from 1960 to 1980 (3.3% a year) it took only 22 years for the population to double in number. This very rapid population growth generated considerable concern among Mexican leaders and presented numerous challenges.

Table 8.2 Population of major countries[5]

	Country	Population 2009 (millions)	Growth rate 2009 (%/year)
1	China	1328	0.58
2	India	1143	1.46
3	USA	306	0.97
4	Indonesia	239	1.16
5	Brazil	188	1.26
6	Pakistan	165	2.45
7	Bangladesh	155	1.67
8	Nigeria	148	2.27
9	Russia	140	−0.51
10	Japan	127	−0.02
11	Mexico	108	1.12
12	Philippines	97	1.72
13	Vietnam	87	1.32
14	Ethiopia	84	2.51
15	Germany	72	−0.07

How could Mexico expand food production fast enough to keep pace? Could enough schools be constructed and teachers trained to educate such a rapidly growing school age population? Could the economy expand fast enough to provide jobs for all the youth that were completing school? To deal with the mounting challenges of very rapid population growth, Mexico embarked on an aggressive family planning program. This program reduced the rate of growth, but Mexico's population still continued to grow.

The growth rate finally started to decelerate during the 1980s. During that decade it was down to just under 2.0% per year. While this was still considered to be too fast, it was far lower than the 3.3% rate experienced in the previous decade. Though the growth rate was decelerating, the total population was still expanding rapidly. By 1990 the population of Mexico reached 81.2 million.

Growth rates continued to slow down in the 1990s. Growth for the decade averaged 1.8% per year. While the growth rate was declining, the rate of decline was considerably less than that experienced in the 1980s. Rapid population growth was still considered a major challenge. During the 1990s the population increased by 16.2 million (a larger increase in numerical terms than during the 1980s) to reach 97.5 million by the 2000 census. An additional 5.8 million were added by 2005.

One of the world's most populous countries

How does Mexico's population compare to that of other countries? Mexico's estimated population of 108 million (January 2009) makes it the 11th most populous country in the world (Table 8.2). This estimate is sufficiently accurate for making international comparisons but cannot be considered precise because it is heavily dependent on the rates of migration to and from the USA, which can change rapidly (see box).

Mexico's estimated population growth rate of 1.12% per year is lower than that of Brazil, Indonesia and the world as a whole (1.17%). The growth rates for Russia, Japan and Germany are negative. By 2050 Mexico's population is expected to overtake that of Russia and Japan but will be overtaken by Ethiopia, the Philippines and maybe Egypt as well.

Will Mexico's population growth rate continue to decline or will it stay constant or perhaps even

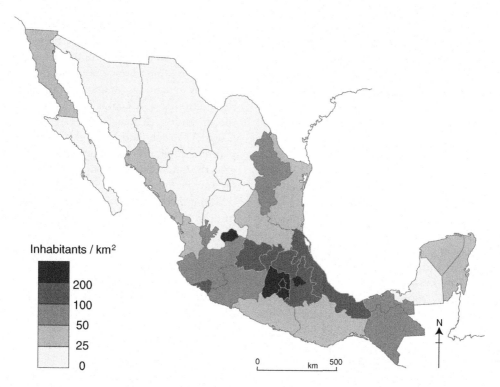

Inhabitants / km²

200
100
50
25
0

N

0   km   500

Figure 8.2 Population density by state, 2009[6]

Table 8.3 Population density of major countries in the Americas[7]

Country	Population density (people/km²)
Mexico	55
Columbia	40
USA	31
Venezuela	29
Peru	22
Brazil	22
Chile	22
Argentina	14
Bolivia	8
Canada	3

increase in the years ahead? This question has serious implications for Mexico's future. Some of these implications will be examined in the next chapter.

Wide open spaces surround crowded cores

Mexicans are not evenly distributed across the Mexican landscape. Some areas have very few people while other areas are very crowded. The population density of Mexico is about 55 persons per km² (142 per mi²), which is not very high by world standards, about the same as Iraq and Kenya. But it is considerably higher than the other large countries in the New World as indicated in Table 8.3.

Where do most Mexicans reside? For the last 500 years most of the population has been largely concentrated in the southern portion of the Mexican plateau. The highest concentration of population is in and around Metropolitan Mexico City, specifically the Federal District and the State of Mexico. These two jurisdictions make up just over 1% of Mexico's area but house over 22% of the country's population. The population density of 950 persons per km² is similar to that of Bangladesh and over twice that of the Netherlands, the most densely populated European country, or of New Jersey, the most densely populated state in the USA.

Population density tends to decline with increasing distance from Mexico City. The population density is quite high in a wide band across the middle of the country from Veracruz and Xalapa, in the east, right across to Guadalajara in the west (Figure 8.2). This band extends north to Aguascalientes and south to Puebla and Cuernavaca. This area covers a little less than 10% of Mexico's land area but is home to over 50% of Mexicans.[8] The population density in this area, over 270 persons per km², is about the same as the densely populated northeastern part of the USA[9] and higher than the UK, Germany or Italy. Surprisingly, this heavily populated core area is relatively mountainous and about half of it is within Mexico's Volcanic Axis which contains numerous active volcanoes.

The 90% of Mexico outside of the high density central band is still relatively well populated and has a population densities comparable to that of the USA. Its population of almost 50 million is larger than that of any other Latin American country except Brazil. While this area is outside the high density central band, it contains some areas of high population density such as around major urban areas in the north: Monterrey, Tijuana, Ciudad Juárez, and Torreón—

Gómez Palacio. The area south of the central band in the states of Michoacán, Guerrero, Oaxaca, Veracruz, Chiapas and Tabasco also has a relatively high population density, significantly higher than any of the other large Latin American countries. On the other hand, vast areas of several northern states are very sparsely populated including Baja California, Baja California Sur, Sonora, Chihuahua and Coahuila.

Disparities of population growth

From 1950 to 2005 Mexico's population increased fourfold from 25.8 to 103.3 million. Where did all this growth occur? Some areas grew extremely rapidly while others grew relatively slowly (Figure 8.3 and Appendix A). From 1950 to 2005 Quintana Roo's population increased over fortyfold from only 27,000 in 1950 to over 1,135,000 in 2005, an average of over 7% per year. This enormous growth of Mexico's easternmost state on the Caribbean resulted from the development of international tourism around Cancún and southward toward the Belize border.

Baja California's population increased more than twelvefold to 2,844,000, about 4.7% per year. Most of this explosive growth resulted from rapid indus-

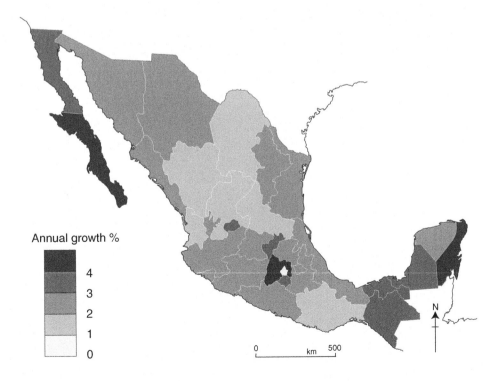

Figure 8.3 Population growth rate by state, 1970–2005[10]

trial and commercial development along the US border in the cities of Tijuana and, to a lesser extent, Mexicali. Tourism development also contributed significantly to population growth on the Baja Peninsula, particularly in Baja California Sur which saw its population increase eightfold.

Rapid population growth in the State of Mexico came from the expansion of the Mexico City Metropolitan Area. Another important factor was the rapid industrial growth of Toluca, the state capital. In 1950 the state had a population of about 1,393,000 and was ranked seventh behind Michoacán and Oaxaca. By 2005 the population had increased tenfold to over 14 million, making it by far the most populous state.

After 1950, the population of the Federal District initially grew quite rapidly but then slowed significantly. From 1950 to 1970 its population more than doubled from just over 3 million to almost 7 million (a growth rate 44% higher than the national average). However, during the 1970s urban expansion spilled over into the State of Mexico, and the Federal District's population growth started to slow significantly. From 1970 to 2005 its growth rate was less than a third of the national average, and its population grew only from 6.9 million to 8.7 million.

The expansion of Metropolitan Mexico City to the south resulted in a rapid rise in the population of the small state of Morelos. Its population increased sixfold since 1950, from 273,000 to over 1.6 million.

Campeche also grew relatively rapidly with the growth of the petroleum industry in the state. Its population increased sixfold from 122,000 in 1950 to 755,000 in 2005.

States in the northern interior of Mexico grew the slowest. The two slowest growing states, Zacatecas and Durango, have experienced limited economic growth and significant out-migration. San Luis Potosí and Hidalgo also grew relatively slowly. Though all four states managed to double their populations after 1950, their growth rates were significantly less than the rest of the country.

Two large southern, mainly rural states with limited economic development also experienced relatively slow growth. In 1950 both Oaxaca and Michoacán were more populous than the State of Mexico. However, by 2005 the State of Mexico had over three times the population of either Oaxaca or Michoacán which both experienced considerable out-migration. Interestingly, Chiapas, another large, rural, relatively underdeveloped southern state grew 20% faster than the total country from 1950 to 2005 and 50% faster than the rest of Mexico for 1970 to 2005. Clearly, out-migration from Chiapas has been significantly less than from Michoacán or Oaxaca.

The next chapter looks beyond Mexico's late 20th century population explosion and examines the key question of whether this extremely rapid growth will continue through the present century.

9

The dynamics of population growth

In the previous chapter we learned that during the second half of the 20th century Mexico's population exploded from 25.8 million in 1950 to 97.4 million by the 2000 census. By the close of 2005 the population reached 103.3 million. These data raise the question, "Will the Mexican population explosion ever end?" To address this question, it is necessary to look at the key factors that underlie population growth.

Population growth dynamics

The dynamics of population growth involve several basic factors including birth rates, death rates, fertility rates, population momentum and migration. This chapter focuses on natural population growth; the complex topic of migration will be examined in detail in later chapters.

At the most basic level population growth occurs when the number of births exceeds the number of deaths. Birth rates are commonly expressed as the number of live births per year per 1000 population. For Mexico in 2008[1] the birth rate was 18.4, compared to 28.6 for Mexico's southern neighbor Guatemala and 14.2 for its northern neighbor the USA.[2]

Death rate is expressed as the number of deaths per year per 1000 population. In 2008 Mexico's death rate was one of lowest in the world at 4.9, compared to 5.2 for Guatemala and 8.3 for the USA.

Natural population growth rate is the difference between the birth rate and the death rate. Mexico's natural population growth rate in 2008 was 13.5 per 1000 or 1.35% per year. Compared to Mexico, the rate for Guatemala was far higher at 23.36 while that for the USA was much lower: 5.87. However,

these natural population growth values do not include international migration, which can be a very important factor to a country's overall population growth rate.

Birth rates receive far more attention than death rates which everyone agrees should be kept as low as possible. The crude birth rate (live births per 1000 population) is of limited value statistically because it does not take into consideration the age and sex composition of a population. A better measure is total fertility rate which is commonly defined as the average number of children that women are having today.[3] In 1976 Mexican women were having an average of 5.7 children. Today in Mexico women on average are having 2.2 children, compared to 4.7 for Guatemala and 2.1 for the USA. The total fertility rate for Mexico has declined over 50% in the last 30 years.

A total fertility rate of about 2.1 children per woman is usually associated with a stable population with an equal number of birth and deaths. However, once a country's fertility rate drops to 2.1, it may take several decades for birth rates to fall enough to equal death rates. This occurs because a high percentage of the population is young and each succeeding year there are more females of childbearing age (assumed to be between ages 15 and 49). Even though these women have on average 2.1 or fewer children, births still outnumber deaths. Eventually, the number of young women (aged 15) entering the childbearing age equals the number of older women (aged 49) leaving this group. At this point the population stabilizes.

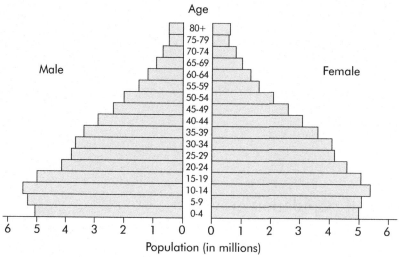

Figure 9.1 Population pyramid for Mexico, 2005[4]

Population momentum is the term used to describe the delay between achieving a fertility rate of 2.1 and stopping population growth. For example, Italy reached a 2.1 fertility rate in 1975 but its births and deaths did not even out until 1995. Population momentum can be understood by looking at population pyramids. A population pyramid indicates the age and sex structure of a population.

Figure 9.1 is the population pyramid for Mexico in 2005. The bottom three steps (for ages 0–4, 5–9, and 10–14) suggest that the number of births in each of the last 15 years has been declining. On the other hand, the pyramid for age groups 15–19 up through 50–54 indicates that 15 to 54 years ago (between about 1950 and 1990) each successive year had significantly more births than the previous year and population growth was very rapid. The large number of females between ages 0 and 14 will enter the childbearing age and begin having babies in years ahead. Even though they may have far fewer babies than their mothers did, the total number of births will greatly outnumber deaths. This population momentum will continue to increase the size of the Mexican population. Notice that in the 80+ group females significantly outnumber males.

Demographic transition

Demographers have analyzed the changes over time of the birth and death rates of individual countries and found that the trends which emerge are relatively similar for all countries. Based on these trends,

demographers have developed the demographic transition model.[5] The model helps to explain the population dynamics of countries over the last few hundred years.

Stage A
Hundreds of years ago, virtually all areas of the world were in a pre-modern demographic situation characterized by very high birth rates and very high death rates of about 40 to 50 (births or deaths) per year per 1000 people. In this stage women have, on average, about 8 or 9 children. But many die off young and perhaps only 50% live to age 15. The average life expectancy is low, usually less than 30 years. Very few people live to an old age. The population grows significantly when times are good and then declines significantly during famines and other difficult times. These ups and downs tend to balance out over time.

In this demographic situation which persisted for thousands of years overall population growth was very slow, perhaps 0.1% per year. At this rate, it may take 720 years for a population to double in number. Some indigenous groups in the Amazon, New Guinea and other places may still be at this stage but no nation on Earth is still in this initial Stage A of the demographic transition model.

Historically, in 1900 Mexico's demographic situation was similar to Stage A. Birth and death rates were relatively high at 34.0 and 32.7 respectively (Table 9.1, Figure 9.2). This resulted in a very slow growth rate of 0.1% per year. Of every 1000 children born, about 300 died before reaching their first birthday. Life expectancy was low at only about 33 years. The demographic situation changed very little during the first decade of the 20th century.

Mexico's demographic transition was interrupted briefly by the Mexican Revolution which began in 1910. During the Revolution, birth rates were lower than death rates and the population declined by about 6% between 1910 and 1920.

Once political and economic stability were achieved following the Revolution, the demographic transition continued into Stage B.

Stage B

With the onset of limited socio-economic development and urbanization, per-person income and nutrition begin to rise. Some improvement is also made in public sanitation, particularly with respect to water. In addition, some improvements are made in health care. As a result of these changes, a country moves into Stage B. Death rates begin to drop relatively quickly by about 20% to 30%, because far more children survive. Life expectancy increases steadily.

During Stage B, birth rates begin to drop a little but remain quite high as people continue to view children as a blessing. Children are also perceived as an economic benefit because at an early age they help produce food. People continue to have about as many children as they can because they fear that many, if not most, will die young. By having many babies, parents feel that some might survive to adulthood and thus will be able to care for them in their old age.

With continued high birth rates and falling death rates, population growth rates increase fairly dramatically, reaching about 2.5% per year. This allows populations to double about every 30 years. There

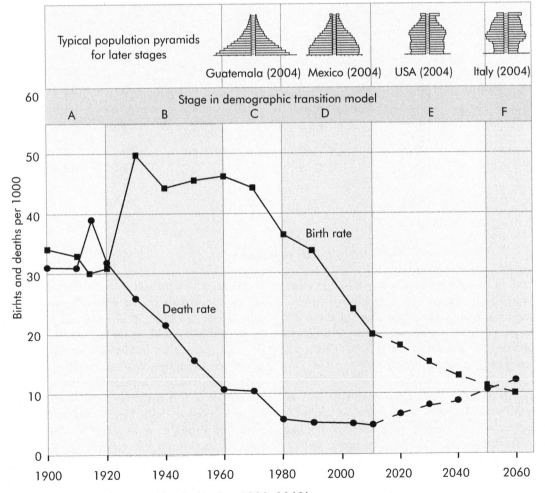

Figure 9.2 Demographic transition in Mexico, 1900–2060[6]

Table 9.1 Basic demographic data for Mexico, 1900–2050[7]

Year	Birth rate (/1000)	Death rate (/1000)	Pop. growth rate (%)	Infant mortality rate (/1000 live births)	Total fertility rate	Life expectancy (yrs)	Total population (millions)
1900	34.0	32.7	0.13	300	7	33	13.6
1910	33.0	32.0	0.10	225	7	32	15.2
1914	30.0	38.0	−0.80	225	6	30	14.7
1920	31.0	33.0	−0.20	225	7	35	14.3
1930	49.5	26.7	2.28	175	9	38	16.7
1940	44.3	22.8	2.15	140	8	43	19.7
1950	45.6	16.1	2.95	120	8	50	25.8
1960	46.1	11.5	3.46	94	8	58	34.9
1970	44.2	10.1	3.41	75	7	62	48.2
1980	36.3	6.5	2.98	53	5	65	66.8
1990	33.8	5.2	2.39	36	3.4	69	81.2
2000	21.1	4.5	1.66	23	2.4	72	97.5
2005	19.3	4.8	1.45	17	2.2	75	103.9
2010	**17.8**	**5.0**	**1.28**	**14**	**2.1**	**75**	**108.4**
2020	15.7	5.6	1.01	10	1.9	77	115.8
2030	13.6	6.6	0.69	7	1.9	79	120.9
2040	11.9	8.1	0.38	5	1.9	80	122.9
2050	11.1	9.8	0.12	3	1.9	82	121.9

Life expectancy

Studies of data from the past few hundred years indicate that life expectancy has increased steadily in most European countries at a rate of about 2.5 years per decade (25 years per century). In the developing world the increase has been higher, between 3 and 5 years per decade.

In Mexico, life expectancy in the 1930s was only 37 years. In other words, Mexican children born in the 1930s were only expected to live for 37 years. Of course, many lived far longer but an equal number died long before they reached age 37. Mexican life expectancy increased rapidly and was up to 54 years in the 1950s. It reached 60 years by the mid 1960s, 64 by the mid 1970s, 69 by the mid 1980s and, by the mid 1990s, was up to 74. Life expectancy in Mexico today is 75 years.

Women live longer than men; the life expectancy today is about 78 years for women and 73 years for men. It is amazing to reflect that in the 75 years since the 1930s Mexican life expectancy has doubled from its earlier level. If Mexico continues to increase its life expectancy by 3 years a decade, today's average Mexican newborn will have excellent odds of living to be 100 or more.

are only a few countries currently in Stage B. such as Ethiopia and Afghanistan.

In Mexico, following the Revolution, birth rates jumped quickly from about 30 births per thousand population all the way up to almost 50. This is approaching the biological maximum. Apparently, health conditions had improved and women had about as many children as they could.

The birth rate remained quite high all the way up until about 1970 when it stood at about 44 births per 1000 population. The death rate dropped steadily and dramatically since the Mexican Revolution when it reached almost 40 per 1000 population. It declined to 27 by 1930, to 16 by 1950 and all the way to 10 by 1970.

Stage C

As a country moves into Stage C, birth rates start to fall rapidly. Parents no longer want eight children, hoping to see three or four grow to maturity. Instead, they may have only five children and begin to believe that most or all their children will survive to adulthood. In addition, people in urban areas begin to view children more as an economic liability than an asset.

Death rates continue declining rapidly with additional improvements in income levels, sanitation, nutrition and health care. Death rates remain far lower than birth rates, thus rapid population increase continues. Countries in Stage C at this time include Guatemala, Kenya and Pakistan.

Mexico went through this stage of the demographic transition relatively rapidly. After 1970, social change and an aggressive family planning program pushed the birth rate down rapidly. The pace of reduction in the death rate slowed a bit, but death rates continued to drop

Stage D

As a society moves into Stage D, death rate reductions slow down and level off because the average age of the population is increasing. Obviously, older populations have higher death rates than younger populations. Eventually the death rate levels off at about 5 per 1000. This means that only about one half of 1% of the population dies each year. Meanwhile birth rates continue to decline rapidly. As a result, population growth begins to slow down.

Mexico is now in Stage D along with Brazil, Costa Rica, Indonesia, India and Israel. By way of com-

parison, the USA and Canada were at this stage in the demographic transition in about 1960. Mexico's current crude birth rate is about 19.0 per 1000 and its crude death rate is less than 5.0 per 1000, one of the lowest ever recorded for any large nation on the planet.

Mexico's death rate is low because it has a relatively young population, fairly good health care and relatively few old people. This enviable situation will undoubtedly change in the years ahead as the Mexican population ages. These changes may be predicted, to some extent, by looking at how the demographic transition has continued in countries like the USA and Canada.

Stage E

As a society approaches Stage E, its death rate starts to climb slowly because there are far more elderly people in the population. The fertility rate dips below the replacement level of 2.1 children per woman. But because there are so many women of child-bearing age, the overall birth rate is still higher than the death rate so the population continues to grow, albeit slowly, as a result of population momentum.

As women entered the labor force in great numbers in the later part of the 20th century, they began to view having children as a clear obstacle to their professional careers. In addition, the need to have children as a guarantee of support in old age diminished as government and other programs began to fill this need. As a result, more and more women decided to have only one or two children or perhaps none at all. In short, in the modern age, having children is no longer viewed as a necessity but as an expensive option. Countries currently in Stage E include Canada, the USA, China, and Thailand.

Stage F

When a society reaches Stage F, birth rates drop to the point where they equal death rates at about 10 per 1000 population. With births equaling deaths, population growth goes to zero. However, this stable population situation does not last very long. Most European countries and Japan are at about this point.

As Stage F continues, birth rates continue dropping. Death rates continue to edge up due to the overall aging of the population but eventually begin to level off. In this stage, death rates are considerably higher than birth rates. Population declines of roughly 0.5% per year are experienced. With very low fertility rates, the number of children is very small compared to the adult population (Figure 9.2).

Countries that appear to be in this stage now are Italy, Germany, Japan, Russia and the Ukraine. The current fertility rate in Italy (1.15 children per woman) is one of the lowest in the world.

With continued declines in fertility rates, by 2030 the populations of Japan, Russia and the Ukraine are expected to be declining by about 1% per year so that by 2070 their populations could be half what they were in 1990. This is quite amazing. For the first time in the modern era the populations of some major countries are declining steadily.

Predicting the future

The demographic transition model appears to be quite accurate and to fit the population changes experienced around the world quite closely. Death rates have fallen rapidly everywhere, despite some brief increases in countries ravaged by famine, war, diseases such as AIDS or similar upheavals.

With rare exceptions, birth rates are falling everywhere. The exceptions are the periods immediately following major wars and economic disasters. Declining fertility is the key factor driving down birth rates and population growth. In general, women all over the world are having two or three fewer children than their mothers and three or four less than their grandmothers.

The early stages of the demographic transition model saw the birth rate in Mexico fall to about 22, and the death rate to about 5. The later stages of the model provide some clues as to the likely changes in population structure that can be expected over the next forty or fifty years. As shown in Table 9.1 and

Figure 9.2, it seems likely that Mexico's birth rate will fall to about 10 per 1000 by 2060. Over the same time period, the death rate is expected to rise slightly before leveling off at about 12 per 1000.

One of the most dramatic population changes in Mexico over the past fifty years has been the huge drop in total fertility rates. In the 1950s women had about eight children on average. By 1976 this figure had dropped to about 5.7. It continued to plummet, to 4.4 in 1981, 3.8 in 1987, 3.2 in 1992, 2.8 in 1996 and to 2.4 in 2000. This trend is expected to put it at 2.1 by 2010 and down to 1.8 by 2060.

The net result of all this is that the mean age of the population will rise dramatically from 27 years in 2002 to 38 by 2030 and to 45 by 2050, with a correspondingly rapid rise in the population aged over 65 and a sharp decline after 2030 in the percentage of working age people.

This change in the population structure will inevitably provoke changes in consumption patterns and in the demands placed on educational systems, healthcare and a host of other services, presenting both challenges and opportunities. The percentage of the population under 15 years old is predicted to drop to 15% by 2050. On the other hand, in 2050 the over 65s will represent 25% of the then total population of about 122 million. Though Table 9.1 indicates that birth rates still exceed death rates in 2050, population is expected to decline slightly as a result of international migration.

The challenge of Mexico's late 20th century population explosion has been addressed successfully. As population growth rates continue to decline and eventually become negative, the new challenge will be coping with a rapidly aging population. Fortunately, Mexico should be able to learn from Europe and Japan who are already facing this challenge.

10
Indigenous peoples

In newspapers and the popular press, "culture" refers to such things as literature, paintings, classics and the performing arts. To social scientists, culture has a broader meaning and relates to specific behaviors, beliefs, social customs and adaptations that summarize the way of life of a specific group of people. The spatial dimensions of these concepts are the realm of cultural geography. The cultural geography of Mexico is an extremely broad field including ethnic groups, religion, cuisine, architecture, music and sports. In this chapter we focus on indigenous populations, ethnic mix and language.

Ethnic diversity

Mexico's identity is closely tied to its indigenous population. Unlike its two northern neighbors, most Mexicans do not regard themselves as transplanted Europeans. Instead, Mexicans generally view themselves as mestizos, a mixture of the native indigenous peoples already living in the region, the Europeans who conquered their land, and others. Mexico's national pride and self image are rooted more in the Native American, rather than the European, side. Mexican art, food and many other cultural traits are more Native American than European. La Malinche, Hernán Cortés' Indian consort and mother of one of the first mestizos, is viewed more as a traitor than a hero.

In contemporary usage, the word mestizo often refers to anyone who has adopted Mexican Hispanic culture. Seen in this cultural context, both those with a European background and those with a mixed European–indigenous background are referred to as mestizos. Mestizo, then, has become a synonym for culturally Mexican. This broad common usage of the term mestizo blurs the distinctions between various cultural groups.

In the abstract, Mexico as a country prides itself on its indigenous roots. However, in everyday life, indigenous groups are placed on the very lowest level of Mexican society. The term *Indio* is derogatory and full of negative connotations. This apparent paradox is a bit more understandable when one realizes that indigenous peoples are the least educated and poorest groups in Mexico.

Given that Mexico is a true melting pot, it is difficult to delineate clear distinctions between ethnic groups. Most sources suggest that the Mexican population is 30% predominately indigenous, 60% mestizo, 9% European and 1% other. These figures are only estimates; the Mexican census does not collect data on ethnicity. Many of those classified as predominately indigenous have merged almost entirely with the mestizo group. Available information suggests that about 9% of the population continue to identify themselves primarily with a specific Native American indigenous group.

Languages

The official language of Mexico is Spanish and Mexico is the world's largest Spanish speaking country. In fact, its population, now numbering over 105 million, represents about one-third of all the 330 million or so Spanish speakers in the world. Mexico's population includes more indigenous people than any other country in the Americas. About nine million Mexicans consider themselves to be indigenous, though only 6 million still speak their native indigenous language.

In 16th century Mexico, as many as 170 different indigenous languages were spoken. This number fell to about 100 by 1900 and has continued to fall since. According to the latest census, there are 62 living indigenous languages in the country, albeit some are spoken by very few individuals. This makes Mexico the world's fourth most language-diverse country, after Papua New Guinea, Indonesia and India.

Characteristics of indigenous peoples and their communities

Most indigenous peoples maintain their own identity and live in indigenous communities. They retain their own cultural values, system of justice and methods of organizing production. Indigenous groups maintain their own relationship with nature which sometimes emphasizes achieving harmony with the environment rather than adopting the European approach of trying to control it.

About a quarter of Mexico's towns or villages have a significant indigenous population. Over 13,000 localities are predominately indigenous in that over 70% of the population speaks an indigenous language. In another 4000 communities, between 30% and 70% speak an indigenous language.[2] Together, these 17,000 communities account for almost 7% of Mexico's population. The majority are isolated rural localities with under 500 inhabitants.

Indigenous Mexicans perceive themselves as clearly different from mestizos. They tend to view mestizos as aggressive, impatient and disrespectful toward nature. Mestizos, on the other hand, often contend that indigenous groups are insufficiently motivated and too constrained by tradition to deal appropriately with the demands of modern society.

Isolated indigenous communities are very disadvantaged compared with other Mexican communities. Indigenous municipalities represent about one-third of all municipalities in Mexico[3] but account for 48% of all highly marginalized municipalities and fully 82% of very highly marginalized municipalities. The incidence of extreme poverty in 2002 was 4.5 times higher in predominantly indigenous municipalities than in non-indigenous municipalities. In other words, the poorest rural communities in Mexico are predominantly indigenous.

Indigenous language speakers trail other Mexicans in virtually all socioeconomic characteristics (Table 10.1). About 33% are illiterate compared to the national rate of only 8.6%. Unfortunately, most leave school prematurely to help their families earn a living. Indigenous females are particularly disadvantaged. They get more than a year's less schooling than indigenous males and about half the national average. The fact that most mothers are functionally illiterate has severe implications for the health of their children. Almost 5% of indigenous infants die before reaching their first birthday. Over half of the children under age five suffer from malnutrition. Indigenous women suffer from poor nutrition and anemia; their fertility rate is 46% higher than the national average.

About 85% of indigenous households are below the Mexican poverty line and over half live in "extreme poverty". Over one third of houses lack electricity and over half lack piped water. Without a doubt, indigenous peoples have a far lower standard of living than other Mexicans.

Table 10.1 Mexico's indigenous population[1]

Characteristic	Indigenous language speakers	All Mexico
Demographic (2005)		
Population (millions)	6.0	103.3
% rural (<2,500)	62.3	23.5
Health (2000)		
Infant mortality per 1,000	48.3	28.2
Malnutrition < age 5 (%)	53.8	38.5
% Infant mortality from intestinal infection	83.6	27.3
Fertility rate (children/ woman)	3.5	2.4
Education (2005)		
Illiteracy (% of those >15)	32.7	8.6
Years of school: male	5.1	8.4
Years of school: female	3.9	7.9
% completing primary school	44.8	71.8
Housing (2000)		
% with electricity	65.0	95.4
% with piped water	42.0	85.2
% with drainage	12.0	75.4
Poverty (2000)		
Below poverty line (%)	85	50
Extreme poverty (%)	54	20

Blacks in Mexico[4]

Following the crash in indigenous population in the first hundred years following the conquest (see chapter 8), imports of slaves became a high priority. By 1570 almost 35% of all the mine workers in the largest mines of Zacatecas were African slaves.[5] Large numbers of slaves were also imported for the sugar plantations and factories in areas along the Gulf coast such as Veracruz. By the mid-17th century, some 8000–10,000 blacks were Gulf coast residents. After this time, the slave trade to Mexico gradually diminished. It is estimated that between 110,000 and 200,000 black slaves were brought to New Spain during colonial times and that blacks outnumbered Spaniards until after 1810.

During the 36 years between the abolition of slavery in Mexico (1829) and in the USA (1865), some US slaves fled south; as many as 4000 entered Mexico between 1840 and 1860. Early in 1850 several states enacted laws offering land concessions for black immigrants, in order that undeveloped areas with agricultural potential might be settled and farmed. Further groups of blacks arrived from the Caribbean after 1870 to help build the growing national railway network. In 1882, 300 Jamaicans arrived to help build the San Luis Potosí–Tampico line; another 300 came in 1905 to work in mines in the state of Durango.

Thousands of Cubans came after 1895, partially in response to their own independence struggles. They favored the tropical coastal lowlands such as Veracruz, Yucatán and parts of Oaxaca, where the climate and landscapes were more familiar to them than the high interior plateaus of central Mexico.

In many areas blacks have become completely assimilated into the mestizo mix. However, the legacy of blacks on local culture, especially musical instruments and forms, is still readily apparent today in several villages in Veracruz, notably the settlements of Coyolillo, Alvarado, Mandinga and Tlacotalpan as well as in several small communities on the Pacific coast along the Costa Chica in the states of Oaxaca and Guerrero.

Despite their extreme poverty, indigenous communities have managed to remain stable while collectively pursuing their relatively well organized survival strategies. Their belief systems and rich knowledge of nature remain intact. Over 90% of indigenous peoples own their homes and farm plots.

Indigenous people and language

As noted earlier, roughly six million Mexicans over the age of five speak one or more indigenous language. This group is the focus of most quantitative analyses. There are another three million Mexicans who consider themselves indigenous but who no longer speak an indigenous language.

Most indigenous speakers also speak Spanish which helps to confuse ethnic distinctions. Spanish capability greatly improves educational and employment opportunities. Even though the number of monolingual indigenous people has fallen sharply in recent years, more than a million indigenous speakers cannot communicate in Spanish which is a clear disadvantage.

The ability to speak Spanish varies by gender and indigenous group. Roughly 9% of indigenous males and 16% of females cannot speak Spanish. Spanish capability is relatively rare for some indigenous groups. For example, amongst the Amuzgo of Guerrero and the Tzeltal and Tzotzil of Chiapas, less than two thirds of the females over age five can speak Spanish compared to nearly 80% of the males. This is an indicator of gender inequality within these three rather large, but isolated indigenous groups which together number more than 720,000 people.

It is also the women rather than the men who tend to retain other local traditions of dress and social customs longer and thus assimilate more slowly into mainstream society.

Spatial distribution of indigenous groups

Indigenous groups predominate in some areas of Mexico and are practically nonexistent in others (Figure 10.1). Over 95% of the indigenous population lives in a belt of 14 contiguous states from San Luis Potosi, Hidalgo and Michoacán eastward to Chiapas and Quintana Roo. The remaining 18 states either have relatively small groups of Náhuatl and Mixtec migrants or isolated indigenous pockets such as the Mayo in Sonora and the Huichol in Jalisco and Nayarit. The main exception is the

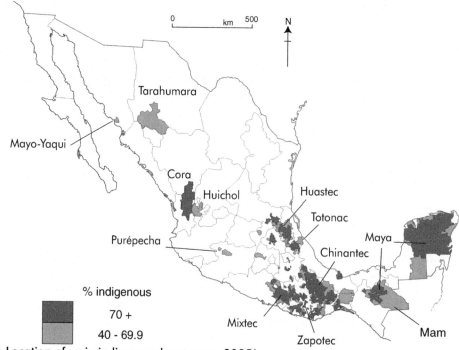

Figure 10.1 Location of main indigenous languages, 2005[6]

50,000 Tarahumara who live in the remote Copper Canyon region of Chihuahua.

As Spain expanded its territorial interests in New Spain in early colonial times, two major axes of economic development assumed considerable importance: the Mexico City–Veracruz corridor, the major trade route linking the capital to the port and Europe, and the Mexico City–Zacatecas corridor, the major route linking the capital to valuable agricultural and mining areas. It is no coincidence that it was along these corridors where indigenous languages and cus-

toms first died out, as the indigenous people were forced to become assimilated into the developing dominant culture.

Oaxaca is the state with the highest number of indigenous speakers—over one million, 35% of the state's population. The state has a mixture of large indigenous linguistic groups including about 350,000 Zapotec, 230,000 Mixtec, 165,000 Mazatec, 100,000 Chinantec, 100,000 Mixe and 40,000 Chatino. Oaxaca's very rugged physical terrain has isolated numerous indigenous groups which are largely cut off from mainstream Mexican society (Figure 10.2). As a result of its large and diverse indigenous population, Oaxaca is one of Mexico's most culturally diverse and interesting states.

Chiapas is the second leading state with nearly a million indigenous speakers representing 26% of the state's population. Indigenous languages native to Chiapas mostly belong to the Mayan language group. Chiapas' indigenous speakers include 320,000 Tzotzil, 360,000 Tzeltal, 160,000 Chol, 43,000 Zoque and 40,000 Tojolabal. Except for the Zoque, from 25% to 40% of these groups cannot speak Spanish and thus are isolated and very disadvantaged. Over 90% of Zoque speakers can also speak Spanish. The changing cultural identity of the Mam of Chiapas is explored in greater detail below.

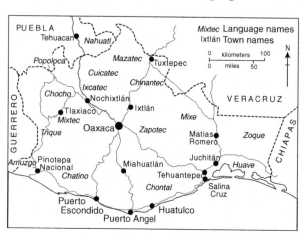

Figure 10.2 Linguistic diversity of Oaxaca state

In Yucatán there are about 530,000 Maya speakers, representing 33% of the state's population. There are virtually no other indigenous groups in the state. Over 90% of the Maya speak Spanish and therefore are not as isolated as most indigenous groups. Together, Veracruz and Puebla have about 1.2 million indigenous speakers including almost 720,000 Náhuatl speakers and 210,000 Totonac speakers. Because the states have large populations, the indigenous percentages are relatively small—12% for Puebla and 9.5% for Veracruz. Smaller states with relatively larger indigenous percentages include Quintana Roo (19%), Hidalgo (16%), Guerrero (14%), Campeche (13%) and San Luis Potosí (11%).

At the other end of the spectrum are several northern and western states that are less than 1% indigenous including Aguascalientes, Coahuila, Colima, Guanajuato, Jalisco, Nuevo León, Tamaulipas and Zacatecas. In most cases, the majority of indigenous speakers in these states are migrants.

Specific indigenous peoples and languages

The most widely spoken indigenous language is Náhuatl, the language of the Mexica (Aztecs). For simplicity, all language names used here, such as Náhuatl, include all minor variants of the particular language.

The 1.4 million Náhuatl speakers mostly live in central Mexico from Veracruz west through Puebla to Guerrero and north to San Luis Potosí (Table 10.2). Náhuatl is part of the Uto-Aztecan language family which includes most of the indigenous languages spoken in northern Mexico. Náhuatl is the principal indigenous language in eleven states though in some of these states there are only a few thousand Náhuatl speaking migrants. About 200,000 Náhuatl speakers over age five do not speak Spanish. Most of these live in small rural Náhuatl speaking communities. It is worth noting that Náhuatl is the source of numerous Spanish and English words of geographic significance such as coyote, chocolate, tomato and avocado.

Mexico's 760,000 Maya speakers almost all live in the Yucatán Peninsula. Over 90% also speak Spanish. This, and the peninsula's flat terrain, mean that Mexican Maya speakers are somewhat less isolated than most indigenous peoples of Mexico. As a result, poverty is slightly less prevalent.

Table 10.2 Main indigenous languages (number of speakers over age five), 2005[7]

Language	Total	% monolingual	Main state/s
Náhuatl	1 376 026	9.6	Puebla, Veracruz, San Luis Potosí, Guerrero, México
Maya	759 000	5.4	Yucatán, Quintana Roo, Campeche
Mixtec	423 216	18.2	Oaxaca, Guerrero
Zapotec	410 901	7.4	Oaxaca
Tzeltal	371 730	27.4	Chiapas
Tzotzil	329 937	28.0	Chiapas
Otomí	239 850	4.4	Hidalgo, México
Totonac	230 930	12.7	Veracruz, Puebla
Mazatec	206 559	19.5	Oaxaca
Chol	185 299	20.6	Chiapas
Huastec	149 532	5.1	San Luis Potosí, Veracruz
Chinantec	125 706	9.8	Oaxaca
Mixe	115 824	18.7	Oaxaca
Mazahua	111 840	1.4	México
P'urépecha	105 556	5.6	Michoacán
Tlapanec	98 573	22.1	Guerrero
Tarahumara	75 371	14.4	Chihuahua

Oaxaca is the home of the third and fourth most important languages, Zapotec and Mixtec. There are over 400,000 speakers of each language. Almost 90% of Zapotec speakers also speak Spanish which enhances their education and employment opportunities. While 23% of Mixtecs do not speak Spanish, tens of thousands of Mixtecs have migrated looking for work. Immigrant Mixtec speakers tend to live in Mixtec-speaking neighborhoods. There are about 16,000 Mixtecs in Mexico City, 14,000 in Baja California, 13,000 in Sinaloa and perhaps 50,000 in the USA. A sizable number of these migrants have very limited Spanish or English capability.

There are roughly 240,000 Otomí speakers in the area north of Mexico City. The Otomí environment and corn-based economy in the Mezquital Valley was essentially ruined in the 16th century when Spanish livestock seriously overgrazed the valley and degraded it into a semi-arid wasteland (see chapter 30). Somehow, the Otomí society managed to survive. Today over 94% speak Spanish and they are slightly better off than more isolated indigenous groups.

The Mam of Chiapas: regaining cultural identity[8]

The Mam (strictly speaking Mexican Mam, since there are also Guatemalan Mam) are an instructive study in cultural geography. Having disappeared from view as a cultural group, losing most of their traditional customs, they subsequently re-invented themselves, finding a viable way forward in the modern world. There are about 8000 Mam living close to the Guatemala border. They first settled in this area in the late 19th century, mainly in the deforested mountains of eastern Chiapas.

Mexican policies from 1935–1950 towards indigenous groups were focused on achieving acculturation so that the groups would gradually assume a mestizo identity. It was widely held at the time that otherwise such isolated groups would inevitably be condemned to perpetual extreme poverty. To the Mam, this period is known as the "burning of the clothes". Almost all of them lost their language, traditional dress, methods of subsistence and even their religion in the process. Indeed, for a time, the term Mam never appeared in any government documents.

From 1950–1970, the Mexican government opted for a modernization approach, building roads (including the Pan-American highway) and attempting to upgrade agricultural techniques in this coffee-growing region. During this period most Mam were peasant farmers, subsisting on corn and potatoes, gaining a meager income by working at least seasonally on coffee plantations. Working conditions were deplorable, likened in one report to "concentration camps". Plantation owners forced many into indebtedness. The Mam refer to this period as the time of the "purple disease" (onchocercosis), spread by the so-called coffee mosquito. Untreated, it causes purple skin, skin lesions and blindness. It reached epidemic proportions, devastating the Mam peasants who had no access to adequate medical services.

After 1970 the Mam gradually re-found themselves as official policy changed to foment a multicultural nation. Some, especially those who had become Jehovah's Witnesses, migrated northwards forming several small colonies promoted by the government in the Lacandón tropical rainforest on the border with Guatemala. Others, spurred on by Catholic clergy influenced by liberation theology, began agro-ecological initiatives.

For instance, one 1900-member cooperative—the Indigenous People of the Motozintla Sierra Madre—specialized in the production of organic coffee. The cooperative's agro-ecological initiatives benefited from the advice of the community's elders and rescued many former sound agricultural practices, such as planting corn and beans alongside the coffee bushes to avoid the degradation that can result from monoculture. It halted the application of agrochemicals and studied methods of organic agriculture and land restoration.

Its coffee, adroitly marketed, commands a premium price, double that of regular coffee sold on the New York market. The Mam have effectively taken advantage of modern technology, from phones to e-mail, to overcome their isolation and compete on their own terms, developing export markets in many European nations as well as the USA and Japan.

At the same time, the Mam have re-invented their cultural identity and helped revive their language and traditional forms of dance. They have also re-written their past. The revisionist version is that they always respected nature and lived in harmony with the environment. In reality, as historical geographers have demonstrated, this was not always the case (see chapter 30). Whatever the historical reality, the defense of the earth, nature and their culture has become central to the Mam.

11

The geography of religion

Catholicism

Mexico's population is predominantly Catholic but Mexican Catholicism is extremely varied in practice. It ranges from those who support traditional folk religious practices to those who adhere to the highly intellectualized liberation theology.

The Roman Catholic Church's role in Mexico goes back to the clergy accompanying the conquistadors. They came seeking souls to save and were relatively successful in that many Indians became nominal Catholics. In actuality, many accepted those aspects of Catholicism that meshed with their traditional belief systems but essentially ignored the rest. This "folk Catholicism" is quite different from Vatican-based Catholicism. Colonial churches were sometimes built directly on top of pre-Columbian pyramids (as in Cholula, Puebla) or employed pyramid stones as building materials (as in Tzintzuntzan, Michaocán), further blurring the distinction between pagan and Christian.

The relentless drive of early missionaries, of all denominations, to find more souls to save drove them to even the most far-flung corners of New Spain. In the process, they founded hundreds of missions, many of which quickly became architectural centerpieces for the towns and cities established by civil authorities as administrative and mining centers. The settlement pattern of northern Mexico, in particular, owes much to the tireless endeavors of these early missionary-explorers. The missionaries also served as agents of diffusion, introducing European agricultural tools, techniques, crops and domesticated animals.

Throughout the colonial period, the Catholic Church was a very powerful political force. Following independence, the Mexican government took numerous actions to limit the Church's influence. In 1857 President Benito Juárez confiscated all Church properties and suppressed all religious orders.

The current constitution, adopted in 1917, institutionalized many of the 19th century secular reforms and essentially precluded any national role for the Roman Catholic Church. It forbade churches from participating in primary and secondary education, denied legal standing to ecclesiastical marriages and ordained that the operation of church buildings required explicit government authorization. It also denied the right of churches to criticize the basic laws of the country.

Initially, federal and state administrations strenuously enforced the constitution, which provoked the bloody Cristero Rebellion of 1926–29 in western Mexico. After the 1940s, the government agreed not to enforce key constitutional provisions in exchange for the Catholic Church's cooperation in achieving social peace.

Since the 1960s, evangelical churches have dramatically expanded their membership. Motivated in part by this evangelical challenge, the leadership of the Roman Catholic Church began to speak out on sensitive public issues, challenging the constitutional ban on clerical involvement in politics. By the early 1980s the Church demanded the right to play a much more visible role in national affairs. Bishops denounced electoral fraud in northern Mexico and accused the government of corruption and human rights violations.

In 1992 the government removed almost all constitutional restrictions on the Roman Catholic

Church and re-established diplomatic relations with the Vatican. Even with improved church-state relations, tensions did not entirely cease. For instance, in 1994 the government was quick to accuse the Catholic Church of supporting the Chiapas rebellion and federal soldiers repeatedly searched diocesan churches in their pursuit of the rebels. The government also expelled foreign clergy who were accused of inciting violence and land seizures. In recent years the church-state relationship has mellowed and the Catholic Church has gradually become a more important political player.

While the population remains predominantly Catholic, allegiance to the church has declined steadily since 1970. In 1970 96% of the population five years of age and older identified itself as Roman Catholic. By the 2000 census the figure had fallen to 88%. Though the proportion of Catholics is declining in Mexico, it is still considerably higher than in Mexico's southern neighbors. For example, only about 70% in Guatemala are Catholic.

There are significant regional variations. Catholicism is strongest in a band of central-western states, extending from Zacatecas to Michoacán, where only one in twenty is not Catholic (Figure 11.1). In such

areas, religion is a strong force in everyday life, with visible manifestations not only in the number of churches and other ecclesiastical buildings but also in the cultural importance and frequency of religious festivals and processions.

In contrast, about one in six is not Catholic in the northern border states. In southeastern Mexico (Chiapas, Campeche, Tabasco and Quintana Roo), about one in four is not Catholic. Interestingly, non-Catholics are concentrated in both the prosperous northern states and in the relatively poor south and southeastern states.

The growth of other religions

The notable shift in religious affiliation and in church-state relations in recent decades has led to an increase in the number of non-Catholics in Mexico from under two million to over ten million.

Mexico's non-Catholic population is very heterogeneous. About three million Mexicans over age five (3.5%) said they had "no religion" in the 2000 census. Indigenous language speakers and males in rural areas were the most likely to place themselves in this category, which is almost 60% male. This group varied from under 1% in the most Catholic western

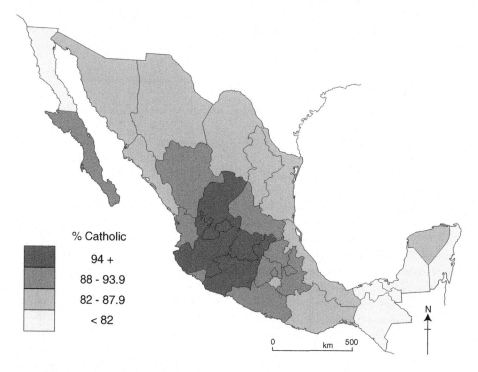

% Catholic

94 +

88 - 93.9

82 - 87.9

< 82

0   km   500

N

Figure 11.1 Extent of Catholicism, by state[1]

The distinctive landscape of Mennonite enclaves[2]

One of the reasons for the Mexican Revolution which began in 1910 was a demand for land redistribution. After the fighting ended (1920), large landowners in northern Mexico looked to sell part or all of their vast holdings before the federal government forced the break up of their estates. The government also wanted to encourage more settlement in northern areas of the country that had unrealized agricultural potential.

Among the settlers were more than 1300 Mennonite families (9263 individuals) of German-Russian descent who arrived from Canada complete with all their possessions in 1922, having been guaranteed by President Obregón tax concessions, freedom of worship and exemption from military service.

The Mennonites founded agricultural colonies near Ciudad Cuauhtemoc, west of Chihuahua city (where they bought 100,000 hectares for 600,000 pesos, or 8.25 dollars an acre), at Patos in northern Durango state and near Saltillo in Coahuila. Today, there are also several Mennonite villages far to the south, in Campeche.

The group's spartan lifestyle is reflected not only in conservative dress habits but even in the fact that their villages (campos) are numbered rather than named. The people are taller than the average Mexican, speak German and have northern European physical features. Today, about 50,000 Mennonites live in the Ciudad Cuauhtemoc area.

The landscapes of Mennonite areas are very distinctive. They transformed desolate areas of semi-arid scrubland into prosperous farms. Houses built of adobe on wood frames line the main street of each campo. These elongated street villages (about sixty in number) are totally different to the compact, nucleated villages found elsewhere in Mexico.

Surrounding the villages, and divided into blocks by wide roads, are large, relatively flat fields, which look more like parts of the US Midwest than Mexico. The farms are neatly kept and dotted with wind pumps used to raise water for irrigation. Tractors are common, though horse-drawn buggies are also used. The main crops are wheat, oats, beans, corn and, in some areas, apples. The Mennonites are experienced dairy farmers and their most famous contribution to Mexican cuisine is the production and marketing of Chihuahuan cheese (*queso menonita*).

While their lifestyles are gradually changing with the times, the Mennonites have made a unique contribution to the complexity of Mexican rural landscapes.

---

states to 13% in Chiapas, a state with large indigenous population.

The census divides non-Catholic church members into two groups, each of which has grown rapidly in recent years. The first is labeled "Protestant and evangelical". It includes Pentecostal and Evangelical churches which have grown very rapidly, especially in indigenous areas, and now make up 85% of this group. It also includes Lutheran, Methodist and Presbyterian churches which have had a small urban presence dating from the late 1800s and are now particularly popular in indigenous areas. The group also includes Mennonites (see box) and Luz del Mundo, a Protestant denomination founded in Mexico. About 5% of Mexicans are in this group but the percentage varies from less than 2% in Western Mexico to over 10% in Southeast Mexico.

The second non-Catholic group is labeled "Biblical, not evangelical." This group is still rather small but has grown very rapidly in the past two decades. It includes the Seventh Day Adventist Church, which is particularly popular in indigenous areas, as well as the Church of Jesus Christ of Latter Day Saints (Mormons) and Jehovah's Witnesses, which have so far had little influence in indigenous areas. The first Mormons arrived in Mexico in 1875. Several English-speaking Mormon colonies were established in Chihuahua (the most prominent today being Colonia Juárez) and Sonora. Mormon membership surged from 248,000 in 1980 to 617,000 in 1990 and more than 1 million in 2005.[3] Mexicans belonging to the Mormon Church have, on average, much higher incomes, higher rates of literacy and, interestingly, lower fertility rates than members of other churches.

Dozens of evangelical denominations have engaged in strong recruitment efforts since 1970, with considerable success in southeastern Mexico. In 2000, Protestants and evangelicals comprised 14% of the population in Chiapas and Tabasco, 13% in Campeche and 11% in Quintana Roo. Yet a significant evangelical presence has also appeared in several other areas, including the states of Veracruz and México where more than 20% of all Protestants and evangelicals live.

The growth of Protestantism in Mexico is associated with a variety of factors.[4] With the exception of the Mormon church, it has grown especially rapidly among low income groups, particularly in poor states and indigenous areas. Growth in the prosperous northern states appears to be related to proximity to the USA. For example, in Coahuila 12.4% of people in border municipalities are Protestants compared to only 8.7% in other municipalities. This increased incidence of non-Catholic religion in border areas may be related to the large influx of migrant workers seeking job opportunities offered by the maquiladora plants.

Protestantism has made particularly strong gains among indigenous groups. These gains are considered less a conversion from true Catholicism than a first time acceptance of a modern religion by people who previously adhered to Indian folk Catholicism. Protestantism, and especially Pentecostalism, is thought to be compatible with indigenous values and spiritual practices. Some Protestant groups have specifically focused their proselytizing efforts in indigenous areas.

The rapid growth of Protestantism in the past few decades is expected to continue for several decades into the future. Aggressive proselytizing by some Protestant groups has caused a backlash. For example, the Catholic hierarchy has encouraged local Catholics in some indigenous villages to expel from the village adherents of evangelical religions. Since the 1970s, some 20,000 indigenous people expelled from villages in Chiapas, including many Tzotzil from San Juan de Chamula, have resettled to form a *cinturón de la miseria* (belt of misery) on the outskirts of the nearest large city, San Cristóbal de las Casas. They lack employment, education and basic amenities. In other cases, some churches, including the Jehovah's Witnesses, have helped exiled followers found small, new settlements in the rainforest.[5]

With continued proselytizing, this backlash is expected to continue into the future. At the same time, the political power of the Roman Catholic Church has expanded greatly during the past twenty years and is likely to continue to expand in the years ahead. These trends mean that religion will probably be as powerful a force in Mexico during this century as it was in the 20th century.

12

The changing political map of Mexico

Political geography deals with the spatial dimensions and implications of political processes. In this chapter we investigate the evolution of Mexico's international and internal borders, the spatial hierarchy of governmental units and their responsibilities and the geographical pattern of voting behavior.

Political entities and boundaries

Before the conquistadores arrived, the area that became Mexico was divided informally into five large regions: Aztecs and Nahuas in the center; Tarascos and others tribes in the west; Maya, Zoques and Totonacs in the southeast; Otomí, Mixtecs, Zapotecs and Chinantecs in the south, and a wide variety of disbursed groups in the north. There were no formal boundaries. The Aztecs were definitely the dominant group in what later became central Mexico.

After the conquest, the Viceroyalty of New Spain had its capital in Mexico City and ruled an enormous territory including present day Mexico, the Philippines, Central America (excluding Panama), the large Caribbean islands, Florida and the southwestern portion of the USA from California through Colorado to Texas. During the 300-year colonial period, some of these territories were lost and the boundaries of internal administrative units changed many times.

How did Mexico's state and national boundaries evolve? In 1824, shortly after independence, Mexico became a federation of 19 states and six territories (Figure 12.1). Guatemala decided to split from Mexico, and Western Chiapas separated from Guatemala and joined Mexico. In 1842, Mexico seized most of the rest of Chiapas. The final piece of Chiapas was taken from Guatemala in the 1880s.

The 19 original states were Chiapas, Chihuahua, Coahuila y Texas, Durango, Guanajuato, Jalisco, México, Nuevo León, Oaxaca, Puebla, Querétaro, San Luis Potosí, Sonora y Sinaloa, Tabasco, Tamaulipas, Veracruz, Yucatán and Zacatecas. The six territories were Baja California, Colima, Tlaxcala, Alta California (which also included Nevada, Arizona, Utah and parts of Colorado and Wyoming) and Santa Fe de Nuevo México (New Mexico, Texas and part of Colorado). A small circular Federal District (8.4 km^2) was also delineated; this was doubled in size in 1854 before being reduced slightly to its current area in 1900.

From 1824 to the present, Mexico's national and internal boundaries changed significantly as a result of wars, political squabbles and conflicts. In 1830, after continual internal disputes, Sonora and Sinaloa became separate states. After putting down a rebellion by Zacatecas in 1835, General Santa Anna persuaded Congress to sever Aguascalientes from the State of Zacatecas. A more romantic version of the story contends that while putting down the rebellion Santa Anna met the beautiful Doña María Luisa Villa and promised her anything for a kiss. He got the kiss and fulfilled her desire of an autonomous Aguascalientes, under the governorship of her husband. Aguascalientes became a state in 1857.

In 1836, Texas declared independence as the Lone Star State. A few years later, in 1840 the states of Coahuila, Nuevo León and Tamaulipas declared independence as the Republic of the Río Grande. They rejoined the Federation after a short and unsuccessful war of independence. In 1841, Yucatán declared independence but was forced to rejoin Mexico two

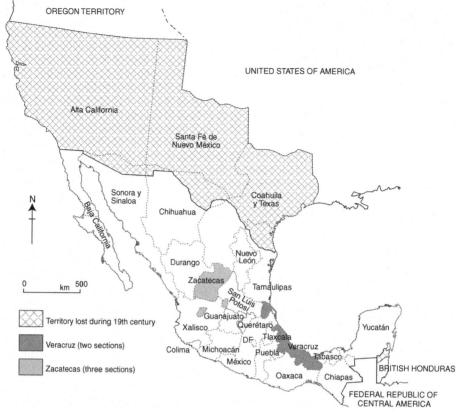

Figure 12.1 Mexico in 1824 and territory lost since independence

years later. It rebelled again in 1846 to form the Republic of Yucatán. It remained officially independent for two and half years before being forced to rejoin Mexico. However, this did not stop the rebellion, known as the "Caste War" which continued off and on for years. Chiapas was equally rebellious.

The 1848 Treaty of Guadalupe Hidalgo, signed after the Mexican-American War, ceded over half of Mexico's territory to the USA. A few years later, under the 1853 Gadsden Purchase (Treaty of La Mesilla), northern portions of Sonora and Chihuahua were transferred to the USA. This established the current border between the two countries. Minor disputes have occurred due to the migrating meanders of the Río Bravo (Grande) which forms much of the border between Mexico and the USA. Flooding during the early 1860s moved the Río Bravo channel south, shifting an area of about 2.6 km^2 (1 mi^2) from Ciudad Juárez in Mexico to El Paso in the USA. Both countries claimed the area, giving rise to the El Chamizal dispute which was resolved in 1963. A similar dispute, the Ojinaga Cut, was resolved in 1970.

The new constitution of 1857 affected many states. It merged Nuevo León with Coahuila. Aguascalientes, Colima and Tlaxcala all had their status changed from territory to state. The state of Guerrero was created from portions of the State of México and Puebla. Campeche split from Yucatán in 1863 to become its own state. A year later, Nuevo León regained its status as a separate state from Coahuila. In 1869, the states of Hidalgo and Morelos were separated from the State of México, greatly reducing its size. The creation of these seven new states ended years of political arguments and concerted efforts by local advocates.

The territory of Tepic separated from Jalisco in 1884 and gained statehood as Nayarit under the new 1917 Constitution. In 1902 the Federal Government carved the territory of Quintana Roo from Yucatán, cutting it to only one quarter of its original size. Baja California Territory was split into northern and southern sections in 1931. The northern section gained statehood as Baja California in 1954. The southern section did not achieve similar status until 1974, the same year that Quintana Roo became a state. This established the 31 states and Federal District which currently comprise the United Mexican States.

The political system

The current political system in Mexico derives from the Constitution of 1917 which emerged from the Mexican Revolution. The Constitution is a sweeping document that captures the ideals of the Revolution, but also reflects three centuries of Spanish colonial rule. The Constitution is "revolutionary" in that it aggressively protects the rights of workers, peasants and their organizations. It guarantees the right to organize, an eight-hour work day, the rights of female and child workers and payment of a minimum wage sufficient to satisfy the necessities of life. The colonial influences are evidenced by highly codified civil law, acceptance of heavy state involvement in civic affairs and business and the relative strength of the executive over other branches of government. Another important influence is Mexico's 19th century history which included foreign military occupations, loss of half the national territory and several virtual dictatorships.

The government of the United Mexican States has three branches: executive, legislative, and judicial. The executive branch is by far the most important and most powerful. The President serves a six-year term, may never be re-elected, and appoints the 18 cabinet secretaries who run their respective secretariats or ministries. The full cabinet meets only rarely. Legislation must be signed by the President to become law. Though the legislature may override a veto, the Constitution dictates that laws can only be enacted after being signed by the President. The President has the power to issue basic rules (*reglamentos*) independent of the legislature. In fact, most Presidents unilaterally issue more Mexican laws than are passed by the legislature.

The legislature consists of a Senate and a Chamber of Deputies. The 128 senators serve the same six-year term as the President and cannot be re-elected. Each state and the Federal District has two senators from the party getting the most votes in that state and one from the party getting the second most votes. These 96 senators do not represent equal numbers of constituents. Smaller states have greater representation. For example, in the State of Mexico there are about 4.7 million people per senator whereas in Baja California Sur there are only about 170,000 people per senator. The remaining 32 senators are elected by proportional representation based on the percentage of the national vote obtained by each party. These senators do not have geographical constituents.

There are 500 deputies in the Chamber. Geographic districts directly elect 300 deputies; the remaining 200 are elected by proportional representation. A party must win at least 2% of the national vote to get a deputy in the Chamber. They serve three-year terms and cannot be re-elected.

The ban against re-election means that every three years there is an entirely new Chamber of Deputies. Every six years Mexico has a new President and all new legislators. The ban on re-election diminishes the continuity as well as the overall experience and expertise of Mexican government at all levels.

The judiciary is divided into federal courts and state courts. The federal courts have jurisdiction over constitutional issues, most civil cases (contracts, labor issues, banking and commerce) as well as major felonies (bank robberies, kidnapping), except murder. State courts handle murders, divorces and minor felonies. The Supreme Court consists of 26 judges, selected by the President and confirmed by the Senate. Legally, they serve for life but actually submit their resignation to the new President every six years. Below the Supreme Court are four chambers of judges dealing with criminal, civil, labor and administrative issues. There are 16 federal circuit courts and 68 district courts.

According to the Constitution of 1917, powers not granted to the Federal Government are reserved for the states. State constitutions roughly mirror the federal constitution. Each state has a popularly elected governor who serves one six-year term and cannot be re-elected. The popularly elected members of the state chamber of deputies serve three-year terms. Non-sequential re-election is permitted. Governors generally have more power than the chamber of deputies. State governments depend on the Federal government for much of their revenue, some of which they funnel to municipal governments. Each state has a Supreme Court of Justice with judges appointed by the state governor.

States are divided into municipalities. There are 2458 municipalities which vary greatly in size and population. For example, the average population of Oaxaca's 570 municipalities is about 6000 while the average population of Baja California's five municipalities is over 500,000. Each municipality elects a new president and local council every three years.

Municipal governments have taxing authority but rely very heavily on financial support from state and federal sources. Municipalities are responsible for a variety of public services, including water and sewerage; street lighting and maintenance, trash collection and disposal, public safety and traffic, supervision of slaughterhouses, and maintenance of parks, gardens and cemeteries. Municipalities are also free to assist state and federal governments in the provision of elementary education, emergency fire and medical services, environmental protection and the maintenance of historical landmarks.

The geography of Mexican party politics

Mexico's three major political parties are the Institutional Revolutionary Party (Partido Revolucionario Institucional or PRI), the National Action Party (Partido Acción Nacional or PAN) and the Party of the Democratic Revolution (Partido de la Revolución Democrática or PRD). The numerous national minor parties claiming to represent such groups as environmentalists (PVEM), workers (PT) and peasants (various) sometimes form coalitions with national parties. Political alliances are the shifting sands of Mexican politics. For instance, whereas the Labor Party (PT) sided with PAN in the 2000 elections, it preferred an allegiance with PRD in 2003 and 2006. There are more than a dozen additional state level political parties.

The Institutional Revolutionary Party (PRI), with the stated intention of maintaining the spirit of the Mexican Revolution and Constitution of 1917, dominated Mexican politics from 1929 until well into the 1990s. During the 1930s President Lázaro Cárdenas championed the cause of workers, expropriating foreign oil companies and aggressively redistributing land to landless peasants under the communal farming system known as *ejidos* (see chapter 15).

By the early 1940s, the political processes and institutions that would broadly define Mexican politics for the next fifty years were well established. These included a strong federal government, dominated by a civilian president and his party loyalists.

A regular and orderly rotation of power among rival factions strengthened the de facto single-party system. Every six years, the outgoing PRI President personally selected his successor who would duly "win" a majority of votes in the next election. The PRI controlled all government ministries and most Mexicans had trouble distinguishing between the PRI and the government.

In the run-up to elections, the sitting PRI President often spent lavishly on inflationary infrastructure projects to impress the public. This led to a succession of financial crises coinciding with new governments. For example, López Portillo began his Presidency in 1976 and was quickly forced to devalue the peso by 50%; his successor Miguel de la Madrid fared no better.

During the late 1970s oil boom, the PRI government initiated a massive public building program funded with loans based on projected future oil revenues. When the price of oil plummeted in the early 1980s, Mexico could not afford to repay these loans and the economy plunged into a serious financial crisis. During this crisis, the stable, ritualistic pattern of Mexican politics began to crumble. Mexico had to obtain structural adjustment loans from the IMF and World Bank which were conditioned on major reforms such as decentralizing the economy, privatizing key industries and removing protectionist tariffs.

The status quo changed dramatically in 1988 when Cuauhtémoc Cárdenas Solórzano, son of the former president, left the PRI party to contest the presidential election as head of a populist coalition of leftist parties. Cárdenas proved popular with both the urban working class and the rural poor. Many observers felt Cárdenas had won the election but the central computerized vote tabulation system crashed. When it came back on-line, the PRI-controlled Elections Commission declared that the PRI candidate, Salinas de Gortari, had won. Fortunately for the stability of the country, the Mexican public begrudgingly accepted this result.

PRI's weak showing in the 1988 election seriously damaged its legitimacy and credibility. This, and strong international pressure, compelled the party to make concessions. After decades in which the ruling PRI monopolized every office, it began to accept electoral defeats in some state and local elections at the hands of PAN, the main opposition party, and PRD, the new leftist party. However, PRI maintained control of most aspects of Mexican politics.

In 1994 Ernesto Zedillo, the PRI presidential candidate, won a close, apparently fair election but faced an immediate economic crisis when he took office. Mexico devalued the peso and eventually accepted a $48 billion bailout loan from the USA. The bailout worked and Mexico repaid the loan before it was due. Zedillo later took steps to make the Bank of Mexico independent from politics, greatly improving future economic stability. The Zedillo administration implemented fundamental political reforms, separating PRI from the government and shifting power away from the Presidency. It made the Elections Commission independent and transparent, and ended the practice of each President appointing his party's next presidential candidate and the Mayor of Mexico City. Instead, they would be chosen by the party and elected by the voters, respectively. These reforms set the stage for clean and fair elections in 2000 and advanced Mexico's transition from a single party state to a relatively modern multi-party democracy.

The PRI is perceived currently as Mexico's traditional, slightly left-of-center political party. Its history and grass roots organization gives it a strong position in state and local politics. The PRI supports policies of mixed economy and nationalized industries, both of which are longstanding Mexican practices. It is nominally socialist but is perceived as a centrist party.

The National Action Party (PAN) was founded in 1939 by business and religious groups as a more conservative, Christian democrat alternative to PRI. The PAN appealed to conservative Mexicans as well as to Catholics in western Mexico who were frustrated with previous government suppression of the Catholic Church.

At first PAN was very weak, but by the 1960s it was winning some local elections and a few seats in the Chamber of Deputies, mostly in northern and western Mexico. Following the political reforms of the 1990s, PAN emerged as a powerful political force and by 2006 was the leading political party.

PAN is perceived as Mexico's conservative party. The official PAN ideology supports policies to address current national problems, rather than pursue a left-wing or right-wing agenda. The PAN supports conservative positions regarding free enterprise, privatization and smaller government alongside Catholic positions such as opposition to abortion and same-sex unions.

The Party of the Democratic Revolution (PRD) was founded by Cuauhtémoc Cárdenas along with other former PRI members and a variety of socialist groups after the 1988 presidential election fiasco. The party has a leftist ideology. The PRD had limited success until 1997 when Cuauhtémoc Cárdenas was elected mayor of Mexico City and the party gained 125 of the 500 seats in the Chamber of Deputies. Since 1997, PRD has gained considerable strength to become a major force in Mexican politics.

Elections in the 21st century

In the Presidential election of 2000, a non-PRI candidate won for the first time in over 70 years. The PAN's Vicente Fox, a former Coca Cola executive and ex-governor of Guanajuato, won the election with 43% of the vote. This election was hailed by many as evidence that Mexico had finally become truly democratic.

Fox's victory was almost a landslide: he won in 19 of 25 northern and central states indicating the strength of PAN in the largest and wealthiest portion of the country. He also was victorious in the southeastern states of Yucatán and Quintana Roo. The PAN did less well in the southern tier of seven states from Michoacán to Campeche and also failed to win in a block of four western states. The PAN also did well in congressional races where it won a plurality, but not a majority, in the Chamber of Deputies (Figure 12.3) and finished second to PRI in the Senate. The geographic pattern of PAN's congressional victories was quite similar to the Presidential voting pattern.[1]

The PAN did less well at the state and local level. It won 8 of 32 state governorships and 31% of state deputies but only 15% of municipal mayors. Its strength was once again in key northern and central states.[2] The 2000 election indicated that PAN was the leading national party and a very strong contender at the state and local level in northern and central Mexico.

The losing PRI presidential candidate, Francisco Labastida, won in 11 states including a block of four in the west (Sinaloa, Durango, Nayarit and Zacatecas), two in the center (Puebla and Tlaxcala) and the southern tier states (Guerrero, Oaxaca, Chiapas, Tabasco and Campeche). The PRI did better in Congressional elections winning a majority in the Senate and finishing a close second to PAN in the Chamber of Deputies. PRI was again strongest in the southern tier states and the block of four in the west as well as in Tamaulipas, San Luis Potosí and Veracruz.

In state and local elections, PRI voters elected 20 governors, 51% of state deputies and 70% of municipal mayors. Clearly, the old party's grip on politics at this level was still very strong. However, the PAN was seriously challenging the PRI in some of the most important parts of the country.

The PRD 2000 presidential candidate, Cárdenas, won 17% of the vote but claimed victory in only one state—Michoacán, his birthplace.[3] Though the PRD placed a rather distant third, it maintained its position

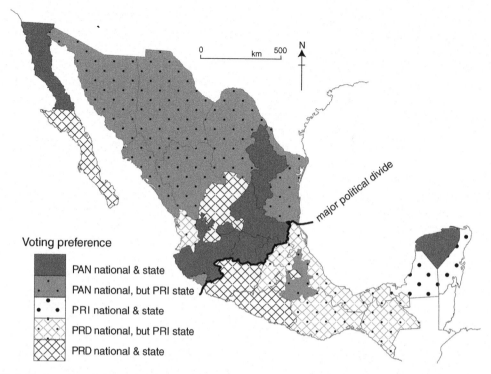

Figure 12.2 National and state election results, 2006
National: Percentage of votes received by candidates for national president, senators and deputies.
State: Percentage of votes for state governor plus percentage of seats in state legislature

as a major party with considerable strength in certain areas of the country, winning state governorships in Baja California Sur, Zacatecas, Nayarit, the Federal District and Tlaxcala.

The lackluster 2000–2006 Presidency of PAN's Vicente Fox demonstrated that Mexico had achieved true political separation of powers within a stable multi-party democracy. The period was characterized by low inflation and slow but steady economic growth. However, Fox was unable to implement his reform agenda because of opposition from PRI and PRD, which controlled the Congress; their control expanded after the 2003 midterm elections, further diminishing Fox's ability to accomplish his agenda.

The 2006 elections

The 2006 elections were a low point for the PRI. Its presidential candidate failed to win even a single state. The PAN candidate Felipe Calderón barely edged out PRD's López Obrador, 35.9% to 35.3%. Massive election protests by Obrador and his supporters did not succeed and Calderón was sworn in as President. Calderón was preferred by urban, higher educated, wealthier and right-leaning voters. Obra-

dor did better with male voters as well as left leaning groups and those with low income. The PRI candidate Roberto Madrazo, a distant third with 22.2%, did relatively better with older, rural, less educated and poorer voters.

The PAN also won a plurality, but not majority, of legislative seats. PAN won 52 senatorial seats compared to 39 for PRI and 36 for PRD. In the Chamber of Deputies, the balance shifted dramatically. PAN won 206 seats compared to only 151 in 2003. The PRD increased its number of deputies from 97 to 127, while PRI deputies declined significantly from 224 to 108.

In state and local elections, the PRI lost some ground to PAN and PRD but still maintained a considerable lead, winning 17 governorships compared to 9 for PAN and 6 for PRD. The PRI also elected the greatest number of officials to state legislatures[4] and municipal level positions.

In the 2006 elections, the PAN maintained its lead in national politics but lost ground in some areas of the country.[5] Six states switched from PAN to PRD (Baja California Sur, State of México, Federal District, Morelos, Veracruz and Quintana Roo) while two states—Sinaloa and Durango—switched from PRI to PAN.

The PRD gained significant ground in presidential politics. It picked up the six states from PAN mentioned above as well as an impressive nine from PRI (Zacatecas, Nayarit, Hidalgo, Tlaxcala, Guerrero, Oaxaca, Chiapas, Tabasco and Campeche). It is worth noting that between the 2000 and 2006 presidential elections only 15 of 32 states did not change parties. All but one of these 15, including a solid block of 12 northern and western states[6], voted PAN in both elections while Michoacán voted PRD in both elections.

Figure 12.2 shows the political geography of Mexico following the 2006 elections. In terms of national politics, Mexico can be divided into two generalized political regions. Northern and western Mexico tends to be more conservative and voted PAN in the 2006 national elections. The rest of the country tends to be more liberal and voted PRD.

The north-south split between PAN and PRD at the national level is quite stark. Virtually all the states south of a line drawn across the country north of Michoacán, State of Mexico, Hidalgo and Veracruz (Figure 12.2) voted for the PRD presidential candidate except Puebla and Yucatán. All the states north of this line voted PAN except for Baja California Sur, Nayarit and Zacatecas. Two southeastern states—Campeche and Quintana Roo—voted for PRD in the presidential election but are considered PRI states at the national level because PRI won impressively in the elections for national senators and deputies. It will be interesting to see if this north-south division is maintained in the next presidential elections in 2012. This of course will largely depend on the characteristics of the presidential candidates and the state of the economy.

When it comes to state and local politics, the clean north–south split breaks down because PRI remains the strongest party at this level in 18 states spread throughout most of the country. Eight states voted PAN in the 2006 presidential election but favored PRI at the state level. All of these states except Puebla are north of the north-south dividing line in Figure 12.2. Six states voted for the PRD presidential candidate but preferred PRI candidates at the state governor level (Nayarit, State of Mexico, Hidalgo, Veracruz, Oaxaca and Tabasco). All of these states except Nayarit are south of the line. Interestingly, two states near the capital—Tlaxcala and Morelos—favored the leftist PRD presidential candidate but at the state level voted for the rightist PAN candidates. This demonstrates the complexity of Mexican politics.

Eight states are aligned with PAN at both the national and state level (Baja California, Nuevo León, San Luis Potosí, Querétaro, Guanajuato, Aguascalientes, Jalisco and Yucatán). This solid block of PAN states also favored PAN in the 2000 election. All the states in the block with the exception of Yucatán are north of the political divide in Figure 12.2. These states are expected to remain PAN in future elections. On the other hand, PAN remains very weak in the three poor southern states (Guerrero, Oaxaca and Chiapas) where it received less than 17% of the presidential vote in 2000.

Six states voted PRD at both the national and state level: Michoacán, Guerrero, Chiapas, Federal District, Baja California Sur and Zacatecas. All of these states are south of the dividing line in Figure 12.2 except the latter two which are in the PAN part of the country. The reasons why Baja California Sur and Zacatecas are solid PRD states in the midst of the PAN-dominated northern region are not obvious. Undoubtedly, the PRD organizations in these two states are strong and their candidates are attractive to voters.

What factors explain the north–south political division? Three of the PAN states—Jalisco, Aguascalientes and Guanajuato—were the core of the 1920s Cristero Rebellion and remain the most staunchly Catholic part of the country. It is not surprising that they align with the PAN and the pro-religious policies it advocates. In addition, the northern states are generally more prosperous than southern states and consequently tend to support the more conservative, business friendly PAN.

The PRD is more liberal and populist giving high priority to worker and peasant issues. As a result, the poorer southern states tend to align with PRD. Interestingly, the Federal District which is the wealthiest and most progressive section of the country is the strongest supporter of the PRD. The PRD has controlled politics in the capital ever since Cuauhtémoc Cárdenas was elected mayor in 1997. In fact, the PRD Presidential candidate, López Obrador got over 58% of the Presidential vote in the capital, higher than in any state. Of course, Obrador had been mayor of Mexico City. He got over 56% in Tabasco, his home state, and 51% in Guerrero. In no other state did he get over 46% of the vote.

One possible reason for Mexico City's strong support of the PRD is the residents' dislike of the other two major parties. Voters in the capital have been so close to the national government for so long that they might have became completely disillusioned with PRI and its practices. Perhaps they still harbor ill feelings from the PRI government's role in the 1968 Tlatelolco Massacre which killed hundreds of students demonstrating in the capital, and its weak response after the 1985 earthquake.

The PRI 2006 Presidential candidate got only 8.5% of the vote in the capital and PRI has only 4 of 66 members in the local legislature. In addition, Mexico City is very progressive; in 2008 it voted in favor of legalized abortion and same sex unions, both of which are very strongly opposed by the conservative PAN.

The 2009 interim elections

The PRI made an amazing comeback in the 2009 interim elections. Aided by an effective campaign, voters blamed Mexico's economic downturn on the PAN, which had held the Presidency as well as the Senate and Chamber of Deputies. This, along with internal feuding among the PRD's leadership, convinced many voters to switch to the PRI which significantly increased its percentage of votes in virtually all states. It won five of six state governorships, giving it 19 compared to 13 for all other parties. The PRI also extended its already significant lead in state legislatures and municipal politics.[7]

In the 2009 election of representatives to the Chamber of Deputies, nine states switched from the PAN to the PRI[8] and five switched from PRD to PRI.[9] As a result, PRI more than doubled its members from 108 to 241, its highest number since the 1997 election. Members from the PAN and the PRD declined dramatically from 206 to 147 and 126 to 72 respectively (Figure 12.3).

The 2009 election suggests that the pattern of voter preferences in national elections has changed dramatically. The PRI can now be considered the leading party in perhaps 10 to 15 states. Six states are still held by the PAN (Aguascalientes, Baja California, Guanajuato, Querétaro, San Luis Potosí and Tlaxcala) while the PRD is clearly dominant in four states (Baja California Sur, Federal District, Michoacán and Zacatecas). There does not appear to be a clear leading party at the national level in the other states.

What will happen in the 2012 election? The attractiveness of the 2012 presidential candidates will greatly influence the political map. Interim elections can be misleading. The PRI performance in 2003 interim election was also strong but it fielded an unimpressive presidential candidate in 2006 and consequently did rather poorly in the 2006 election.

The geographic pattern of political voting has changed significantly in the past two decades. Such change will probably continue into the years ahead. Consequently, it is difficult to anticipate what geographical voting patterns will look like in future decades.

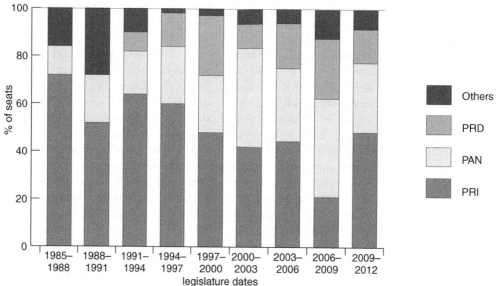

Figure 12.3 Changing composition of Chamber of Deputies, 1985–2012[10]

13

Mexico's cultural landscape

The term culture refers to a group's shared attitudes, values and practices. In chapters 10 and 11 we looked at two important aspects of Mexico's cultural geography: indigenous peoples and religion. However, the concepts connected to "culture" extend well beyond indigenous peoples. There are numerous manifestations of culture that we could have selected for this chapter but we have opted to focus on beauty pag-

eants, language, cuisine, music and dance. We then describe one possible subdivision of the country into distinct cultural regions.

Language

In chapter 10 we examined in some detail the pattern of indigenous languages in Mexico. However, linguists have also recognized patterns in the Spanish

Dialects of Spanish

- North
- Center
- West
- South
- Gulf Coast
- Yucatán Peninsula
- Chiapas

Figure 13.1 Regional varieties of Spanish in Mexico[1]

spoken in the world's most populous Spanish-speaking country. Figure 13.1 shows the regional pattern of Spanish dialects first proposed by Pedro Henríquez Ureña in 1921. Each distinct region has some significant differences in grammar, pronunciation and vocabulary. Many minor differences exist within each region, making it possible for someone with a good ear from Tamaulipas, for example, to easily distinguish between a speaker from Sonora and one from Zacatecas

Beauty pageants

Beauty pageants are one expression of popular culture. The first *Señorita México* (Miss Mexico) national beauty pageant was held in 1952 and won by *Señorita Chihuahua*. The contest was held annually (with three exceptions) until 1993. In 1994 it was replaced by *Nuestra Belleza México* (Our Mexico Beauty). The winner of Mexico's national beauty pageant represents Mexico in the Miss Universe competition. *Nuestra Belleza México* was founded by Lupita Jones (Miss Mexico 1990) who went on to become Mexico's first Miss Universe.

Location quotients allow us to look at the degree of unevenness in a spatial distribution. Have some states won Miss Mexico more often than would be expected by chance? Does the frequency of winners from a particular state match that state's share of the national population?

Figure 13.2 shows the location quotient for the states whose beauty queens have won Miss Mexico. The location quotient is worked out by multiplying the percentage of all winners from a particular state by 100 and then dividing the result by the percentage of the national population that resides in that state. For example, Yucatán has 4 winners out of 54 = 7.4%. 7.4% x 100 = 740. Yucatán has 1.76% of Mexico's population; 740 divided by 1.76 = 420.

The results reveal that *señoritas* from Mexico's northern states have dominated the competition. The popularly-held view, among single young Mexican males, that the country's most beautiful young ladies come from Sinaloa is borne out by the results of Miss Mexico: Miss Sinaloa has won no fewer than seven times. While there have been more winners from the Federal District than any other state, when relative population sizes are taken into account, Sinaloa comes out on top. These results do, of course, raise more questions than they answer about the possible reasons behind them.

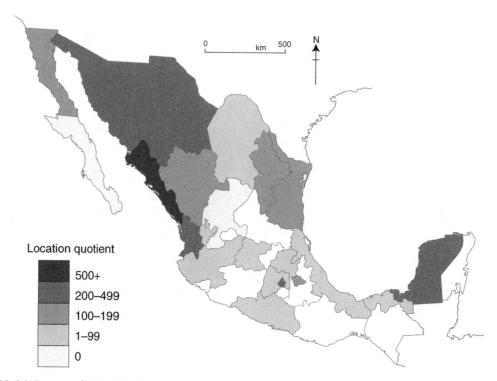

Figure 13.2 Winners of Miss Mexico

Figure 13.3 Regional types of music and dance[2]

Music and dance

Numerous different regional music styles are found in Mexico (Figure 13.3), some strongly influenced by indigenous instruments but most relying on the string and brass instruments brought by early Spanish settlers. Curiously, mariachi music, which is often considered Mexico's national musical style, is believed to owe its origin to French immigrants and refer to wedding (*mariage*) music. Other popular music types include *rancheras* (country style songs), *corridos* (songs telling stories, often about heroes), *norteño* (northern), rock and pop.

Musical instruments vary regionally as well. For instance, the marimba, a kind of wooden xylophone, is most often heard in Chiapas whereas the harp is more characteristic of Veracruz.

Regional dance styles have provided the stimulus for Mexico's numerous *baile folklórico* (folkloric ballet) groups, many of which tour internationally. Some examples of regional dances are provided on Figure 13.3

In addition to these cultural manifestations there are significant spatial variations among many other facets of culture, including sport, dress, architectural styles and handicrafts. Regional differences are also found in some forms of literature.

Cuisine

Mexican cuisine is extraordinarily varied and has become one of the most popular in the world. Diana Kennedy, the foremost authority on the subject, has devoted her life to researching the regional variations in ingredients, cooking methods and typical local dishes.

The ingredients used reflect different climates and ecosystems (chapters 4 and 5). For instance, corn (maize) tortillas predominate in southern and central Mexico while wheat tortillas are more commonly found in the north of the country. Pork and hominy stew (*pozole*) is largely restricted to the Pacific coast states of Jalisco and Guerrero. The grilled beef of cattle ranges in the northern interior of Mexico contrasts with the seafood found along the coast.

Cuisines are strongly influenced by trade routes and migration, especially the arrival of immigrant groups. Mexican cuisine is a fusion of indigenous and Spanish cooking, influenced in some regions by Cuban, Italian, French and other migrants.

On a more local scale, miners from Cornwall in the UK who came to work in the silver mines of Real del Monte in the state of Hidalgo brought with them their meat and vegetable-filled pastries called Cornish pasties. These were quickly assimilated into the local cuisine, and *pastis*, admittedly with some chilies added, are still sold in the town.

Main cultural regions

Factors such as ethnicity, language, music and cuisine all show clear spatial patterns and have enabled cultural geographers to propose the regional division of Mexico into distinct regions. One such division, first suggested by geographers Robert C. West and John P Augelli, is shown in Figure 13.4.

The major dividing line separates Indian–mestizo southern Mexico from European–mestizo northern Mexico, the former larger in area than the latter. The boundary between these two major regions is very similar to where archeologists place the northern limit of sedentary Mesoamerican cultures such as the Aztec and Maya. This is clearly no coincidence. Within Mesoamerica, the Spanish were unable to obliterate all traces of the existing indigenous societies. North of Mesoamerica there appear to have been few organized, sedentary pre-Columbian cultures and consequently little serious resistance to colonization. The cultural regions reflect the areas' pre-Columbian and colonial pasts as well as post-independence changes continuing to the present. Some cultural regions match physical regions (chapters 3, 4 and 5) suggesting that some cultural characteristics are strongly influenced by the nature of the land.

Most of Mexico's population inhabits Indian-mestizo southern Mexico, which is divided into several regions. The core area, centered on Mexico City and its surrounding conurbation, extending into neighboring states, has been the main cultural center and seat of power for centuries. Even before the Conquest, its lakes and fertile volcanic soils supported a high density of population. Many trading routes date back to pre-Columbian times. Cultural diffusion of Hispanic traits along these routes led to strong similarities of language and culture throughout this region; the remaining Indian enclaves are few and far between.

The mestizo west, which includes the Lerma–Chapala basin, is also very important in terms of population, agriculture and industry. It includes the second city, Guadalajara, as well as interior industrial centers such as Silao and León, and tourist resorts such as Puerto Vallarta. Pre-Conquest population density was not as high in this area as in the core and post-Conquest mortality rates were higher, resulting in a general lack of strong Indian traditions in this area. Rural house types are predominantly Hispanic rather than indigenous. The west remains strongly Catholic and is very conservative. In some regards, it is the most Mexican of all regions, being the birthplace of such distinctive cultural practices as Mexican horsemanship (*charrería*), the Mexican hat-dance (*jarabe tapatío*), mariachi music and tequila, the national drink.

The small, mainly agricultural, tropical Balsas depression is sandwiched between the core area and the southern highland. This rugged southern highland region includes almost all of the states of Guerrero

Ancient kitchens[3]

The three most important ingredients in ancient Mexican cuisine—corn, beans and squash—had all been domesticated by 5000 BC. Spiced up by chili peppers, this quartet of foods fully met people's nutritional needs.

Detailed analyses of soil by archeologist Linda Manzanilla, working at Teotihuacan close to Mexico City, now provide an idea of what was on the menu a thousand years before the arrival of Europeans. At its height in 500 AD, Teotihuacan was one of the largest cities in the world, with an estimated population of 200,000. Its elaborate water supply and drainage systems and a precisely aligned grid demonstrate masterful urban planning.

The city was so prominent that it became a magnet for craftsmen from far-away regions like Oaxaca and the Gulf Coast Plain. These migrants formed their own neighborhoods in the city. The food ideas and preferences they brought with them made Teotihuacan an excellent place for a cosmopolitan eating experience. The residents of Teotihuacan enjoyed a varied diet of plants and animals. They not only prepared corn, beans, squash and chilis but also ate potatoes, prickly pear cacti, hawthorns and cherries. For additional protein, rabbits, deer, duck, dogs, turkeys and fish were all on the menu, at least occasionally.

To liven up their cuisine, they had a plethora of herbs and spices as well as chocolate. Chewing gum and tobacco could satisfy their cravings, and various hallucinogens were available to stimulate their imaginations.

and Oaxaca. This is a generally impoverished region despite the fact that it includes several major tourist resorts, such as Acapulco and Huatulco, and the important provincial city of Oaxaca. The population of this region is unevenly distributed. Several indigenous groups such as the Miztecs and Zapotecs express a strong local identity through their distinctive economy, dress and social organization. They interact with each other and the outside world at regular, vibrant markets.

East of the southern highland is the strongly indigenous region of Chiapas, already identified as being economically very poor. Most settlements are small. During colonial times, neither the highlands nor the rainforest of Chiapas held much interest for the Spanish. The culture of some indigenous groups has changed relatively little since the Conquest except for the introduction of sheep and their wool. Non-Catholic religions have made considerable inroads into the culture of this area. The southern boundary of this cultural region extends well beyond the political boundary that separates Mexico from Guatemala.

The Gulf Coast region, comprised of Veracruz and Tabasco, is a major oil-producing and refining area.

It also produces a variety of tropical crops. The mestizo inhabitants, known as *Jarochos*, of these coastal lowlands have a strong regional identity expressed through language, cuisine, dance and music. The rural house types found on the lowlands are often distinctively indigenous in style.

The Yucatán Peninsula has transformed itself from a largely agricultural and somewhat isolated area in colonial times to a tourism-oriented one today, where dozens of archaeological sites and other attractions are supported by resorts such as Cancún. Many of this region's inhabitants view themselves more as *Yucatecos* than Mexicans. The local Maya Indians, now living in poverty, fiercely resisted Spanish settlers; many still practice slash-and-burn cultivation today, just as their ancestors did thousands of years ago. Some villages have Hispanic street patterns but individual huts of indigenous design.

The European–mestizo north accounts for 60% of Mexico's land area but houses only 26% of its population. As a whole, the settlement forms, rural house types and economic activities in this region reflect many more impacts of Hispanic culture than the area to the south. Remnants of indigenous culture survive only in small pockets in the northwest.

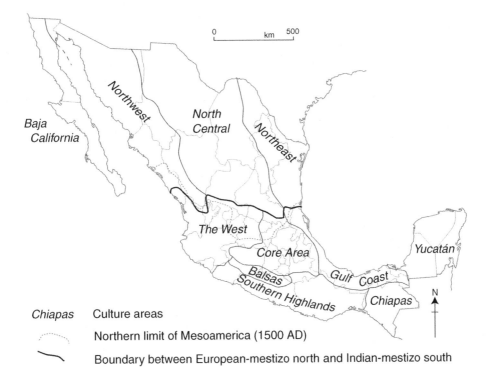

Figure 13.4 Main cultural regions[4]

Throughout the area, access to water is a fundamental constraint on settlement and economic activity. The northward movement of both settlement and economic activity during the colonial era has continued in recent times (see chapters 26 and 27). The mestizo population shows few signs of any indigenous heritage. This area is divided into four regions.

The northeast includes the industrial and commercial center of Monterrey, home to many of Mexico's largest industrial firms and conglomerates. The region has coal and gas deposits, agricultural areas and close ties to the USA. Its people are considered entrepreneurial and progressive. The cultural landscape is predominantly Hispanic in character, with an overlay of traits more commonly associated with the USA.

Besides the very arid Chihuahuan desert, the vast north-central area has large ranches and some intensively cultivated irrigated areas. This cultural region is very similar in extent to the natural physical region of the arid and semi-arid northern central plateau. Hispanic economic activities such as mining and stock-raising dominated this area in colonial times. Oasis settlements, numerous large haciendas, and rural house types also reflect Hispanic and Moorish influences. At the end of the nineteenth century and during the early twentieth century, state and federal authorities encouraged immigrant groups such as Mormons, and later Mennonites, to settle in this region.

The northwest, principally the states of Sinaloa and Sonora, includes not only the inhospitable Sonoran desert but also several highly productive irrigated areas of coastal lowland, and many important mineral deposits. Isolated pockets of indigenous people such as the Tarahumara and Seri Indians continue to eke out a living in this region, but mining, commercial agriculture and coastal tourism are the mainstays of the local economy.

The long, arid peninsula of Baja California remains quite isolated from the rest of Mexico. Old missions still stand in Spanish or North African-looking oasis towns. Manufacturing industry is concentrated along the Mexico–USA border. Many workers live on one side but have jobs on the other. Parts of Baja California have become the playground for well-heeled tourists, mainly coming from the USA.

The northern sections of all four European–mestizo regions have so many similarities today that some geographers have proposed a northern border (maquiladora) region. This new region has become culturally distinct to anywhere else in Mexico.

From this brief description, it should be clear that the boundaries between neighboring regions are not absolute, independent of time or set in stone. The boundaries will differ depending on the precise defining characteristics used. The characteristics which serve to define a particular region include every aspect of culture not just ethnicity, language and religion. Different regions tend to exhibit variations in building styles, music, cuisine, dance types, sports, consumption patterns, shopping habits, and so on. The full discussion of these is worthy of a book in its own right and goes well beyond the scope of the present work.

One potentially contentious issue related to consumption and shopping habits is the extraordinarily rapid rise in Mexico of major multinational chains such as Wal-Mart which first entered Mexico in 1991 and is now the country's largest retailer. Does the rise of major retailers signal the demise of the traditional corner stores or can they continue to compete? Will it take long for any changes to be reflected in the urban fabric and layout? What will be the effects on employment, culture and community life?

In chapter 18, we examine the processes of cultural diffusion and consider the important role played by several culturally-significant forms of mass communication, including *telenovelas* (soap operas) and *historietas* (comic books).

14

Economic activity: is Mexico a world player?

The Mexican economy changed significantly during the 20th century. Though agriculture is still important, its contribution to total economic activity declined dramatically and currently accounts for less than 5%. The economy today is similar to that of wealthy countries in that services account for about 69% of all economic activity. Industry is also important, accounting for about 26%. Mexico has a free market, export-oriented economy composed of a mixture of modern and pre-modern activities. Public enterprises such as Pemex, the state owned petroleum monopoly, are important but in recent years the government has made efforts to expand private competition in railroads, airports, shipping ports, electricity, telecommunications, and natural gas distribution.

Mexico is sometimes considered an insignificant economic player because it is over-shadowed by its large and economically very powerful northern neighbor, the USA. However, a comparison of Mexico with the other large countries of the world reveals that the Mexican economy is actually quite significant.

The size of the economy

What yardstick can be used to compare Mexico with other countries? The commonly used measure is Gross Domestic Product (GDP), the total value of all final goods and services produced within a nation in a given year. GDP numbers are normally generated using national systems of accounts. Such accounts usually do not include informal sector economic activity such as petty trade or part-time household help. They also exclude important, but unreported or illegal, economic activity such as drug trade. Fur-

thermore, GDP figures do not include unpaid work such as that performed by housewives. Official GDP figures tend to underestimate the total GDP of a country but do provide a relatively good yardstick for comparing countries.

Mexico's estimated GDP in 2008 was $1.58 trillion (Table 14.1). This figure is based on purchasing power parity (PPP) which overcomes gross distortions resulting from differences in exchange rates. For example, a haircut of the exact same quality might cost $15 in the USA, $5 in Mexico and $1 in China. Using the PPP approach, this same haircut would count as a $15 contribution to the GDP of each of the three countries.

If the informal sector and other unreported activities were added, Mexico's GDP would be closer to $2 trillion (see box). The Mexican economy is the 11th largest among the world's 200 or so countries. Though it is small compared to the USA, Mexico's GDP is more than two-thirds that of the United Kingdom or France, and greater than Spain and Canada. Mexico's economy is over twice as large as the economies of the Netherlands, Argentina, Saudi Arabia and Poland, and over 20 times larger than Guatemala, its southern neighbor. Clearly, Mexico is a significant player in the world economy even if still overshadowed by its northern neighbor.

GDP growth rates are important because they reveal trends and give insights into what the economy will do in future years. The Mexican GDP growth rate in 2008 was estimated at 2.0%. Growth rates can change dramatically from year to year and declined significantly following the worldwide economic crisis that started in late 2008.

Economic activity per person

What are the economic characteristics of a wealthy country? Most of us think of a country's overall wealth or relative level of economic wellbeing in per person terms as opposed to the overall size of the economy. For example, we tend to think of Switzerland as a richer country than India, although India's economy is over ten times larger than Switzerland's.

There are numerous theories which seek to explain why some countries are wealthier than others[1].

Table 14.1 Gross Domestic Product (purchasing power parity) and Gini coefficient, 2008[2]

	Country	2008 GDP ($ billions)	GDP / person (US$)	Gini coefficient
	WORLD	51 410	10 500	na
1	USA	14 960	48 000	45
2	China	7 800	6 100	47
3	Japan	4 487	35 300	38
4	India	3 319	2 900	37
5	Germany	2 863	34 800	27
6	UK	2 279	37 400	34
7	Russia	2 225	15 800	42
8	France	2 097	32 700	33
9	Brazil	2 030	10 300	57
10	Italy	1 801	31 000	32
11	Mexico	1 578	14 400	48
12	Spain	1 378	34 100	32
13	Canada	1 336	40 200	32
14	South Korea	1 312	27 100	31
15	Indonesia	932	3 900	39
16	Turkey	931	12 900	44
17	Iran	860	13 100	45
18	Australia	825	39 300	31
19	Taiwan	757	33 000	33
20	Netherlands	688	41 300	31
21	Poland	685	17 800	35
22	Saudi Arabia	600	21 300	na
23	Argentina	585	14 500	49
24	Thailand	570	8 700	42
25	South Africa	506	10 400	65

Adam Smith in his 1776 classic *The Wealth of Nations* posited that nations become rich through individual self-interest, capitalist investment, free trade and the invisible hand of markets based on supply and demand. Capitalist imperialism holds that capital invested in poor countries promotes growth but that the benefits of this growth accrue to capitalists in wealthy countries. Colonialism supports capitalist imperialism; colonial powers control or exploit colonies to ensure a flow of wealth to colonial governments or their capitalists. According to modernization theories, which first appeared after the second world war, countries become wealthier by passing through a series of stages from traditional, fatalistic pre-modern cultures to societies characterized by capitalism, meritocracy and democracy. The problem with modernization theories is that they ignore interrelationships among economies, implicitly assuming that economies operate in a vacuum.

Dependency theories, which emerged in the 1960s, posit that wealthy, core, manufacturing countries control the terms of trade and keep poorer, agricultural periphery countries in their impoverished dependent situation. These theories, which draw heavily from Marx, argue that the dependency relationships are fostered by very powerful transnational corporations, core country governments and international organizations like the International Monetary Fund (IMF). Critics of dependency theory argue that several developing countries, like Korea, Taiwan, Mexico and Brazil, have managed to industrialize and grow economically by working closely with the wealthy core countries. Some have dubbed these middle income countries as semi-periphery countries which remain dependent upon wealthy core nations. However, many of these countries, such as Korea, have large industrial investments in developing countries and thus behave like core countries. Some political scientists have argued that these so-called semi-periphery nations have essentially bought into the world economy and thus act as a stabilizing buffer between the core and periphery countries.

In the latter part of the 20th century the concept of globalization gained widespread popularity. Capitalists, generally from wealthy countries and often acting through transnational corporations, started investing heavily in developing countries to take advantage of low wages and looser environmental and other restrictions. As a result, there has been very rapid expansion of developing world manufacturing of consumer goods, mainly destined for the wealthy core countries. While this has increased employment and incomes in the developing world, the dominant core-periphery dependency relationships have grown even stronger. Furthermore, with rapidly expanding world trade and the growing strength of transnational corporations, economic analysis focused on the nation-state is becoming less relevant.

Mexico is in a group of "middle income" or semi-periphery countries which also includes Brazil, Argentina, and most of Eastern Europe. These countries are somewhere between the wealthy core countries and the so-called developing world countries. Many Mexicans are involved in typical developing country economic activities such as small scale farming, petty trading, low skill wage labor and the like. On the other hand, some Mexicans are billionaire capitalists and control very powerful transnational corporations. Millions of Mexicans work in typical core country positions as entrepreneurs, corporate executives, engineers, accountants, doctors, lawyers, etc. There is no distinct line between these core and periphery type economic activities, only hundreds of shades of grey. The core-periphery dependency model operates between countries on the world scale but also within countries such as Mexico.

Table 14.1 shows the GDP per person for the world's 25 largest economies on a Purchasing Power Parity (PPP) basis. Mexico's per person GDP in 2008 was an estimated $14,400. This is a significant amount. It suggests that, on average, the Mexican economy produces almost $60,000 worth of goods and services each year for a typical four-person Mexican family. Mexico's figure is about 37% above the world average. It is almost the same as that of Argentina and a bit higher than that of Turkey and Iran. Mexico's per person GDP is about a third that of the USA and Canada but more than twice that of China, about five times that of India and almost three times that of its neighboring Central American countries.

Structure of the economy

What does Mexico do to produce its national income? In looking at economic activities, it is useful to break the economy into three basic types of activities. Definitions vary, but we consider primary activities to include agriculture, fishing, forestry and mining (including petroleum extraction). Secondary

How important is the informal sector?

Studies carried out by INEGI and various academic researchers suggest that people working informally (without paying tax) generate economic activity equivalent to 22.2% of GDP. By way of comparison, the world average is believed to be around 33% of GDP.

Firms operating in the informal sector may enjoy a competitive advantage over legally established enterprises but it is not entirely a one-way street. For instance, they provide employment for an estimated 12.5 million people, or 28% of the non-agricultural workforce. In addition, 28.3% of the revenue received by informal activities is spent on power, water, telephone, fuel and other raw materials.

Informal businesses account for a significant proportion (21.5%) of total activity in the restaurant and commerce sectors but also play an important part in other service industries (16.4%), transportation (11.5%) and construction (11%).[3]

activities include electricity generation, manufacturing (which transforms raw materials into useful products) and construction. Tertiary activities are all types of services such as wholesaling, retailing, health care, education, entertainment, accounting and transportation. However, it should be noted that INEGI chooses to classify mining and petroleum extraction as secondary activities rather than primary activities.

Though Mexico used to be a predominately agricultural country, it no longer is. In fact, these days, agriculture (including fishing and forestry) accounts for only about 4% of the total economic production, compared to 1% in the USA and 2% in Canada (Figure 14.1). However, about 15% of the labor force is engaged in agriculture. With 15% of the labor force producing only 4% of economic production, it is clear that those engaged in agriculture are not as productive and do not earn as much as those working in other sectors. Agricultural workers in Mexico are amongst the poorest members of society.

Secondary activities account for 27% of the economy in Mexico, compared to 29% in Canada but only 20% in the USA; they provide 26% of all jobs. Unlike the USA and Canada, where manufacturing jobs are declining every day, manufacturing jobs in Mexico seem to be more or less holding their own.

The tertiary sector accounts for 59% of all jobs in Mexico and 69% of the economy, compared to 79% of the economy in the USA and 69% in Canada. By comparison, services account for only 53% of the GDP in India and 30% in Nigeria because these countries have higher percentages in agriculture. In general, as a country develops (see Figure 14.2), people move from agriculture to manufacturing and then to services. But this does not necessarily mean that service jobs are higher paying; doctors and lawyers have service jobs, but so too do fast food employees, petty traders and street sweepers.

Income distribution

Per person income data indicate average income levels but do not usually tell us much about income levels for the majority of people in a country. In virtually all countries, there are some extremely rich people whose incomes boost the averages significantly. For example, if an area has ten people, nine of them with incomes of only $3000 a year ($250 a month) and one with an income of $1,000,000 a year, the average income for the area is over $100,000 a year. This suggests that people in the area are rather wealthy. Actually, one is extremely wealthy while nine are extremely poor. Therefore, when looking at per person income levels it is important to look at income distribution.

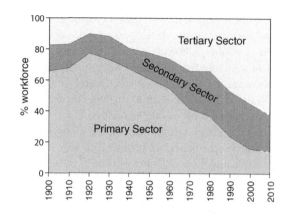

Figure 14.2 Employment structure, 1895–2005[5]

Income distribution information is important for several reasons. When combined with per person income data, it indicates the standard of living of the majority of people as well as that of the poorest segments of society. It also indicates a country's concern for equity. Countries focused on social equity put in place tax and social systems that reduce the gap between the richest members of society and the middle and lower income groups.

Income distribution information can also reveal information about relative poverty and the way middle and lower income groups feel about their situation when compared to the wealthiest people in their country. For example, a family of four with an income of $30,000 might feel wealthy if they lived in India but poor if they lived in the USA. Relative poverty is an important aspect of the quality of life, discussed more fully in chapter 29.

There is considerable literature on the relationship between income inequality and economic growth. Simon Kuznets' classic model of income distribution holds that as an economy begins to industrialize, inequality increases.[6] Then it levels off and later, as the total economy becomes modernized, declines. Thus, in the long term, inequality first goes up, levels off and then comes down in the form of an inverted "U". According to Kuznets' model, we would expect premodern economies to have low levels of inequality, industrializing economies to have high levels of inequality, and post-industrial economies to have lower levels of inequality. However, the Kuznets' classical model has not been consistently supported by empirical studies, which indicate that inequality does

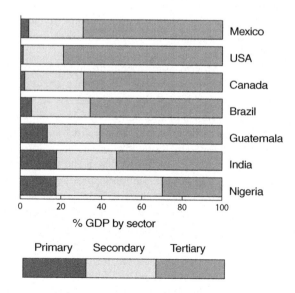

Figure 14.1 Economic structures, 2007[4]

not necessarily change very much as economies grow from lower to middle to upper income levels.

Numerous empirical studies have been conducted on the impact of income inequality on economic growth as well as the impact of economic growth on inequality. The results of these studies are inconclusive. Obviously, the relationship is complicated. An important aspect is whether the cause of income inequality is from differences in asset ownership, differences in productivity, or due to external events such as regional wars, famines, market collapse, drastic technological change, etc. Government policy can also play an important role.

What is the distribution of income in Mexico? In 2005 per person income for the richest 10% in Mexico was $44,035. This figure is over four times the national average, indicating that per person income in Mexico is very unequally distributed. In fact only two countries—Brazil and South Africa—in the top twenty-five economies are more unequal. The average for all twenty-five countries (Table 14.1) is about three times the national average. The distribution in Japan and Italy is far more equitable; in both countries, the highest 10% get only about twice the national average.[7]

The richest 10% in Mexico are wealthy even by world standards. Their income is about 30% more than the vast majority (middle 60%) in the USA. A four person Mexican family in this group has an annual income of over $175,000, an impressive income level in any society.

The vast majority of Mexicans, the middle 60%, had a per person income of $6882 in 2005. This group gets about 35% less than the national average and less than one sixth that of the richest 10%. Many people in this group feel relatively poor when they compare themselves with the life style of the upper 10% which is often portrayed in TV shows, magazines and films.

The poorest 20% in Mexico, over 20 million people, had per person income of only $1848 in 2005. This is only slightly more than the lowest 20% in Indonesia even though Mexico's overall per person income is three times greater than Indonesia's. In other words, on average, Mexicans are three times as wealthy as Indonesians but the low income group in Mexico is about as poor as Indonesia's low income group.

Mexico's lowest 20% get only 1/24th of what the highest 10% receive. In Brazil the situation is

> ## Mexican billionaires
>
> Carlos Slim, the telecommunications magnate, is worth about $60 billion, according to the 2008 Forbes Magazine list of the world's billionaires, making him the richest person in Latin America and the second richest man in the world.
>
> Nine other Mexicans made the Forbes billionaires list: Jerónimo Arango (Wal-Mart de México), Lorenzo Zambrano (Cemex), Alberto Bailleres (Industrias Peñoles, mining), Roberto Hernández (banking), Alfredo Harp Helú (banking), Ricardo Salinas Pliego (Grupo Electra, Banco Azteca), Germán Larrea Mota-Velasco (Grupo Mexico, mining), Isaac Saba Raffoul (Grupo Casa Saba, pharmaceuticals) and Emilio Azcarraga Jean (Grupo Televisa).

far worse: the low income group receives only about 1/44th as much as the wealthiest 10%. In contrast, the income distribution is far more equitable in Japan where the low income group gets about one-quarter as much as the highest 10%.

The Gini index is another way of quantifying inequalities of wealth or income. Without going into all the mathematical details, Gini index values range from 0 (perfect equality) to 100 (extreme inequality with all wealth in the hands of a single individual). The Gini index at a national scale usually falls between 25 and 70. It provides a very useful way to compare income inequalities between countries or to analyze trends in income inequality over time.

In general, the Gini index (Table 14.1) loosely correlates with development since most developed countries have lower Gini values (usually below 36) than more developing countries where the values often exceed 40. However, there are many notable exceptions including the USA which has a Gini index of 45, higher than might be expected, and Bangladesh and Ethiopia, which have relatively low Gini values of 33 and 30 respectively.

Mexico's Gini index of 48 is high, indicating that inequality remains a real issue. There is little evidence that the index has fallen significantly since the 1990s.

In Mexico's case, its informal sector, not reflected in Gini calculations, may serve to ameliorate the

Table 14.2 GDP per person by state, 2007[8]

Rank	State	GDP per person ($)
1	Federal District	23 130
2	Nuevo León	16 342
3	Campeche	15 175
4	Quintana Roo	13 342
5	Coahuila	12 474
6	Chihuahua	12 338
7	Baja California	11 365
8	Baja California Sur	10 820
9	Aguascalientes	10 663
10	Sonora	10 336
11	Tamaulipas	10 200
12	Querétaro	9 940
13	Jalisco	8 631
14	Colima	8 618
15	Durango	8 140
16	Morelos	7 902
17	Yucatán	7 160
18	Sinaloa	7 046
19	San Luis Potosí	6 935
20	Guanajuato	6 794
21	State of México	6 251
22	Puebla	6 091
23	Tabasco	5 802
24	Veracruz	5 417
25	Nayarit	5 252
26	Michoacán	5 147
27	Zacatecas	5 132
28	Hidalgo	5 119
29	Guerrero	4 981
30	Tlaxcala	4 928
31	Oaxaca	4 003
32	Chiapas	3 657

degree of income disparities suggested by the Gini figure taken on its own. Some economists suggest that countries with such high Gini indexes need to double their rates of economic growth before they will succeed in reducing their incidence of poverty.

The spatial distribution of economic production

Mexico's economic production is not distributed equally in all areas of the country. On a per person basis, some areas produce far more than the national average while others produce only a fraction of the average. However, for areas within a country, per person production is not closely aligned with per person income because the benefits of production may go to individuals or entities in others areas of the country. For example, an area with a large natural resource such as oil might have very high levels of per person production, but the incomes associated with that production might go to other areas of the country.

Table 14.2 indicates the per person GDP for Mexico's 32 states. The table reveals a very broad range. The Federal District, the financial, commercial and governmental center, is by far the highest with a per person production level over three times the national average. Nuevo León has a level over twice the national average as a result of Monterrey's industrial and financial activities

The high level for Campeche primarily results from petroleum extraction and processing. Most of the benefits of this petroleum production do not go to Campeche residents but rather to Pemex, the national oil corporation. Likewise, the high level for Quintana Roo comes from the tourist industry, the profits from which mostly go to large tourism corporations with headquarters outside Quintana Roo and often outside Mexico altogether. In conclusion, the high per person production levels for these two states are a bit of an anomaly and do not mean high per person income levels for the states' inhabitants.

The map (Figure 14.3) suggests that within Mexico there is a core-periphery dependency pattern. The primary core is clearly Mexico City. The secondary core area is in the northern border states, particularly Baja California, Chihuahua, Coahuila and Nuevo León. These states, with production levels over 60% above the national average, include the rapidly growing, relatively dynamic cities of Tijuana, Mexicali,

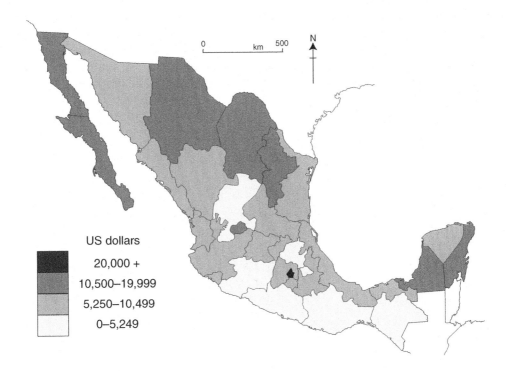

Figure 14.3 GDP per person, 2007[9]

Ciudad Juárez, Monterrey, Nuevo Laredo, Reynosa and Matamoros. Guadalajara, in the state of Jalisco, could be considered a tertiary core area.

The clearest periphery area consists of the four poorest states (Oaxaca, Chiapas, Guerrero and Michoacán) which lie along the south coast. Other relatively peripheral states tend to surround the main Mexico City–Guadalajara core areas. These states include Nayarit, Zacatecas, Hidalgo, Tlaxcala, Puebla, Veracruz and Tabasco. Though there are some economically dynamic areas within these states, their per person levels are significantly below the national average. By the same token, there are many marginalized, periphery areas within the so-called core states. Unfortunately very limited data are available on the spatial distribution of production for areas smaller than states.

Trends in income distribution: are the poor getting poorer?

Many proponents of the North American Free Trade Agreement (NAFTA) which came into effect in 1994 argued that it would stimulate Mexico's economic development, leading to an increase in employment, and (in due course) higher wages. This would have a beneficial effect for the entire workforce but the effect would be most pronounced among the poorest 20%. It would help reduce the differential between their incomes and those of the middle income earners. Opponents of NAFTA argued that free trade would have the opposite effect and would lead to a widening gap between the haves and the have-nots. Which argument is right? Has the gap widened or narrowed?

Research addressing this question reveals the complexity of the issue.[10] Complicating the situation is the economic instability which followed the passage of NAFTA as well as the significant urban–rural and regional inequality that persists in Mexico. Available data suggest that inequality increased during the 1980s and again slightly between 1996 and 1998 but then declined until 2002.

Researchers conclude that the giant gap between rich and poor will not decline naturally as the economy grows, but will require specific policy actions. The overall impact from the global economic downturn which started in 2008 is not yet clear but past experience suggests that the gap tends to decline during economic hard times.

Some economists argue that a trend of a widening gap between rich and poor was already evident in the years prior to NAFTA. If so, this suggests that globalization and Mexico's support for free trade are not the only factors responsible for the apparently growing disparities of wealth in the country.

Even if the disparities are widening, it does not necessarily mean that the poor are getting poorer. It is perfectly possible that their real incomes (and standards of living) could increase, by say 10%, while those at the top increase by 15%. Both groups would therefore be getting richer, even though the gap between them widened. On the other hand, it is possible that both could be getting poorer, with the gap increasing or declining. Clearly, income data are difficult to analyze and we should be very cautious to avoid making any overly-simplistic statement about the poor getting poorer.

15

Agriculture, forestry, fishing, mining

Primary activities were extremely important to Mexico in the past, accounting for most of the country's gross national product. They are still relatively important but (excluding petroleum) currently account for less than 5%. This chapter and the next analyze census data to look at individual economic activities and where they take place within Mexico.

Agriculture

How important is agriculture to the Mexican economy? Agriculture represented over 20% of Mexico's gross national product in the 1960s. Now, it accounts for about 4%. However, agriculture is still very important in terms of employment. Currently, about 15% of working Mexicans are engaged in agriculture; this figure was 77% in 1921. Productivity and wage levels in agriculture are far lower than in other sectors of the economy.

Just over 20% of Mexico is considered potentially appropriate for agriculture but only about 14% is cultivated.[1] The total area of cultivated land is 21.7 million hectares (53.8 million acres). More than 6 million hectares (about a quarter of the total area) are irrigated. Worldwide, only China, India, USA, Pakistan and Iran have larger areas of irrigated farmland.[2]

Mexico does not have a broad, widely recognized farming belt, like the USA mid-west stretching from Ohio to Nebraska. Given the country's very diverse climate, a wide variety of crops is grown depending on local conditions. Mexico's extraordinary biodiversity includes native varieties of numerous plants of economic importance including corn (maize), beans, squash, tomatoes, chilies, avocados, cacao (chocolate), vanilla, papaya, chicle (chewing gum), agaves, tobacco and cotton as well as a vast array of tropical fruits. All parts of Mexico are engaged in agriculture, but some areas are far more dependent on farming than others.

Where is farming concentrated in Mexico? The leading agricultural state is Jalisco with 10% of all Mexico's agricultural production. Other important agricultural states are Veracruz (8%), Michoacán (8%), Sinaloa (6%) and Chihuahua (6%). Sonora, Durango, Puebla and Guanajuato each produces between 4% and 5% of the total.[3] Though Jalisco is the leading agricultural state, agriculture accounts for only 5.5% of its total economic production. This is a similar situation to California, the leading US agricultural state. We can look at agriculture from a different perspective by asking which states are most dependent on agriculture. Agriculture accounts for more than a tenth of total economic production in five states: Durango (13%), Zacatecas (13%), Michoacán (13%), Sinaloa (12%) and Nayarit (10%) The states with the least amount of agricultural production are the Federal District, Quintana Roo, Tlaxcala, Colima, Campeche and Baja California Sur.

Crops

Corn production has been the core of Mexican agriculture throughout its history. Corn continues to be very important. Production has increased by more than 40% since 2000 (Figure 15.1). Currently corn is grown on about half of all agricultural land. However, corn is a rather low value crop and accounts for only about 14% of total crop value. Corn, which is consumed by both humans and livestock, is grown

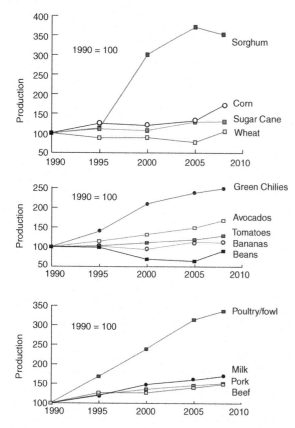

Figure 15.1 Agricultural production by volume since 1990[4]

virtually everywhere in Mexico and is the leading crop in 17 of the 32 states. The leader in value of corn produced is Jalisco with 17% of the national total. Other major corn states are Sinaloa (14%), State of Mexico (9%), Chiapas (8%) and Michoacán (7%).

Sugar cane is the most important crop in terms of tonnage. Most years, Mexico produces more than 50 million tons of sugar cane, compared with about 34 million tons of corn. Veracruz leads in sugar production followed by Tamaulipas, Jalisco and Sinaloa.

Other economically important crops include sorghum, beans, tomatoes, avocados, potatoes, green chili, wheat, bananas and coffee. These crops each contribute between 2% and 5% of the total crop value and thus are far less economically important than corn or sugar.

Sorghum is mainly used for animal feed. Its production, which has more than tripled since 1995 (Figure 15.1), is largely concentrated in Tamaulipas and Guanajuato which account for about half of all production.

Beans, a very important source of protein, are grown all over the country. Production has been in decline; it is highest in Zacatecas (27% of the national total) followed by Sinaloa, Durango, Nayarit, Chiapas and Chihuahua.

Production of tomatoes, potatoes and green chilies is mostly concentrated in Sinaloa which produces about 30% of the tomatoes and potatoes and 20% of the green chilies. Baja California is also an important tomato producer. Exports of tomatoes alone are worth over $1 billion a year. Chihuahua is important for potatoes and green chili. The output of green chilies has almost tripled since 1990 (Figure 15.1).

Half of Mexico's wheat production comes from Sonora. Most production in these arid northwestern states is only possible with intensive irrigation.

Mexico is the world's leading avocado producer, with about 80,000 hectares devoted to the crop in the main growing region, the state of Michoacán where avocados have been cultivated for more than a thousand years. State-of-the-art technology, modern cultivation methods and ideal natural conditions have combined to give Michoacán's 10,000 avocado growers yields of up to 2.24 tons per hectare (0.9 tons per acre). Avocado exports to the USA were resumed in 1997 following the partial lifting of an embargo that had lasted since 1914.

The avocado "season" runs from October to April. The annual harvest is usually over one million tons, most of which is for the domestic market. Mexicans are the world's largest avocado consumers with a per person consumption of eight kg (18 lbs) a year.[5] After fresh vegetables and tomatoes, avocados are Mexico's most valuable agricultural export, bringing in about $600 million a year.

Banana production has remained static since 1990. It is focused in the tropical southern states of Chiapas and Tabasco. Together, they produce 70% of Mexico's annual banana harvest of 2 million metric tons.

Mexico is seventh in the world in coffee production and one of the leading suppliers of organic, shade-grown coffee. The nation's 480,000 coffee growers, most working small parcels of land less than 5 hectares (12 acres) in size, are concentrated in Chiapas, Veracruz and Oaxaca, and produce 268,000 metric tons a year. While Mexican coffee consumption per person is rising, 62% of the harvest is exported, bringing in $400 million annually.

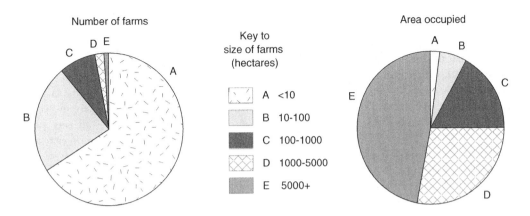

Figure 15.2 The number and size of farms, 1970[6]

Ejidos

One of the fundamental causes of the Mexico Revolution in 1910, though by no means the only one, was the demand by landless *campesinos* (peasant farmers) for access to the means to control their own supplies of food. Revolutionary leaders called for the expropriation of the large estates or haciendas, which had been the principal means of agricultural production since colonial times, and the redistribution of land among the rural poor. A law governing this radical change in the land tenure system came into force in 1917 and the process has continued, albeit sporadically, into modern times.

About half of all cultivated land in Mexico was converted from large estates into *ejidos*, a form of collective farming. In most *ejidos*, each individual *ejidatario* has the rights to use between 4 and 20 hectares (10-50 acres) of land, depending on soil quality and whether or not it is irrigated. In addition, members of the *ejido* share collective rights over the use of local pasture and woodland. The system is similar to that in place in Aztec times. The maximum area of land that hacienda owners were allowed to keep varied with its potential use, from 100 hectares in the case of irrigated arable land to 300 hectares for land without irrigation.

By 1970 land redistribution had been more or less completed. Even so, most farming land still remained in the hands of a very small minority of farmers (Figure 15.2). Only 1% of farms were larger than 5000 hectares (12,355 acres) but between them they shared 47% of all farm land. Meanwhile, 66% of farms were smaller than 10 hectares (25 acres) yet they shared only 2% of all farm land.

The *ejido* system did not produce the anticipated increase in food production or food security. Hacienda owners opted to keep their most productive land, meaning that many *ejidos* had to work land that was marginal at best. Many *ejidatarios* saw no need to pursue profits provided their families were well fed. Many individual plots were too small for mechanization, and nutrients were rapidly depleted through constant use. Collective ownership of the land meant that individuals could offer no collateral for improvement loans. Many *campesinos* abandoned their *ejidos* and sought their futures elsewhere, migrating either to the big cities, for their range of manufacturing and service jobs, or to the USA. A sizable proportion of *ejido* land is no longer economically productive, but only in the 1990s was any mechanism put in place for *ejido* lands to be sold and revert back to private status.

Dairying

Dairy products are becoming increasingly important in Mexico. Milk production has increased by 15% since 2000 (Figure 15.1). Jalisco produces 17% of Mexico's milk. Other important milk producing states are dispersed around the country and include Durango (13%), Chiapas (10%), Coahuila, Guanajuato, Veracruz and the State of Mexico. It is not surprising that Jalisco is a leading dairy state since much of its corn is used to feed livestock, including dairy cows. Jalisco's corn is also fed to egg-laying chickens and the state produces over 41% of the nation's eggs. Behind Jalisco in egg production come Puebla (21%), Sonora (7%) and Nuevo León (6%).

Meat

Meat production (5.4 million tons in 2007) is pretty much spread throughout the country. Jalisco leads the country in total meat production with 15% of the national total. Other important meat producers are Veracruz (10%), Sonora, Guanajuato, Puebla, Yucatán, Querétaro, Coahuila and the State of Mexico.

Veracruz and Jalisco are the leading beef producers, each with about 13% of Mexico's total. Beef production is also significant in the northern and western states of Coahuila (6%), Sonora, Durango, Colima (5% each), Baja California and Sinaloa.

Pig raising is an important industry all over Mexico. Pork production has increased by 50% since 1990, the same increase as that recorded for beef (Figure 15.1). Jalisco leads in the production of pork with 21% of the national total, followed by Sonora (15%), Guanajuato (10%), Yucatán and Puebla (8% each), Veracruz and Michoacán.

Poultry (fowl), mostly chicken and turkey, has now surpassed beef as the leading meat in the Mexican diet. Production of chicken and turkey meat increased by 40% between 2000 and 2008. Chicken and turkey raising in Mexico ranges from traditional methods, with only a few birds, to very modern large scale operations. Again, Jalisco is the leading producer with 13% of Mexico's total followed by Veracruz (9%), Querétaro (9%), Puebla (8%), Aguascalientes, Guanajuato, Durango, State of Mexico, Chiapas, Yucatán and Nuevo León.

Community-based sustainable forestry: a multi-use forest

An alternative approach to commercial forestry has been adopted by the small indigenous P'urépecha community of Nuevo San Juan Parangaricutiro in the state of Michoacán. Founded in 1944 by refugees fleeing the eruption of Paricutín volcano, the community manages 11,000 hectares of forest and has established more than a dozen successful eco-enterprises based on sustainable forestry, timber products (including furniture, packing cases for fruit and resins used in shoe polish), ecotourism, agroforestry (avocados and peaches) and wildlife management (Figure 15.3). Nuevo San Juan Parangaricutiro was awarded the prestigious United Nations Development Programme Equator Prize in 2004.[7]

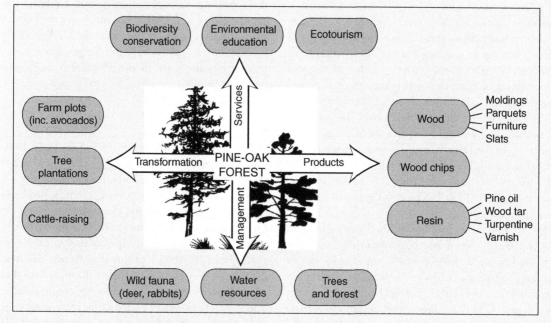

Figure 15.3 Multi-use, community-based forestry[8]

Forestry

About 70% of Mexican forests are owned by local communities. Mexico's forestry industry is not large, accounting for only about 0.1% of gross national product. Lumber is relatively unimportant in construction; where it is used, it is mostly for doors and windows. Its main use is in the manufacture of furniture. Pine is by far the most important timber product accounting for 83% of total production. Of secondary importance are oak and fir, but they each contribute less than 5% of the total. Tropical forests are of little significance in terms of lumber production. About half of all timber production comes from two northern states, Durango (29%) and Chihuahua (22%). Other important forestry states are Michoacán (9%), Jalisco (8%) and Oaxaca (6%). Forestry production has declined in volume since 1990.

Fishing

Mexico's 11,122-kilometer coastline is one of the world's longest yet the national fish catch ranks only 16th in the world. During the 19th and early 20th centuries the Sea of Cortés was the world's leading source of pearls, including much-prized black pearls. The annual harvest was worth up to $2 million. By 1940 production had fallen as oyster beds were overfished, and cultured and artificial pearls were substituted for natural pearls.

The fishing industry now accounts for only 0.24% of gross national product. The relatively shallow waters off the Pacific coast and abundance of plankton in waters cooled by the Californian current make for particularly good fishing in the north-west. Together, Sinaloa (23%) and Sonora (22%) account for about 45% of the national total. Fishing is also economically important in Veracruz (8%), Baja California Sur (6%), Campeche and Baja California (5% each) and Yucatán. Almost three quarters (72%) of the total annual catch of 1.5 million metric tons is landed at Pacific coast ports such as Guaymas, Mazatlán and Manzanillo. Gulf coast ports like Tampico, Veracruz and Campeche, together with Caribbean coast ports such as Puerto Morelos and Progreso, account for a further 25% of the catch. The remaining 3% comes from inland lakes, rivers and fish farms. In terms of value, the most important species are shrimp, tuna and sardines. Fresh-water fish farms are becoming more common, with many of them specializing in the production of high value species such as trout and indigenous white fish.[9] Mexicans consume only 13 kg (29 lbs) of fish per person per year on average, considerably less than the equivalent figures for the USA (21 kg), Canada (24 kg) or Spain (44 kg).

Shrimp

The total shrimp production in 2007 was 178,000 tons. This total masks a significant trend in shrimping. The high-seas catch has declined since 1990. Less than a third of the total catch now comes from the 2,100-vessel specialist shrimping fleet based in the port of Mazatlán. Fish-farmed shrimp account for the remainder, almost 70% of the total. Shrimp fishermen are worried about the overfishing of shrimp stocks in shallow coastal waters, allegedly due to clandestine fishing by non-authorized boats. Pollution of coastal waters from agricultural chemicals is also a major concern.[10] Shrimp exports are worth $360 million a year.

Dolphin-safe tuna

Mexico's tuna catch (mainly yellowfin tuna) peaked at 166,000 tons in 2003 when more than 20,000 tons were exported, mainly to Spain, and has since declined to around 115,000 tons. The USA is the world's largest importer of tuna. Following the resolution of an acrimonious dispute with the USA which included a nine-year embargo against tuna caught by Mexican boats, tuna fishermen can now stamp "dolphin-safe" on tuna exported to that nation. The labels certify that tuna fishing is in compliance with the International Dolphin Protection Program. Part of the conflict revolved around the very different methods of fishing employed in the two countries. Mexican tuna fishermen use the encirclement method which involves locating tuna by chasing dolphins that swim with the tuna schools. Large nets are then employed. Any dolphins trapped in the nets are released by hand and returned (alive) to the ocean. USA tuna fishermen use long-line fishing in which every species hooked is killed. About 20,000 families in Mexico depend on tuna fishing for their livelihood. This figure includes not only fishermen but also those working in associated processing and packing plants. Mexico's 130-vessel tuna fleet[11] is the largest in Latin America.

Overfishing in the Sea of Cortés

The Sea of Cortés (Gulf of California) is one of the world's top five seas in terms of ecological productivity and biological diversity. Among rivers feeding

it are the Colorado, Fuerte and Yaqui. Its coast includes more than 300 estuaries and other wetlands,
of which the delta of the Colorado River is especially
important. The vast reduction in the Colorado's flow
(see chapter 6) has negatively impacted wetlands and
fisheries. These wetlands are also threatened by the
development of marinas, resorts and aquaculture,
especially shrimp farms. The plant and animal communities in these wetlands provide a constant supply of nutrients which support large numbers of fish
and marine mammals. These include the humpback
whale, California gray whale, blue whale, fin whale,
sperm whale and the leatherback sea turtle. The region
is world famous for its recreational sports fishing.

Changes in technology, coupled with high demand (especially in Japan), and greed, explain the
demise of fish stocks. Commercial shrimp fishing
started here in the 1940s. The introduction of out-
board motors in the 1970s allowed small fiberglass
boats (*pangas*) to travel further afield in search of fish.
Up to 20,000 *pangas* using gill nets had an immediate adverse impact on fish stocks, with large decreases
in roosterfish, yellowtail and sierra mackerel.[12]

In the 1980s, as the sardine stocks close to Guaymas had been depleted, new sardine boats were built
with refrigeration facilities which allowed them
to catch sardines further offshore, in their feeding
grounds near Midriff Island.

In the 1990s a longline fishing fleet began to operate out of Ensenada. Licensed boats were required to
fish beyond a non-fishing zone extending 80 km (50
mi) from the coast. A single longline boat may have
5 km (3 mi) of line with 600 to 700 baited hooks in
total. The swordfish populations outside the protected zone were quickly depleted, leading fishing boat
owners to apply for permits to catch shark inside the
80-km limits.

The Sea of Cortés faces numerous pressures. Decades of commercial overfishing are causing a total
collapse of fish stocks. As late as 1993, the area, less
than 5% of all Mexico's territorial waters, produced
about 75% of the nation's total fish catch of 1.5 million metric tons; however, by some estimates, fish
populations have declined by 90% since.

Wetland degradation and declining fish stocks
had inevitable consequences on many marine mammals. Concern over endangered mammals such as
the vaquita porpoise, which is endemic to the area
and was being taken as by-catch in gill nets, led to
the establishment of the Biosphere Reserve of the

Upper Gulf of California and Delta of the Colorado River in 1993. Its management aims to protect
breeding grounds and conserve endangered species,
including the vaquita, the totoaba, the desert pupfish
and the Yuma clapper rail. This reserve, the first marine reserve established in Mexico, opened the way
for several other marine protected areas on Mexico's
other coasts.

What are the solutions? Reversing decades of overfishing requires more effective enforcement of fishing
regulations, especially the 80-km zone of no commercial fishing; vessel monitoring systems; a ban on
the use of gill nets; and a prohibition on the catch of
certain fish such as bluefin tuna.

Fish farming may be a viable alternative and several commercial tuna farms, where wild tuna are
raised in nearshore pens, have been established in
Baja California[13] but more research on the ecological
pros and cons of establishing such farms is urgently
needed.

Mining, petroleum and natural gas

Minerals

Historically, mineral production (even excluding
petroleum and natural gas) has been very important
in Mexico but it now accounts for less than 1% of
gross national product.[14] Currently, the most important metals mined in Mexico are copper, gold, zinc,
silver and lead.[15] Copper accounts for roughly 20%
of the mineral sector and is mostly concentrated in
Sonora. Other important copper producing states
are Zacatecas, San Luis Potosí and Chihuahua. A
Mexican corporation, Grupo México, is the world's
third largest producer of copper. Zacatecas leads in
the mining of silver and Chihuahua leads for gold.
Other important silver and gold mining states are
Durango, Sonora, Mexico State and San Luis Potosí.
Gold output has more than quadrupled since 1990
(Figure 15.4). Most lead and zinc mining is in Za-
catecas, followed by Chihuahua, Mexico State and
Durango. Mexico has only limited reserves of iron
ore, producing about 7 million tons a year.

Mexico's important non-metallic minerals are coal,
gypsum, fluorite, salt, sulfur and limestone. The vast
majority of Mexico's coking coal (1.5 million tons a
year) comes from Coahuila. The production of coal
has almost tripled since 1990 (Figure 15.4). The ex-
cavation of sand and gravel is economically very important because it is needed in great quantities for

virtually all construction in Mexico. In fact, sand and gravel might be economically more important than any other single mineral resource in Mexico.

Mexico is the world's second largest producer of silver (see below), producing 2,400 tons annually, about 13% of the world total, and also places second for bismuth (20% of world total) and fluorite. In addition, Mexico is one of the world's ten largest producers of celestite, wollastonite, lead, zinc, cadmium, barite, graphite, salt, manganese and molybdenum. It is the world's 12th largest gold producer, contributing about 40 tons a year.[16] These numbers show that Mexico is an important player in world mineral production.

The legacy of silver

Even today, the cities and landscapes of many parts of central and northern Mexico reveal the historical significance of silver mining. The legacies of silver mining include not only the opulent colonial buildings in numerous major cities such as Zacatecas and Guanajuato, as well as innumerable smaller towns, but also the deforestation of huge swathes of countryside.

The landscape of states like San Luis Potosí, Zacatecas and Guanajuato was forever changed by the frenzied exploitation of their woodlands. Silver mining needed pit props. The smelting of silver ore required vast quantities of firewood. Barren tracts of upland testify to the success of those early silver mines. Mining played a crucial role in the pattern of settlement and communications of most of northern Mexico. The need to transfer valuable silver bullion safely from mine to mint required the construction of faster and shorter routes, helping to focus the pattern of road and rail communications on a limited number of major cities.

Once workable ores ran out, smaller mining communities fell into obscurity and many became ghost towns. Some of these settlements, such as Real de Catorce and Angangueo, have enjoyed a new lease of life in recent years due to tourism. The importance of silver mining in colonial New Spain can not be over-emphasized. For instance, during colonial times nearly one third of all the silver mined in the world came from the Guanajuato region.

Petroleum and natural gas

The extraction of oil and natural gas is very important to the Mexican economy. It is a major source

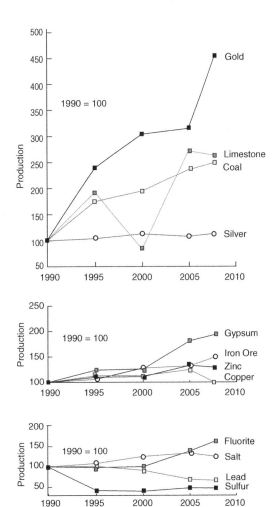

Figure 15.4 Changes in mineral production by volume since 1990[17]

of foreign currency and accounts for about 4% of the gross national product. Production increased about 23% in the 1990s but has pretty much leveled off since then. In 2008, Mexico produced 3.2 million barrels a day placing it 7th in the world, behind Saudi Arabia, Russia, the USA, Iran, China and Canada.[18] Mexico exported about 44% of its oil in 2008 earning roughly $50 billion. Mexico's proven oil reserves of 10.5 billion barrels (15th in the world) will last Mexico less than 10 years at current rates of extraction.[19]

Over 80% of the crude oil comes from offshore wells in Campeche (Figure 15.5). The remainder comes from onshore wells which are concentrated in

Figure 15.5 Oil and gas in Mexico

Tabasco, but also found in Veracruz, Chiapas and Tamaulipas.

The state-owned oil giant Petróleos Mexicanos (Pemex) is preparing to explore and develop new off-shore oil fields to make up for the eventual decline of its supergiant Cantarell oil field, the country's main source of heavy crude since the mid 1990s. They include the Chicontepec oil field, known since 1926, which straddles the states of Puebla and Veracruz. Pemex has one of the lowest production costs per barrel of any major oil company.[20] In 2000, Pemex's cost per barrel was only $4.63, compared with $8.65 for Exxon Mobil and $7.62 for BP Amoco.

Mexico is the world's 11th largest producer of natural gas. Over 40% of Mexico's natural gas comes from Tabasco; Campeche provides about 30%. The rest of the natural gas comes from Veracruz and Tamaulipas. While proven reserves of natural gas place Mexico in 35th position in the world, a 2003 report from the U.S. Energy Department claims that Mexico has probable natural gas reserves of over 135 trillion cubic feet. One major field alone, the Burgos basin natural gas field in Tamaulipas, is believed to contain up to 75 trillion cubic feet. Demand for gas is rising very rapidly. Domestic production, despite doubling between 1985 and 2007 to 6 billion cubic feet a day, has been unable to keep pace with demand, so considerable quantities of natural gas have to be imported from the USA.[21]

16

Manufacturing, construction and services

Secondary activities use raw materials provided by primary economic activity to produce finished manufactured goods. Tertiary or service industries include a myriad of different economic activities from banking and insurance to education, research, commerce and tourism.

Manufacturing

Manufacturing accounts for about 18% of the Mexican gross national product and covers a broad category of activities that process raw materials into useful products. Table 16.1 shows the nine categories of manufacturing used in the Mexican economic census, together with their percentage contributions to the total of the manufacturing sector.

Where is Mexico's manufacturing? It is generally concentrated in the area around the capital. The Federal District (14%) and the State of Mexico (15%) account for 29% of all manufacturing. When the surrounding states of Morelos, Puebla, Tlaxcala, Hidalgo and Querétaro are added, the full core area produces about 40% of the national total.

The six northern border states account for 32% of manufacturing. Nuevo León is the third leading manufacturing state with 10% of the national total, mostly in the Metropolitan Monterrey area. Jalisco is fourth with 7%, largely in the area around Guadalajara. The remaining 21% of Mexico's manufacturing is mostly disbursed among other central and northern states. Only about 4% of all manufacturing is found in the seven southern and eastern states of Guerrero, Oaxaca, Chiapas, Tabasco, Campeche, Yucatán and Quintana Roo.

Which states are most heavily dependent on manufacturing? Over 35% of Coahuila's economy is manufacturing. Other heavily dependent states are Aguascalientes (30%), Querétero (29%) and México (28%) as well as Tlaxcala, San Luis Potosí, Guanajuato, Puebla, Hidalgo and Nuevo León (23%-25%). The states where manufacturing is least important are Campeche (1.4%), Chiapas (3.4%) and Baja California Sur (4.3%).

Metal products, machines and equipment

This is the largest and most important manufacturing category. It includes the manufacture of such things as vehicles (see box), household appliances, tools, consumer electronics and office equipment.

The largest concentration is in Mexico's central core. The State of Mexico leads with 18% of the country's total, followed by the Federal District with 16%. These two, combined with the surrounding core states of Morelos, Puebla, Hidalgo and Querétaro, account for 46% of the national total. The six states along the northern border account for another 40%. The remaining 14% is concentrated in other central and northern states. The seven southern and eastern states listed above produce only 0.4%. In other words, these relatively poor states must import virtually all of their machines, vehicles, appliances, electronic equipment and other metal products.

Food processing, beverages and tobacco

These industries are spread throughout the country, with the heaviest concentrations near the most populous areas. The three leading states—Jalisco, the State of Mexico, and the Federal District—each produce about 13% of the national total. Jalisco's economy is the most heavily dependent on food, beverage and tobacco processing; this is not surprising given that Jalisco is the country's leading agricultural state.

Mexico's Grupo Bimbo is the largest bread maker in the Americas and the world's fifth largest food producer behind Nestle, Kraft, Sara Lee and Unilever. Mexicans are the world's largest consumers of soft drinks with a per person consumption equivalent to about 150 liters a year. In terms of total volume, Mexico is the world's second largest producer after the USA.[1]

Chemical, rubber and plastics

These valuable industries, which include petroleum derivatives, are most important in and around the national core. The highest concentrations are in Querétaro, Tlaxcala, State of Mexico, Veracruz, Tamaulipas, Hidalgo and the Federal District.

Textiles, clothing, and leather products

The vast majority of this type of manufacturing activity is located in central and northern states. The concentration is highest in Aguascalientes and

Table 16.1 Contribution of manufacturing categories to total manufacturing[2]

Manufacturing category	% of all manufacturing
Metal products, machines and equipment	32
Chemical, rubber and plastics	23
Food processing, beverages, tobacco	21
Non-metal mineral products	7
Textiles, clothing, and leather products	7
Paper, paper products, printing and publishing	4
Basic metal processing	3
Wood processing and products	1
Other manufacturing industries	2
TOTAL	100

Guanajuato, followed by Hidalgo, Puebla and Tlaxcala. Interestingly, these are all land-locked states. The textile, clothing and shoe industry is under-represented in virtually all coastal states. This distribution would appear to be market-oriented.

Non-metal mineral products

This industrial group includes things like cement, processed gypsum, sodium and salt. The industry is particularly important to Hidalgo where it represents over 8% of the total economy. It is also relatively important in Coahuila, Nuevo León and Tlaxcala.

Cemex, based in Monterrey, is the world's third largest cement producer and distributer, with operations in fifty countries worldwide. In 2004 Cemex received the Wharton Infosys Business Transformation Award for its creative and efficient use of information technology. Before Cemex, who had ever heard of cement mixers, armed with GPS devices, satellite links and computer systems hooked up via satellite links to the parent company's HQ, cruising cities? The strategy allowed the company to achieve enviable levels of operating efficiency while meeting demanding delivery deadlines even in congested urban areas such as Mexico City. In 2007 Cemex received the Organization of American States Corporate Citizen of the Americas Award for its program to provide housing for low-income Mexican families.[3]

Basic metal processing

This is an important industrial group because it includes the production of steel. which is a basic input for almost all construction in Mexico as well as for numerous manufacturing industries. Historically, Mexico's steel industry was located in Monclova (Coahuila) and in Monterrey (Nuevo León), both relatively near the coal fields of Sabinas in Coahuila.[4] Why is this? Traditionally it took about 20 tons of coal and two tons of iron ore to produce one ton of steel. Transportation costs were very significant and steel manufacturers opted for the "least cost" location by building steel plants near coal mines (see box). These days it takes less coal and much of the iron comes from scrap, though the shipping of coal remains a critical variable in locating some steel plants. Of course, if the producer uses an electric arc furnace instead of a traditional coal furnace, then much less coal is needed and the price of electricity becomes an important locational variable.

Table 16.2 Mexico's largest private enterprises, 2008[5]

Rank [a]	Company name	Activity	Sales ($ billions)
1	América Móvil	telecommunications	26.59
2	Wal-Mart de México	retail stores	18.84
3	Cemex	cement, construction	18.71
4	Carso Global Telecom	telecommunications	15.24
5	Femsa	diversified: Coca-Cola bottling; beer; OXXO retailing; food packaging	12.92
6	BBVA-Bancomer	banking; financial	10.46
7	Telcel	telecommunications	10.40
8	Telmex	telecommunications	9.55
9	GM de México	motor vehicles	9.52
10	Grupo Alfa	diversified: petrochemicals; auto components; telecommunications; food	8.94

[a] excluding Pemex, a parastate corporation, which had sales of about $100 billion

Vehicle production in Mexico

Mexican vehicle production started in the 1920s and grew relatively slowly until the start of the North American Free Trade Agreement (NAFTA) in 1994. NAFTA linked Mexico's low labor costs with ready access to the US market. Automobile companies invested billions in Mexico and distributed their various industrial processes across Canada, the USA and Mexico to lower their overall production costs within NAFTA.

By the late 1990s, vehicle production approached two million units a year placing Mexico in the world's top ten. Though output has fluctuated during the past decade, in 2008 Mexico produced 2.2 million units, edging past Canada and back into the top ten. There are 20 assembly plants in Mexico and more than 1000 vehicle parts manufacturers. Vehicle and vehicle part production contributes roughly $75 billion to Mexico's GDP each year and about 500,000 direct and indirect jobs.

Trade in vehicles and vehicle parts are a dominant activity in NAFTA. About 70% of the vehicles produced in Mexico are exported, with roughly three-quarters of the exports going to the USA or Canada. On the other hand, about 60% of vehicles sold in Mexico are imported, and three-quarters of these come from the USA or Canada.

Where and by whom are Mexico's motor vehicles produced? Vehicles are made by numerous companies with plants spread across central and northern Mexico. In 2000 five of Mexico's twenty largest private enterprises, including two of the top ten, were motor vehicle companies.

The largest producer is General Motors with about 24% of the total in 2008. GM plants are located in Mexico City, Toluca, Silao (Guanajuato) and Ramos Arizpe (Coahuila). Nissan and Volkswagen are tied for second with 21.4%. Nissan's plants are in Aguascalientes and Cuernavaca, while the large Volkswagen plant is in Puebla. Ford plants in Hermosillo, Chihuahua and Cuautitlán (just north of Mexico City) contribute 15%. Chrysler adds 13% from its plants in Toluca and Saltillo. The remaining 5% comes from Honda and Toyota whose main plants are in El Salto (near Guadalajara) and Tijuana, respectively. Chinese auto companies are also now reported to be planning to build vehicle plants in Mexico. A Mexican car company, Mastretta, is scheduled to begin production of its MXT sports model in 2010.

The 2008–2009 economic downturn had an enormous impact on the Mexico auto industry (see chapter 20). Any prolonged downturn can seriously damage the Mexican vehicle industry as well as the economies of the cities where auto plants are located.

Industrial location theories

Early attempts at explaining the spatial distribution of industries, such as that by Alfred Weber[6], were mainly based on the principle of "least cost" locations. In general, because of transport costs, industries which lose weight during manufacturing (smelting of metal ores, most food processing) tend to be located near sources of raw materials. Industries which gain weight or bulk during manufacturing (vehicle assembly, brewing) tend to be located near markets.

However, the least cost location is not necessarily due to transportation costs. In some industries it may depend on labor costs. For instance, instead of making garments at the site of a market such as New York it may be cheaper to ship garment pieces to a cheaper labor location, perhaps an in-bond maquiladora plant in Matamoros, and then ship the finished garment back to New York.

Numerous alternative approaches have been developed by geographers and economists. These include the idea of "maximum profit location."[7] This idea used space-cost curves to define the spatial margins of profitability and the point of maximum profit. It is also common for many firms to opt for "sub-optimal locations" resulting from their imperfect knowledge. Many locational decisions are probably taken as investment decisions, one of several sets of decisions faced by any firm.[8]

Other researchers have focused on examining the specific reasons for the locations of individual industrial plants. Many industries, it appears, whose location is otherwise hard to explain, are the consequence of the climatic preference of an entrepreneur (the "sun-seeking mentality") or a fondness for a specific recreational activity ("amenity proximity" or the so-called "golf course mentality").

In the cases of long-established industries, the original reasons for a factory's location may no longer apply. Nevertheless, the company may remain in the same location and continue to thrive, demonstrating the principle of "industrial inertia".

Additional factors often apply in the case of transnational and multinational corporations.

Paper, paper products, printing and publishing

This group is quite diverse in that it includes the manufacture of paper as well as printing and publishing. Of the two, printing and publishing is more important in Mexico because much of the raw paper is imported. Printing and publishing industries tend to locate in major populated areas. In Mexico, this industry is concentrated in the densely populated core in the states of Querétaro, the Federal District and State of Mexico.

Wood processing and wood products

This group of industries is rather small compared to other categories and is concentrated in the leading forestry states of Durango, Chihuahua and Michoacán. This is no surprise because it far more expensive to ship trees than lumber or wood products. Thus lumber companies located in forestry areas can deliver lumber cheaper to urban markets than companies located elsewhere.

Construction

Construction is an important economic activity in virtually all areas of Mexico. It contributes about 5% to the gross domestic product. Construction is particularly important in Nayarit, Chiapas and Veracruz, where in each case it represents over 9% of the economy. On the other hand, it accounts for only 3% of the economy in Durango and Coahuila.

Electricity, water and gas

These utilities are very important to all economic activities, but they only amount to 1.4% of the gross domestic product. Utilities are economically very important in Colima (10% of that state's economy)

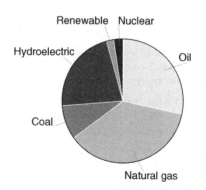

Figure 16.1 Sources of electricity, 2009[9]

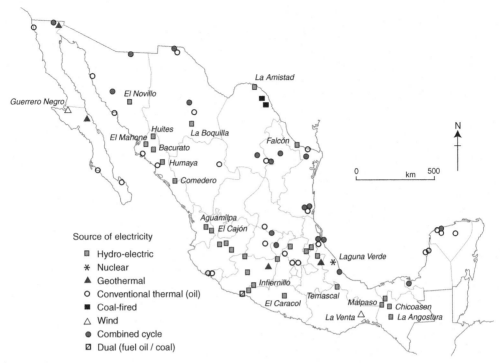

Figure 16.2 Location of main power stations

and Chiapas (9%), both of which have large power generation plants, as well as Guerrero (5%).

Mexico's national electrical system serves about 97% of all Mexicans. In recent years electrical generation has not been able to keep pace with demand for electricity, which is increasing at about 6% to 7% per year. Attempts to increase private sector investment in energy as a means to keep up with surging demand have met opposition in the Mexican Congress. Under current law, private investors may generate electricity but transmission and distribution are restricted to the Federal Electricity Commission.

About 30% of Mexico's total installed electricity generating capacity of 60,000 MW comes from conventional power plants burning oil (Figure 16.1). Natural gas-fueled power plants account for about 35%, while coal plants contribute about 9%.[10] Altogether, fossil fuel burning facilities account for almost three-quarters of Mexico's generating capacity.

Many of Mexico's newer power plants are highly efficient, gas-fired, combined cycle plants which integrate gas and steam turbines. On a per megawatt basis, they are relatively economical to build. Their major disadvantage (equally true for conventional thermo-electric power stations) is that their emissions contribute to air pollution (particularly sulfur dioxide) and global warming. About 25% of Mexico's annual emissions of carbon dioxide are due to electricity generation.

Hydroelectric power has been important since the early part of the twentieth century. Currently about 22% of the electricity generating capacity is from hydroelectric plants. The largest hydroelectric plants are on the Grijalva River in Chiapas. Other rivers providing significant hydropower are the Balsas, Santiago, Fuerte, Papaloapan and Moctezuma.

Mexico has one nuclear power plant at Laguna Verde in Veracruz (Figure 16.2), which provides about 2.6% of the nation's generating capacity. No additional nuclear plants are planned.

Mexico has the world's second largest geothermal electrical potential, after Indonesia. This resource might be more important in the future but at present it accounts for less than 2.4% of Mexico's electricity capacity.

The region of Mexico with most potential for wind power is the low-lying and flat Isthmus of Tehuantepec in southern Mexico where annual wind speeds, at a height of 30m (100 ft) above the ground (the height of modern windmills), average more than

30 kph (19 mph). Despite the success of the wind-farms already operating in La Venta (Oaxaca) and Guerrero Negro (Baja California Sur), wind power is responsible for less than 0.05% of all electricity. The government hopes to boost wind power capacity significantly within the next five to ten years.[11]

Most solar power interest is focused not on large-scale plants but on small-scale photovoltaic (PV) systems providing electricity in remote rural areas. About 3 million people (3% of the population) live in small or remote settlements not yet connected to the national electricity grid. More than 60,000 PV systems have been installed nationwide, benefiting 250,000 rural inhabitants.

Services

Services account for about two-thirds of the total Mexican economy. Services include all economic activity that does not involve extracting something from the ground, or growing or fabricating something. It includes everything from commerce, travel and transportation through banking, government services, health care and education to such mundane services as haircutting, dry cleaning and car washing.

Many services in a local area focus almost exclusively on local clientele. As such, they do not bring in outside money and thus do not really contribute much to the economic base. On the other hand, services such as tourism bring in lots of money from outside and may be the mainstay of the local economy.

The Mexican census provides data on four general categories of services: commerce (including hotels and restaurants), transportation, finance (including insurance and real estate) and public and personal services. Each of these is discussed below.

Commerce, which accounts for 21% of Mexico's total economy, includes retail and wholesale trade as well as restaurants and hotels. Commercial services are essential to the economies of all Mexican states because retail trade is a dominant activity virtually everywhere in Mexico.

Most tourist expenditures fall within this category, which is particularly important to states with major tourist attractions (see chapter 19). Quintana Roo, the state containing Cancún and many other Caribbean tourist destinations, is heavily dependent on tourism. In fact, income from commerce, hotels and restaurants makes up 47% of the total economy of Quintana Roo. The level of tourism on the Pacific coast around Acapulco in the state of Guerrero has tapered off in recent years. Still, commerce, hotels and restaurants account for 25% of Guerrero's total economy. Other states with economies relatively dependent on commerce include the northern border states of Chihuahua (33%) and Baja California (29%), along with Jalisco (27%).

Transportation and communications

This category covers all the services that move people, things or ideas from place to place (see chapters 17 and 18). It includes telecommunications, postal and courier delivery services as well as taxi, bus and air travel. Also included are all shipping services whether by truck, railroad, ship or pipeline. Furthermore, all warehousing, transshipment and port activities fall into this category. Altogether, these activities contribute about 11% to Mexico's gross domestic product.

Transportation activities are Mexico's largest consumer of energy, accounting for 36% of the total.[12] Industry and mining use 33% of the energy, households and service enterprises consume 27% and agriculture uses the remaining 3%.

The telecommunications sector is very important. Four telecommunications firms are among the ten biggest Mexican private sector enterprises: América Móvil, Carso Global Telecom, Telcel and Telmex (Table 16.2). All four are directly or indirectly controlled by Carlos Slim Helu, Mexico's wealthiest individual, and his family. The family also controls Grupo Carso which owns retail chains such as Sanborn's and Sears México.

Colima, with its major port of Manzanillo, is the state most dependent on transportation which accounts for 16% of its total economy. Other states dependent on transportation include Querétaro, Aguascalientes, Guerrero, Tamaulipas and the Federal District (about 12% each).

Finance, insurance, rental income, real estate

This category contributes 13% of Mexico's gross domestic product. The category is a bit confusing because real estate and rental income are much larger than finance and insurance income in almost all states except the Federal District, which houses almost 80% of all of Mexico's financial and insurance workers. Despite the capital's dominance in finance and insurance, this category accounts for slightly less than 15% of its total economy.

Over 25% of the economy of Baja California Sur is dependent on this category. Though finance and insurance are not very important, real estate is a dominant business activity in Baja California Sur. Other states heavily dependent on this category of services include Chiapas (18% of its economy), Oaxaca (18%) and Michoacán (16%). These three states are very dependent on remittances sent to families from workers outside the state. Processing of these remittances requires financial services. Furthermore, a sizeable portion of these remittances is probably being used for property purchasing, construction and improvements to properties that are being rented while their owners are working in the USA.

Public, social and personal services

This broad category is responsible for 26% of Mexico's gross domestic product. It covers a wide range of services such as government administration, police, courts, education, health care, tailoring, hairstyling and cleaning. These services are a very important component of the economy in all Mexican states.

The economy of the Federal District, the country's center of government, is very dependent on public, social and personal services. They make up 39% of the Federal District's total economy. A large percentage of employees in the Federal District either work for government or provide goods and services for government or government workers. Other states dependent on public, social and personal services include: Chiapas (32%), Nayarit (31%) and Tabasco (31%).

Economic specialization

Individual states tend to specialize in goods or services that they can produce more efficiently than other states. The economies of some states are very specialized. The economies of other states are quite diversified and pretty much mirror the Mexican economy as a whole.

Economic specialization is an important concept and is often used to classify states, regions or cities. For example, Quintana Roo is known for tourism and Campeche for petroleum production. Historically, many Mexican towns specialized in silver mining. When the silver ran out, the local economy collapsed and they became ghost towns. In contrast, Cancún has specialized in tourism, which continues to grow (see chapter 19), stimulating local economic development and population expansion. The economic success of an area is often dependent on its economic specialization or its existing economic base (discussed in chapter 20).

There are several approaches to measuring economic specialization, each with advantages and disadvantages. One common approach is to use the locational quotient which compares the percentage of a state's workforce engaged in a particular activity with the percentage of the national workforce in the same activity. Unfortunately, employment data at the state level in Mexico are notoriously unreliable, so we have opted for an alternative approach.

Figure 16.3 shows the economic specialization for each state, defined here as the activity or activi-

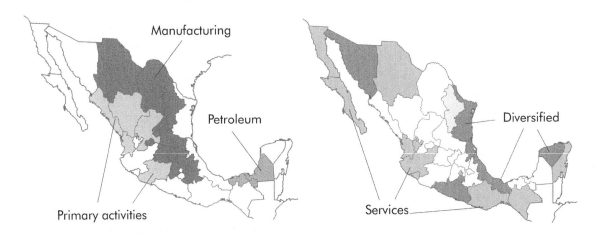

Figure 16.3 Economic specialization, by state[13]

ties where production is at least 5 percentage points more than the national average for that activity. For example, manufacturing is 30% of the economy of Aguascalientes, compared with 18% for Mexico as a whole. As a result, Aguascalientes is considered to specialize in manufacturing. Of course, if we used the location quotient or some other approach, the results would be somewhat different.

Yucatán is the only state in southeast Mexico that has a diversified economy. Campeche is extremely specialized in petroleum which accounts for 53% of its economy, compared to only 4 % for Mexico as a whole. Petroleum is so dominant that the percentages in the other sectors are all very small compared to national averages

Quintana Roo is also highly specialized with 47% of its economy derived from the commerce, hotels and restaurants sector, compared to 21% of Mexico's overall economy. Like Campeche, there is relatively little other economic activity in the state. However, it is important to remember that much of the revenues from petroleum and tourism flow to national or international enterprises and not to the residents of Campeche and Quintana Roo, who have per person income levels below the national average.

The Chiapas economy is rather unique in that it is specialized in three sectors: public and private services; finance, insurance, rental income and real estate; and utilities. How can a state specialize in three separate sectors? The share of Chiapas's total production from each of these three sectors is more than 5 percentage points greater than the Mexican average for these sectors. The three sectors make up 59% of Chiapas's economy compared to only 40% for all of Mexico. On the other hand, manufacturing represents only 3% of the Chiapas economy compared to 18% for the whole country.

Several of the states surrounding the capital city specialize in manufacturing. These include the State of Mexico, Tlaxcala, Puebla, Hidalgo and Querétaro. The Federal District itself is fairly specialized in public, social and personal services, which make up 39% of its economy compared to only 26% for the rest of Mexico. Morelos, the other state in the core, has a diversified economy. Manufacturing is also the specialization of San Luis Potosí, Guanajuato and Aguascalientes, to the north and west of the core.

Manufacturing, particularly in maquiladoras, is also an important economic activity in the northern border states. Chihuahua, Nuevo León and Coahuila are all classified as manufacturing specialists. Chihuahua also specializes in commerce as does Baja California, while Sonora and Tamaulipas have diversified economies.

The four contiguous western states of Sinaloa, Durango, Nayarit and Zacatecas all specialize in primary sector activities: agriculture, forestry and fishing, and, in the case of Zacatecas, mining. The contribution of primary activities to their economies is three to four times the national average. One state south of this group, Michoacán, also specializes in agriculture.

17

Transportation: the movement of people and goods

The analysis of spatial interactions—the movements of people, goods, information, and ideas from one place to another—is central to geography. Spatial interactions involve both transportation, the focus of this chapter, and communications, the subject of the next. Transportation may take place over road and rail networks, or by ship, pipelines or air. The evolution of transportation networks has played a key role in Mexico's history and has had numerous impacts on its present-day geography.

Spatial interactions allow the supply of an item at one place to meet the demand for that item at another place. A complementarity of supply and demand is the basis of all geographic flows. For example, the complementarity formed by Mexico's abundant supply of workers and the USA's demand for a large number of them results in the migration of Mexican workers to the USA (see chapters 26 and 27).

Tourist flows (chapter 19) are also subject to complementarity. The cold winter months in northeastern USA and Canada create ample demand for winter vacations in warm, sunny Mexican beach resorts. A complementarity is also evident in the trading of agricultural goods such as bananas and pineapples grown in southern Mexican for markets in Mexico City and northern Mexico. In the communications sector, TV shows and films produced in Mexico City flow out to meet the demands of viewers throughout the Spanish-speaking world. Without complementarity, none of these flows would take place.

Flows of people and goods must overcome distance. In general, the greater the distance, the greater the cost in terms of time and money. As a result, we would expect steel produced in Monterrey to cost more in Cancún, 2400 km away, than in Reynosa, only 220 km away. This presents an intervening opportunity for a supplier in Mexico City to stockpile some steel and then supply demand in Cancún more rapidly than is possible direct from Monterrey.

Intervening opportunities need not be on a direct route between points of supply and demand; the important factor is that they are closer. For example, a family in Guadalajara wanting a beach vacation is more likely to vacation in Puerto Vallarta than in Cancún because Puerto Vallarta is much closer and constitutes an intervening opportunity.

The cost of overcoming distance and intervening opportunities give rise to the concept of distance decay. In short, flows of goods and people (interactions between places) generally decline or decay with distance. On any given day, therefore, there are probably more bus passengers traveling from San Luis Potosí to Zacatecas, 190 km away, than to Chihuahua, 1050 km away.

However, distance is not the only factor influencing the level of spatial interaction between places. The relative size of the places is also important. This explains why more bus passengers from Guadalajara travel 560 km to Mexico City than go 350 km to San Luis Potosí: Mexico City is much bigger. This gives rise to the gravity model of spatial interaction, which holds that the amount of interaction between two places is directly related to the relative size or level of importance of the two places and inversely related to the distance between them.

The model has been applied to many different types of interaction, including the number of buses per day, telephone calls, tons of goods shipped, and airline flights. Depending on the type of interaction being analyzed, the relative size of places can be measured by indicators such as population, economic production, sales floor area, purchasing power or number of car registrations. Typical distance indicators include not only kilometers but also travel time and cost.

In order to reduce costs, businesses focus considerable attention on movements of their raw materials and products. Complex mathematical network analysis is employed to assist suppliers such as Coca-Cola to ensure that distribution trucks make timely deliveries to dozens of different grocery stores in up to 50 different locations each day. Knowledge of the road network and traffic patterns helps to reduce the total time and cost.

At a larger scale, the company must forecast the demand for their product throughout the country and decide the optimum locations for bottling plants to minimize the total cost of supplying their product to retailers. Similar network analysis is required by banks, convenience store chains, department stores, police departments, fire stations, emergency medical services and numerous other activities. We saw in chapter 16 how Cemex, Mexico's largest cement manufacturer, cut its costs and delivery times by fitting its delivery trucks with sophisticated computerized systems.

Movements of people and goods require some type of transportation network, whether shipping lanes, railroads, highways, pipelines or air routes. These networks tend to become more efficient with time, often by adding additional links. At the same time, transport technologies are always evolving:

cars, for example, have become faster and more fuel efficient.

Changes in technology and in transport networks can revolutionize the flows of particular goods. In 16th century Zacatecas, silver bullion was transported by mules along rough trails before being loaded on a ship for Spain. It is now moved by armored car or by air more securely and more quickly. Effectively, Spain is much closer to Mexico today than it was in the 16th century. This concept is known as time-space convergence. The time and cost of moving goods or people over a given distance has been reduced. The world has shrunk. First proposed by Donald Janelle[2], time-space convergence means that the friction of distance has been greatly reduced.

Figure 17.1 shows how time-space convergence has changed travel times between Mexico City and Veracruz since 1820. Note that the time scale is logarithmic. In the pre-railway era, travel times varied greatly from dry season to rainy season. The journey could sometimes take up to three months! People could travel much faster than their valuable possessions could be transported between the two cities. New designs of stagecoach and road improvements slashed the travel time in the 1860s to 3.5 days for the 400 km (250 mi) road trip.

With the inauguration of the railway line from Mexico City to Veracruz via Orizaba in 1873, travel time was reduced to about 17½ hours. The steam locomotives were fuelled by coal imported from the UK. By 1909, trains completed the 425 km (260 mi) "rail trip of a thousand wonders"[3] in about 12 hours. Train travel on this line never did become any faster. Passenger services ended in 1997. Freight trains, even today, require 16 hours to complete the journey.

Motor vehicles took as long as trains for this route until the 1950s. Since then, travel times have been steadily reduced to about 4.5 hours for cars and about an hour more for passenger buses.

The first scheduled air service covering the 340 km (210 mi) straight line distance between the cities was in about 1930. The first flights took more than two hours; modern airlines allow 55 minutes.

The graph reveals the huge benefits in terms of travel times brought about by changes in transport technology since 1820 and by the concomitant improvements in the transport network.

In the next sections we take a closer look at the developments of each of these different kinds of transportation.

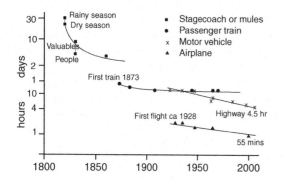

Figure 17.1
Travel times between Mexico City and Veracruz[1]

Pre-1850 transportation

Pre-Columbian societies had neither wheels nor beasts of burden to transport themselves or their goods. Obviously, this limited transportation to the speed, range and endurance of foot power. A system of trails stretched throughout the Aztec Empire, which covered most of present day central and southern Mexico. The system, with rest stops every 10–15 km (6–9 mi), was maintained through tribute. In the Yucatán, the Mayas built an extensive and impressive network of stucco-covered *sacbes* (white roads) linking major cities. The alignments of many of these routes, and their use of specific mountain passes, are still used today.

The Spanish conquistadors found these ancient roads to be completely unsuitable for horse traffic and animal-drawn carts. They were forced to undertake expensive re-routing and upgrading of sections that were critical to their rule. Their highest priority was to connect Mexico City, the capital, with Spain via the port of Veracruz (Figure 17.1). To this end, they starting building the Camino Real (Royal Highway) in 1550. The chosen route went from Veracruz to Xalapa to Perote to Puebla to Mexico City. This required numerous bridges and is essentially the same route between the port and the capital currently used by federal highways 180, 140 and 150. The opening of this first section of the Camino Real facilitated communication, and the transfer of Aztec gold to Spain and Spanish goods to Mexico's interior. To counter bandits, the road was patrolled by soldiers.

Towns along this route gained new importance. They collected tolls to pay for road maintenance. The Camino Real helped Puebla become the second largest and most important city in New Spain, a position it was to hold for 300 years. In the 1550s, the road was extended north to Zacatecas to facilitate transporting gold and silver back to Mexico City and then on to Spain. The Camino Real was later extended to other important cities and mining districts. By 1600 it reached as far north as Chihuahua and was later extended to Santa Fé in what is now New Mexico. Many other roads were also built to facilitate administration, communication and economic exploitation, though some sections of the system were not suitable for wheeled vehicles.

It is far easier to move people and goods, especially heavy bulky loads, by water than by land. However, unlike in the USA, there were, and still are, virtually

Joining the Atlantic and Pacific via the Isthmus of Tehuantepec

Ever since the 16th century, the Isthmus of Tehuantepec has been viewed as an attractive route connecting the Pacific and Atlantic Oceans. Numerous schemes for building a canal were considered but all were rejected as being too expensive. After numerous failures, the first rail line across the isthmus was completed in 1894, but its use was limited because the ports on either end were unsuitable for large vessels. Significant shipping finally became possible in 1907 when the Government built the necessary port facilities and upgraded the rail connection. Unfortunately for Mexico, the Panama Canal was opened in 1914 and quickly captured most inter-oceanic freight traffic.

no navigable internal waterways in Mexico. Proposals to use the Lerma–Chapala–Santiago system as a navigable waterway from Guanajuato State to the Pacific Ocean proved to be impractical.

Ocean-going transport was a different story. Ships were used to move goods and people along the coasts, especially since the only connection to Yucatán in colonial times was by sea. Unfortunately, Mexico's economic centers were almost all located well inland.

In 1565 the Spanish decided that bringing Asian goods from their colony in the Philippines back to Spain by crossing the Pacific, transshipping the cargo across Mexico and then sailing from Veracruz to Spain was preferable (more secure) to any alternative. To support this, a Camino Real for pack mules was built between Mexico City and Acapulco. A road suitable for wheeled vehicles between these cities was not completed until well into the 20th century. Demonstrating strong complementarity, for 250 years Spanish galleons carried Mexican silver to Manila and returned with spices, silk, porcelain, lacquer ware and other exotic goods from the Orient.

These "China galleons", the largest seafaring vessels of their time in the world displacing 2000 tons, greatly stimulated spatial interactions between Acapulco and Manila, 15,000 km away. Many Mexicans settled in Manila and a sizable Filipino community was established in Acapulco. Scores of Nahuatl words entered Tagalog, the main Filipino language. The Filipino currency is still called the peso. In the return direction, Filipinos taught Mexicans the distillation process which enabled the production of tequila. This is an excellent example of how transportation developments can encourage cultural exchanges and diminish the social, economic and cultural distance between places. Independence from Spain brought an end to the Manila–Acapulco galleons but expanded shipping traffic from Veracruz to New Orleans and New York.

By 1850 reasonable roads connected most parts of the country, even if the use of animal power meant that travel continued to be slow and difficult. For example, in 1800 it still took more than a week to go from Mexico City to Guadalajara. In the mid 19th century, Mexico was still an enormous country in terms of the time required for travel or trade.

The railroad age

The advent of steam trains revolutionized travel times (Figure 17.1). Railroads greatly reduced the cost and time of moving people and freight. Early concessions (the first was in 1837) came to nothing. By 1860 Mexico had less than 250 km of short disconnected railroad lines and was falling way behind its northern neighbor, which already had almost 50,000 km.

Political, administrative and financial issues, coupled with Mexico's rugged topography, prevented Mexico from keeping up with other Latin American nations. Mexico City was finally linked by rail to Puebla in 1866 and Veracruz in 1873.

In deciding the best route for the Veracruz-Mexico City line, Arthur Wellington, a British engineer, developed the concepts which later became known as positive and negative deviation.[4] At first glance, it might be assumed that the optimum route for a railway is the shortest distance between points, provided that the maximum possible grade is never exceeded. Negative deviations lengthen this minimum distance in order to avoid obstacles such as the volcanic mountains east of Mexico City: the Veracruz line skirts the twin volcanic peaks of Popocatepetl and Ixtaccihuatl before entering Mexico City from the north-east.

During the successive presidencies of Porfirio Díaz, railway building leapt forward (Figure 17.2). Díaz aggressively encouraged rail development through generous concessions and government subsidies to foreign investors. By 1884 Mexico had 12,000 km of track, including a US-financed link from Mexico City to the USA through Torreón, Chihuahua and Cuidad Juárez.[5] A British company had completed

Figure 17.2 The development of the railway network

The Copper Canyon railway

The Copper Canyon region is one of the most remote parts of Mexico. This remoteness helps to explain why the area is the home of about 50,000 Tarahumara Indians, and how they have managed to preserve much of their highly distinctive culture to this day.

The Copper Canyon railroad line, "the most dramatic train ride in the Western Hemisphere" (*Reader's Digest*), begins in Ojinaga and continues, via Chihuahua, to Los Mochis and Topolobampo. The railroad was started in the 1870s to enable produce grown in southern Texas to be exported via a Pacific port. Simultaneously, the twin settlements of Los Mochis and its port Topolobampo were developed on the other side of the Western Sierra Madre. The railroad project floundered and successive attempts to complete it all failed. Some innovative engineering finally led to the line being completed in 1961. Total cost? Over $100 million. The highlights include a 360° loop at El Lazo (km 585 from Ojinaga), one of only three comparable examples anywhere in North America), and a 180° turn inside a tunnel near Temoris at km 708. The line crosses the Continental Divide three times, reaches a maximum height of 2400 m (at km 583) and skirts the rim of the Copper Canyon. Between Chihuahua and Los Mochis, there are 37 bridges (totaling 3.6 km) and 86 tunnels (totaling 17.2 km). Almost all passenger rail services in Mexico ended in the 1990s but daily services continue along this line, mainly for tourists.

Unlike the railway, Los Mochis and Topolobampo both soon flourished. Topolobampo was started by US engineer Albert Kimsey Owen who chose this previously unsettled area for a socialist colony based on sugar-cane production, and as the terminus for the railway. Topolobampo has one of Mexico's finest natural harbors, a drowned river valley or ria, which affords a safe haven in the event of storms. Los Mochis was officially founded in 1893 by a second American, Benjamin Johnston, who built a sugar factory there.

Los Mochis became especially important in the second half of the twentieth century as a major commercial center, marketing much of the produce grown on the vast El Fuerte irrigation scheme. Much of this produce is still exported to the USA via the famous Copper Canyon railway. Los Mochis and Topolobampo are unusual—there are few other examples of such "new towns", with no colonial or pre-Hispanic antecedents, anywhere else in Mexico.

lines from Mexico City to Guadalajara, and from Mexico City via Monterrey to Nuevo Laredo.

Different gauge tracks typified a system based on numerous concessions but no overall national plan. By the turn of the century, additional tracks connected Guadalajara, San Luis Potosí and Monterrey to the Gulf coast port of Tampico. A line connecting the Pacific and Gulf coasts was also completed (see box). Durango was now connected to Eagle Pass on the US border. A second line to Veracruz was constructed, with a spur to Oaxaca.

Laws passed in 1898 sought to bring order to the rapid and chaotic expansion of Mexico's rail system. Foreign concessions were restricted. Subsidies were only made available for the completion of missing links such as lines to Manzanillo and the Guatemala border. Efforts were made to standardize track gauges.

However, the country's 24,000 km railroad network still had serious deficiencies. There were only three effective connections from the central plateau to the coasts. There were no links from central Mexico to either the Yucatán Peninsula or to the northwestern states of Nayarit, Sinaloa, Sonora and Baja California. The only efficient way to move inland freight from Chihuahua, Torreón, Durango or Ciudad Juárez to the Pacific was either north through the USA or all the way south and through Guadalajara to Manzanillo. The Sonora railroad linked Guaymas and Hermosillo to the USA, but not to the rest of Mexico.

Despite their weaknesses, railroads revolutionized Mexico. The railroads had average speeds of about 40 kph (25 mph) and ran through the night. They were five to ten times faster than pre-railroad transport. They lowered freight costs by roughly 80%. They shrank the size of Mexico in terms of travel time by a factor of between five and ten. They were also much cheaper and far more comfortable than stagecoaches. The estimated savings from railroad freight services in 1910 amounted to over 10% of the country's gross national product.[6] Between 1890 and 1910, the construction and use of railroads accounted for an estimated half of the growth in Mexico's income per person. In addition, the railroads carried mail, greatly reducing the time needed for this form of communication. Clearly, the benefits of railroads far outweighed their costs.

Foreign companies gained mightily from their investments building railroads, which were almost entirely dependent on imported locomotives, rolling stock, technical expertise, and even fuel. But Mexicans also benefitted enormously; in the early 1900s over half of the rail cargo supplied local markets and industries. The railroads thrust much of Mexico into the 20th century.

Cities with favorable rail connections grew significantly during the railroad era while those poorly served were at a severe disadvantage. The speed and economies of scale of shipping by rail encouraged mass production for national markets. For example, cotton growing expanded rapidly on irrigated farms near Torreón because the crop could be shipped easily and cheaply to large textile factories in Guadalajara, Puebla and Orizaba. Manufactured textiles were then distirbuted cheaply by rail to national markets. Elsewhere, the railroads enabled large iron and steel, chemical, cement, paper, shoe, beer and cigarette factories to supply the national market.

On the other hand, most Mexicans still lived far from railroad lines and relied on foot or mule transport while practicing subsistence agriculture. In addition, the cost of rail tickets was prohibitively expensive for many Mexicans; paying for a 70 km (43 mi) trip required a week's pay for those on the minimum wage. The railroads greatly expanded the gap between the 'have' and the 'have not' areas of the country. Almost all the Pacific coast and most of southern Mexico did not benefit from the railroads. Such growing inequalities contributed to the Mexican Revolution.

After the Revolution, network improvements were hindered by poor administration, corruption, labor unions and a shift of government priority to roads. The west coast railroad from Sonora to Guadalajara was completed in 1927. The Yucatán Peninsula was joined to the national network in the 1950s and the Chihuahua to Los Mochis line through the Copper Canyon (see box) was completed in 1961, finally linking Texas and Mexico's northern plateau to the Pacific Ocean.

A rapidly improving road network and competition from private autos, buses and, later, airplanes caused railroad traffic to decline significantly in the second half of the 20th century. Freight traffic on the nationalized railroad maintained a competitive advantage for some heavy shipments that were not time sensitive, but for other shipments trucks be-

---

Yucatán's independent railroad system

Yucatán developed its own, extensive and unique system of narrow gauge railroads in conjunction with the 1870 to 1920 economic boom based on the production of twine from sisal (oro verde or green gold). Yucatán became Mexico's richest state with thousands of prosperous plantations (haciendas) producing sisal as well as sugar and corn.

To move sisal from the fields to processing centers and eventually to ocean ports, 4500 km (2800 mi) of narrow gauge track were laid. The tracks fanned out from Yucatán's capital, Mérida, up to 100 km (62 mi) in all directions, forming the densest rail network in the world. Rolling stock and complete sections of track, with steel ties, were imported, mostly from Europe but also from the USA. The small trains were powered by mules, steam engines, electric batteries and, later, by gaso-

line motors. There was no standard design and several distinct gauges were in use, ranging from 400 to 930 mm (15.7 to 36.6 in).

Foreign competition, the Mexican Revolution, and synthetic fibers brought an end to the sisal boom. During the 1930s many of the plantations closed. Soon, the tracks were put to use providing rail passenger services between the scores of towns in the area. Many families used the small sisal hauling cars as personal transport, powered by a horse or mule. This was far more efficient than animal drawn carts on rough dirt roads, but required occasional de-railing in order to allow others to pass! Some of the Yucatán's narrow gauge lines have survived into the 21st century, and some of the former sisal haciendas have re-opened as luxury hotels for tourists.

Figure 17.3 Mexico's highway system, 2009

came the preferred mode of transport. The current system, with its roughly 21,000 km of track, is far less important to Mexico's economy than it was a century ago.

The age of motor vehicles

At the time of the Revolution (1910) there were very few motorcars in Mexico and poor roads kept speeds down, well below the speed of trains. After the Revolution, the government gave far higher priority to the road system than to railways. The road system had the potential to provide flexible access to all areas of the country while railroad access was limited to specific corridors between major cities. Realizing that Mexico would be a big market, Buick started making cars in Mexico in 1921. Ford opened a plant in 1925 and has been manufacturing cars in Mexico ever since. Though private automobile ownership was still very limited, trucks and buses began to have a significant impact.

The government invested heavily in road improvements. For example, between 1935 and 1945, over one quarter of the national budget was dedicated to road improvements. By the mid 1950s the national road system exceeded the railroad network in length.

Publicly-built toll roads were beginning to appear, though some major gaps remained.

Mexico's rugged relief makes road construction and maintenance very challenging and expensive. As a result of the topography, many roads and highways are very winding with steep grades in places, leading to low average speeds. By the 1960s Mexico's paved national highway system reached all regions of the country. Private car ownership was growing rapidly. Buses were the dominant form of intercity transport and trucks were gaining a growing portion of freight shipments.

By the mid 1980s there were almost 3000 km of free four lane highways, mostly around major cities. By 1992 about 1300 km of new toll roads were in operation and a further 2300 km were in the works.

The number of concessions and pace of construction led to poor standards. Some toll roads were very expensive. The Autopista del Sol (Sun Highway) connecting Mexico City to Acapulco is a good example of the problems related to many private toll roads. It opened with great fanfare in 1993. However, relatively few motorists were willing to pay the $75 toll for the 300 km (190 mi) trip. The toll has since been reduced by more than 50% but is still expensive by

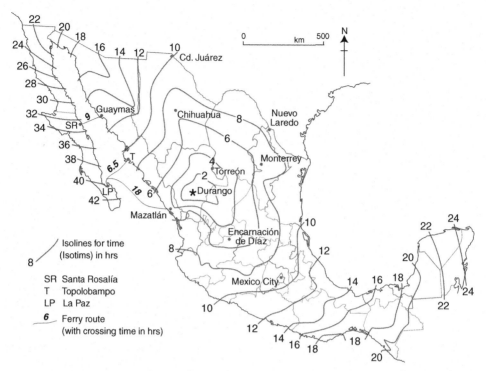

Figure 17.4 Driving times from Durango, 2009[7]

international standards. The quality of construction was so bad that within a few years the highway was full of cracks and potholes. Eventually, the toll operator quit the project and the government was forced to take over and spend heavily to repair the road. About 20 other concessions had to be bailed out in the 1990s at a cost of about $14 billion.

The current road network in Mexico (Figure 17.3) is extensive, covering virtually all areas of the country. Mexico has over 120,000 km of paved roads, far more than any other country in Latin America. By contrast, Brazil has about 96,000 km. There are over 10,000 km of controlled access toll expressways, even if they are among the most expensive in the world. There are an additional 10,000 km of free four lane highways. Mexico also has over 200,000 km of unpaved roads.

On the other hand, there are still some notable gaps in the highway system. Traffic between Monterrey and Guadalajara, Mexico's second and third largest cities, must still negotiate some sections of winding two lane road. Numerous cities lack by-passes to speed through-traffic. Neither the Yucatán Peninsula nor Baja California is connected by expressway to the rest of Mexico.

The Western Sierra Madre still constitutes a major barrier between the Pacific and the north-central plateau between Zacatecas and the USA border. The highways from Durango to Mazatlán, and Chihuahua to Hermosillo, are slow, windy and largely unimproved two lane roads. Durango is actually about 10% closer to Mazatlán than Torreón but the drive from Durango to Mazatlán takes twice as long (Figure 17.4).

If travel times depended only on distance, isolines such as those shown on Figure 17.4 would be arranged in concentric circles around the point of origin. The main factors causing deviations away from concentric circles are relief (especially gradient), the alignments of existing highways in the network and variations in the quality (speed) of these highways.

Durango is only 245 km (152 mi) from the Pacific coast resort of Mazatlán by air. The road distance is 312 km (194 mi). The driving time from Durango to Mazatlán is five hours and requires crossing the Western Sierra Madre. The most spectacular 9-km, gravity-defying section is known as the Devil's Backbone. As the isolines show, driving five hours in any other direction takes you a lot further. Encarnación de Díaz, 460 km from Durango, is the same driving

The impact of improved transport systems on rural areas[8]

Transportation dramatically changed the rural economy of Chilapa, a town about 40 km (25 mi) east of Chilpancingo, the capital of Guerrero. Prior to 1970, the area was almost self-sufficient, as it had been for hundreds of years. It produced cotton shawls (rebozos) and later woven palm goods which were sold to obtain money for salt, iron, cotton, matches and other essentials not produced locally. All the corn and most of food consumed in Chilapa came via pack animals from farms within 12 km (7 mi) of the town.

In the 1970s the road to Chilpancingo (national highway 92) was upgraded and paved, dramatically reducing transport time and costs. This had a very profound impact on the area. Corn and other goods from the rest of Mexico and abroad poured into the area, leading to significantly lower prices. The local farmers could not compete; many stopped farming altogether. Some started commuting by bus to low paying jobs in Chilpancingo. Others produced woven palm goods which were subsidized by the government. These subsidies were curtailed in the 1980s but new subsidies were available for chemical fertilizers. Farmers began producing good quality corn again, which was sold outside the area. Chilapa continued importing cheap, low quality corn for local consumption.

The new road completely changed the economy of the area around Chilapa, brought it farther into the national economy and improved, to some degree, its standard of living.

There are thousands of communities in Mexico that are not served by paved roads (see chapter 24) and are essentially as self-sufficient and poor as Chilapa was before the 1970s. In addition, there are thousands of other communities not reached even by dirt roads; they are even poorer and have to be highly self-sufficient.

time away as Mazatlán. The north-trending bends in the isolines clearly show the influence of the main highways to the border cities of Ciudad Juárez (via Chihuahua) and Nuevo Laredo.

Note that while the Baja Peninsula appears to be extremely isolated, there are several vehicle ferry routes linking it to the mainland which reduce travel times. The greatest savings from Durango are by taking the Topolobampo-La Paz crossing. Assuming good connections, this cuts a staggering 24 hours off the total travel time to La Paz.

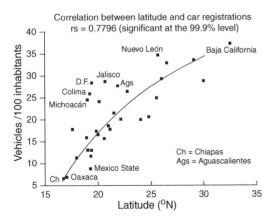

Figure 17.5
Does northern Mexico have more vehicles?[9]

On average there are about seven people per car in Mexico, compared to about six in Argentina, ten in Chile and less than two in the USA and Canada. There are far more cars in urban areas with their many businesses, taxis, and wealthy residents. In poor rural parts of southern Mexico, private car ownership is quite rare.

The road network is heavily used, accounting for over 95% of domestic travel. Mexico's inter-city bus system is one of the finest in the world. The nation's fleet of more than 70,000 inter-city buses enables passengers to amass almost half a trillion passenger-km per year. On a per person basis, Mexicans travel an average of 4500 km (2800 mi) by road each year.[10]

Where are Mexico's vehicles?

Mexico has about 20 million registered vehicles, about one for every five persons (2005). Which areas have the most and least vehicles? It turns out that the northernmost state, Baja California, has the most with 37 registered vehicles per 100 people. The southernmost states, Chiapas and Oaxaca, have about one sixth as many with 6.6 and 6.9 respectively. In fact there is a very strong statistical relationship (using Spearman's rank correlation[11], rs =0.78, significant at the 99.9% level) between latitude and vehicles (Figure 17.5). How can this be?

We are not suggesting a direct causal relationship. Many factors are interrelated. First, the states in the north tend to be wealthier (see Figure 14.2); the correlation between GDP/person and latitude is 0.58. Vehicle ownership is closely related to GDP/person (rs = 0.59). Both these correlations are significant at the 99% level. In addition, northern states are close to the USA, a vehicle-oriented society.

However, there are some anomalies to the general pattern. The very wealthy Federal District has 50% more vehicles than would be expected from its latitude alone. States with many migrants, such as Jalisco and Michoacán, also have more vehicles than expected given their latitude. An added complication is that more than a million foreign-plated cars in Mexico, imported temporarily by returning migrants or foreigners, are not included in these figures.

Transportation by sea and ocean

Ocean transportation has been important since the first arrival of the Spaniards. Since the arrival of the Spaniards, Veracruz has been the most important seaport because it provides the easiest access to central Mexico and the capital. Today it handles a full array of cargo including containers, automobiles, pe-

troleum and grain shipments. Over half of Mexico's grain imports arrive in Veracruz.

There are numerous other important seaports (Figure 17.6). The linked ports of Tampico and Altamira on the Gulf of Mexico have grown in importance since becoming linked to Monterrey and the rest of Mexico by rail late in the 19th century. The port gained additional importance as a petroleum shipping center in the mid 20th century.

Coatzacolcos and Salina Cruz are important ports at either end of the railroad across the Isthmus of Tehuantepec. Their importance has increased dramatically since the 1970s oil boom. Though much of Mexico's oil and gas is transported via pipeline (see Figure 15.1), there are several other important petroleum ports on the Gulf, such as Cayo Arcas and Don Bocas. In terms of tonnage, petroleum and derivatives shipments dominate all other goods.

Acapulco, which was a very important colonial port, retains importance but has been eclipsed by other Pacific ports. As a result of its natural harbor, modern port facilities and excellent rail and road connections, Manzanillo has evolved into Mexico's busiest container port. The port of Lázaro Cárdenas, linked to Morelia and central Mexico by rail and

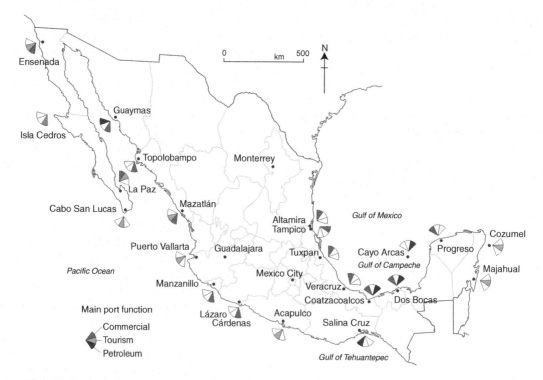

Figure 17.6 Mexico's major ports

expressway, has also emerged as an important Pacific container port. Guaymas on the Sea of Cortés is another important port.

Shipments from Asia to the USA through Mexico's Pacific ports have increased significantly as a result of the large back-ups and long delays experienced at the ports of Los Angeles and Long Beach. In early 2009, Mexico's government was planning to go ahead with a $5 billion megaport at Punta Coronet, 240 km south of Tijuana, to handle Asian shipments bound for the USA. With the economic downturn of 2008–2009, it is questionable whether this project will go forward as scheduled and be completed as planned by 2012.

Mexico's ports now handle more cruise ship passengers than any other nation. The importance of ports such as Cabo San Lucas, Puerto Vallarta and Cozumel for tourism is examined further in chapter 19.

The ferries linking the Baja California Peninsula to the mainland cut travel times and have strategic importance. The two main routes are La Paz–Topolobampo and La Paz–Mazatlán which between them carry 400,000 passengers a year. On the Caribbean side, however, passenger movements are much larger. The ferries operating to the tourist islands of Isla Mujeres and Cozumel off the coast of Quintana Roo (from Puerto Juárez and Playa del Carmen respectively) each carry almost 3 million passengers a year.[12]

Air travel

Air travel is becoming more popular. Of the roughly 50 million air passengers each year, about half are domestic and half international. The initial flights in Mexico were all private and made use of small landing stripes. Before they were accessible by road many remote towns had rough landing strips which were easy and cheap to build. However, these were rarely used, normally only by important officials and elites.

Commercial air service started in Mexico in the 1920s. The main route was Mexico City–Tuxpan––Tampico–Brownsville, Texas. By the 1930s, flights were available to Los Angeles, Cuba, Guatemala and El Salvador. Jet services to USA and European cities started in the 1960s. The routes have expanded steadily and now connect Mexico's 29 national and 57 international airports. Mexico City's airport is by far the busiest in the country with over 24.6 million commercial passenger movements annually, 35% of the national total. Cancún is second with

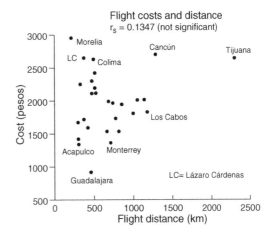

Figure 17.7 Does the price of a flight from Mexico City depend on distance?[14]

about 10.5%, followed by Guadalajara with almost 9%, Monterrey with 7.4%, Tijuana with 5.3% and Puerto Vallarta (Jalisco) and San José del Cabo (Baja California Sur), each with 3.6%.[13] Mexico averages about 370 air passengers per year per 1000 population, compared to 2430 for the USA, 1400 for Canada, 202 for Brazil and 179 for Argentina. While air travel is growing, it remains a distant third behind automobile and bus travel.

Air travel greatly distorts the map of Mexico and the world. In terms of travel time on public transport, Mexico City's airport is closer to Guadalajara, in the state of Jalisco, than to some areas in the Mexico City Metropolitan Area! Similarly, Guadalajara is closer to Hong Hong by air—21 hours for the 13,000 km—than to some communities only 200 km away in northern Jalisco which require a trek of over 24 hours by bus, taxi and foot. Business executives fly 2300 km from Tijuana to Mexico City, work for six hours in the city, and fly back the same day. Commuting to the same office takes longer for some Metro area residents who live only 50 km away.

Air travel, coupled with familiarity, significantly influences our perceptions of distance. A Guadalajara traveling executive perceives Mexico City as being closer to his home than slum areas within 20 km of his house. Downtown Mexico City seems much closer to a person who commutes there daily from 40 km away than to a neighbor who works locally and only goes downtown once a year.

Transportation systems greatly affect our perception of distance. Depending on connections, air travel is not always the quickest means of transport. The straight line distance from Mazatlán to Durango is 245 km. The fastest air connection goes through Mexico City and involves flying over 1500 km. It takes seven hours, longer than the inter-city bus! A direct flight would take about 45 minutes. If an expressway connected the two cities, the drive would take just over two hours. Though the straight line distance between them is about the same as that between Querétero and Mexico City, the travel and perceived distance is far greater. This example demonstrates how existing transportation systems affect our perceptions of distance.

The distinction between absolute distance measured in kilometers and relative distance in terms of cost is illustrated by Figure 17.7 which shows the price of one-way economy-class direct flights from Mexico City to 28 cities for a random mid-week day in April 2009. There is clearly no connection between flying distance (or flight times) and the ticket price (rs = 0.14). Remarkably, the shortest flight, to Morelia, is actually the most expensive. Flights to Lázaro Cárdenas and Colima also cost more than might be expected while the best value fares on a per kilometer basis are those to Guadalajara, Monterrey and Tijuana, all very popular routes.

This chapter has focused on the development of Mexico's national transportation networks. The significance of changes in transportation technology and networks in the context of city growth in general is discussed in chapter 21 and in the context of Mexico City in particular in chapter 22. Some additional aspects of transportation in rural areas are examined in chapter 24.

18

Communications: the movement of information and ideas

Similar to transportation, communication from one place to another is very basic to geographic inquiry. Spatial communication can take many forms including word of mouth, mail, newspapers, telegraph, telephone, radio, television and internet. Like travel and transportation, spatial communication can only take place if there is complementarity, a supply or source of information at one place and a demand or interest at another place. For example, TV shows and films produced in Mexico City flow out to meet the demands of viewers in all Mexican states as well as many other Latin American countries and the USA.

As with the transport of people and goods, communications must overcome distance and are subject to distance decay. Communications also adhere to the gravity model: the volume of spatial interaction is related to the distance between two places and their size. For example, Tepic is much closer to Mexico City than Monterrey but the latter city has far more telephone communications with the capital because it is far larger and more important.

The movement of information and ideas requires some means of communications, such as a telegraph system, telephone lines, fiber optic cables, radio waves or satellite television signals. Some of these means of communication have well-defined networks, others are best defined by the extent of their overall reach or "footprint."

One important concept in the communications sector, somewhat analogous to time-space convergence in the transportation sector (chapter 17), is the process identified by David Harvey as time-space compression in which social relations are stretched across space.[1] Harvey views time-space compression

as a central element of the capitalist system and its adage that "time is money." The term refers to how changing technologies have dramatically changed the speed and nature of communications, leading to several fundamental shifts in how people work and interact. This is illustrated by the workplace revolutions resulting from the introduction (in chronological order) of telephones, fax machines, e-mails and instant messaging. In many ways, these changes have annihilated conventional distance as measured in kilometers. This book is a perfect example: the product of frequent simultaneous technologically-enabled collaboration between two authors living 3700 km apart.

The next sections examine the evolution and characteristics of communication networks in Mexico.

Early communications

Early communications relied on people power and their speed was limited to about 100 km a day.[2] Couriers or runners (*paynani*) traveled the Aztec road system keeping the rulers informed of events and delivering orders from the capital. These roads deteriorated rapidly during the 16th century population crash. In 1580 the right to operate the communications system was assigned to selected members of the nobility. By far the most important part of their operation was the carrying of written messages between the Viceroy in Mexico City and the port of Veracruz, and the ships bound for Spain.

In 1765 the government established a formal postal system with regular routes, including a weekly service to Oaxaca. These routes extended all the way north to upper California and Santa Fe. If you think mail services today are slow, it was even slower in those days; for example, Santa Fe had only four mail deliveries and pick-ups each year!

Some idea of the historical importance of the postal service is gleaned from the fact that by 1801 it already had 400 offices and moved 1.1 million pieces of mail. Following independence (1821), the new Mexican government continued the colonial postal service for domestic mail. For international service, the British and French established packet services, picking up and delivering mail to Veracruz and Tampico. These packet services lasted into the 20th century.

Mexico issued its first adhesive postage stamps in 1856. Stamps issued in 1899 included images of Popocatepetl volcano, the cathedral in Mexico City and the Juanacatlán Falls ("Mexico's Niagara") on the River Santiago near Guadalajara. These are three of the earliest landscape images on stamps anywhere in the world.

Mexico's first airmail service in 1917 operated sporadically between the mining town of Pachuca and Mexico City. In 1928 the first airmail service running to a set schedule linked Mexico City to Tuxpan and Tampico. It was organized by Compañia Mexicana de Transportación Aérea, which later became better known as the airline Mexicana.

In 2005 Mexico's postal service delivered approximately seven letters per person. By comparison, the US Postal Service delivers over 700 items per person,

even if this does include junk mail. Comparable figures for other countries are (in descending order): UK 335, Australia 254, Brazil 45, China 17, Argentina 12 and Peru 0.5. Consumer surveys invariably find that a third of all Mexicans prefer private courier services to the postal service for the delivery of documents. Private courier companies in Mexico share a market worth over $1 billion a year.

Telegraphy

With the coming of telegraphy in 1851, the speed of communications went from very slow to virtually instantaneous. By 1867, Mexico City, Veracruz, Querétaro, Guanajuato, León, San Luis Potosí and Oaxaca were connected by telegraph. Telegraph lines were built in conjunction with railroads but, since they were far, far cheaper than rail lines, they were also extended rapidly to areas without railroads.

With strong government support and subsidies, Mexico had over 10,000 km of teleragraph lines by 1880. There were lines to Acapulco, to the border cities of Nogales, Cuidad Juárez and Matamoros, which connected to the US system, and to Europe via a transatlantic cable. Telegraphy brought speedier communications between Mexican cities and to cities around the world but most rural areas had no service and remained outside the network.

Within a few years Mexico was also connected to the USA via a cable under the Gulf of Mexico and to Chile on the west coast of South America via a

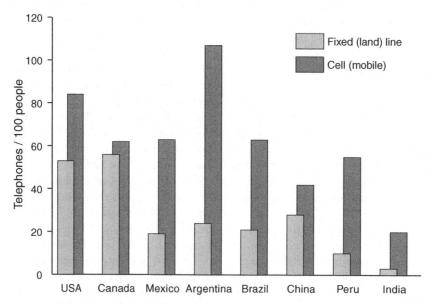

Figure 18.1 Access to fixed line and cell phones by country

cable under the Pacific Ocean. The telegraph system continued to expand through the 20th century. In 1990, the system's 1470 offices handled 28 million telegraphs. The wiring of remittances from migrant workers in the USA to families in Mexico (chapter 26) was extremely important until electronic bank transfers replaced them in the 2000s.

Telephony

Mexico's first telephone line was erected in Puebla in the early 1880s. Before long, the Mexican Telephone Company, a subsidiary of Bell, was operating in Mexico City. The first telephone lines did not work very well and were limited to downtown areas. Only public officials, police stations, a few select businesses and the wealthy used the telephone service.

The growth of telephony was slow because it lacked strong government support, was expensive and had a very limited range. By 1893 telephone services had spread to 13 more cities even though intercity lines would not become available until much later. In about 1950 all Mexico's telephone companies were purchased by a single group of investors to form Teléfonos de México (Telmex) which established a monopoly. Even after the government nationalized the company in 1972, few incentives were offered for expansion and it was still almost impossible to obtain a new telephone line.

In 1990 Telmex was reprivatized in one of Mexico's largest, most complicated and most controversial privatizations. The government sold majority voting rights and a 20% stake in Telmex to a consortium of investors for $1.8 billion and it sold $3.7 billion in shares to the public. The newly privatized Telmex invested significantly in the mid 1990s, enabling millions to get new lines but raising rates dramatically. Competitors were allowed to enter the telephone market but Telmex has remained the dominant player, especially for residential services. It remains fashionable for its customers to complain about its poor service and very high long distance rates.

Mexico and the USA are closely linked by telephone. Over 90% of the international calls from Mexico go to the USA whereas roughly 13% of all US international calls go to Mexico.

For a country of Mexico's wealth and sophistication, it lags behind most of the world in telephony (Figure 18.1). In 2007, Mexico had 19 fixed telephone lines per 100 population compared to 53 in the USA and 56 in Canada. The Federal District had the best service with about 50 fixed telephone lines per 100 people, followed by Nuevo León with 33 and Baja California with 27. Chiapas had the fewest with only 5 per 100, not far behind Oaxaca with 6 and Tabasco with 7. Telephone communications are difficult or inconvenient in these southern states; this limits their residents' quality of life and economic competitiveness. Other states with poor telephone service (less than 12 lines per 100 people) are Hidalgo, Zacatecas, Campeche, Tlaxcala, Guerrero, Veracruz and San Luis Potosí.

Mexicans have better access to cell phones than fixed lines (Figure 18.1) with 63% of the population owning one in 2007, compared to 84% in the USA, 62% in Canada and a staggering 107% (more than one cell phone per person) in Argentina. While lagging slightly behind Guatemala where 76% of the population has a cell phone, a higher percentage of people in Mexico use cell phones than in China or India. Cell phone use in Mexico has grown rapidly in the capital and other big cities but has also grown spectacularly in southern and rural areas where there are few wired telephones. Many rural villages with only a few fixed line phones now have dozens of cell phones, mostly used by those under age thirty. When asked why they don't use cell phones more, some older rural adults say they find cell phones too complicated because of their many small buttons.

Many rural residents get cell phones from relatives who have migrated to the USA. They avoid monthly fees by buying pre-paid cell phone cards when they have the money. When the card runs out, they make no calls until they can afford to buy another one. Some enterprising rural residents use their cell phone as a pay phone. In short, cell phone technology has greatly improved communications in many Mexican rural areas.

Internet

ITESM, a university in Monterrey, established Mexico's first internet connection in 1989. Other universities soon followed. In the late 1990s Telmex started to provide internet service to businesses and the general public. Other providers entered the market but by 2005 Telmex still had about 80% of the market.

Public access via internet cafes is relatively inexpensive. With computers in many schools and cyber cafes in most Mexican towns, about 21%

The adoption of innovations and spatial diffusion

Figure 18.2 shows the adoption of three agricultural innovations by barley-growing farmers in the wetter areas of the central Mexico states of Tlaxcala and Hidalgo.[3] The adoption of each innovation follows the general model (upper graph) quite closely. Researchers introduced farmers to a package of reforms which could improve their crop yields. Interestingly, in this area, most farmers preferred to adopt a single innovation at a time rather than a package of related innovations all at once. This suggests that farmers preferred to limit their risk in any one growing season by only making a single change (usually introducing an improved crop variety) to their traditional methods. However, once a particular innovation had proven effective, they were prepared to adopt the other innovations.

The spread of innovations can also be studied in spatial terms. The spatial diffusion of information or adoption of innovations is an important subset of spatial interaction. There are three basic types of diffusion. The first is relocation diffusion where people travel or migrate and bring their cultural and technological practices with them. For example, modern studies in the genetics of corn (maize) have established that ancient Mexicans first domesticated corn in the Balsas valley. They then migrated both northwards and southwards, taking the practice of cultivating corn with them.[5]

The second is contagious diffusion, which generally spreads from person to person and exhibits strong distance decay. An example is the spread of the Jehovah's Witness faith in Mexico which required a considerable amount of face-to-face personal interaction.[6] Many diseases also spread by contagious diffusion.

The third is hierarchical diffusion, which spreads across higher levels of a hierarchy and then down to lower levels. This is often how information from the top of an organization reaches those at the bottom. An example is the government's 1970s family planning program that was first adopted in large cities, then smaller cities, and eventually penetrated into rural areas.[7]

Combinations of these three types are possible. A recent example is the spread of the H1N1 influenza virus in early 2009. First reports were that it started in a rural village, probably in Oaxaca, and spread by contagious diffusion to others in the village. From there an infected person temporarily relocated to Mexico City where the flu again spread by contagious diffusion. From Mexico City, the top of the Mexican hierarchy, it spread down the hierarchy as carriers of the virus traveled to smaller Mexican cities and to other cities worldwide.

Figure 18.3 shows the spatial diffusion of commercial dairy farming in the central part of the state of Aguascalientes from 1943 to 1968. Only a handful of commercial farms existed in 1943. Over the next 25 years, many more dairy farms began operating. Influencing the rate and direction of spread were such factors as highways, the milk collection routes established by Nestlé, the age of the farmer, and proximity to an existing dairy farm.

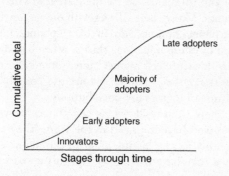

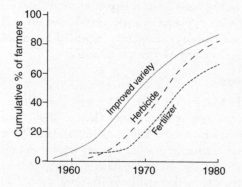

Figure 18.2 The adoption of innovations
(a) general model
(b) adoption of three innovations, 1960-80[3]

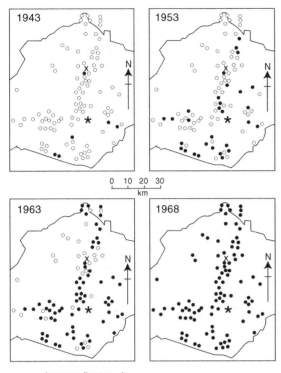

* Aguascalientes city
x Milk collection depot at Pabellon de Arteaga
• Already adopted   ○ Future adopter

Figure 18.3 The diffusion of dairying in Aguascalientes[8]

of Mexicans used the internet in 2007. This is relatively low compared to 94% in South Korea, 73% in Canada and the USA, 27% in Peru, 35% in Brazil and 26% in Argentina. Though Mexico is ahead of China (16%), Guatemala (10%) and India and Nigeria (7%), it is still lagging in internet use relative to its overall level of development.

An impressive three-quarters of Mexico's personal computer internet connections are broadband. Internet use is highest in urban centers but is making steady inroads into rural areas. The highest usage is among 12- to 18-year-olds, with slightly more males than females. However, less than a third of those in this group use the internet. Just under half of internet use is in the home, the rest is in schools, offices, public centers or cybercafes. About 44% of all users visit the internet for educational purposes, 40% for e-mail, 35% for general information, and 21% for online telephoning. The internet is having an enormous impact on Mexican society.

The digital divide

Overall, just how well does Mexico do in terms of the digital divide? The Digital Access Index[9] (DAI) is a compound index assessing the level of information and communications technologies (ICTs) that a country possesses. The DAI combines variables measuring infrastructure, affordability, literacy and educational level, the availability of broadband, international internet bandwidth per person and internet usage. Sweden placed highest in 2002 with a score of 0.85 out of a maximum possible score of 1.0. Canada and the USA were in equal 10th place. Mexico (index: 0.50) placed a lowly 65th of the 180 countries in the rankings, level with Brazil but well ahead of China (0.43). Though digital communications in Mexico are expanding rapidly, Mexico lags behind rival countries in these important technologies. This could possibly hamper Mexico's future ability to compete economically in the increasingly flat world of free trade.

There are some encouraging signs that Mexico is catching up. For example, data for 2008 show that it has become the country with the 8th highest number of internet hosts, the services which provide access to internet servers (Figure 18.4).

Mass communications

Mass communications are important for keeping people informed of national and world events and in promoting unity and nationalism. Mexico has had newspapers for centuries but their importance has diminished as people switched to television and internet sources of information. Newspaper circulation in Mexico is relatively impressive with 6 per 100 people, compared to 23 in the USA and Canada, 6 in

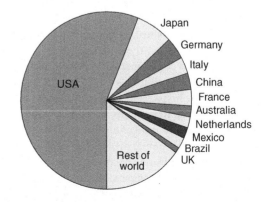

Figure 18.4
Mexico's share of global internet hosts, 2008[10]

Telesecundarias[11]

About one million secondary (junior high) school students live in remote areas where there is a shortage of teachers, especially subject specialists, and where the number of students in any particular grade is too small for regular educational provision to be cost-effective. Mexico's solution has been to embrace satellite technology.

These students receive their lessons in a specially adapted schoolhouse–a *telesecundaria*–from TVs connected to satellite receivers, often powered by generators or batteries charged by wind turbines or photovoltaic panels. The students, some of whom have to walk two hours to reach their classrooms, are supported by 55,000 teachers who help with all subjects at all grades.

The *telesecundarias* program has operated for 40 years and now reaches students from Central America to Florida. It also provides national and international news to the villages. Each TV lesson is 15 minutes long, followed by 35 minutes of focused discussion. Students then take a short break before the next TV lesson. A number of Mexico's 13,000 *telesecundarias* use internet connections for two-way communications between the village school and educators in the capital. Increasingly, classes are internet-based, allowing greater flexibility in delivery. Upon completing the program, the students wanting to continue their education must move to larger towns with preparatory (senior high) schools.

Are *telesecundarias* successful? It certainly seems so. On a per school basis, they are cost-effective for classes as small as 10 or 12 students. An estimated 79.4% of students in *telesecundarias* complete grade 9 compared with an equivalent figure of 78.8% for regular junior highs.

Brazil, 10 in Argentina and less than 3 in Colombia and Peru. Mexicans in large cities are far more likely to read daily newspapers than those in smaller communities. In terms of circulation, the four leading newspapers (*Esto, La Prensa, Excelsior* and *El Universal*) are all in the capital.

Radio broadcasting started in the 1920s and within a few years all major cities had radio stations. Virtually all Mexican households have access to radio broadcasts where they obtain news headlines and more in-depth coverage. Mexico made its first experimental television transmission in 1931 but regular television broadcasts for the public did not begin until the 1950s. By 2005 Mexico had 460 television stations (almost 25% of all stations in Latin America), most of them owned by or affiliated with either TV Azteca or Televisa, the largest Spanish language communications conglomerate in the world.

Over 90% of households have TVs in 24 Mexican states. In Chiapas and Oaxaca only about 70% have TVs because these states are relatively marginalized and have many indigenous speaking families as well as many very remote areas where TV reception is poor. These conditions occur to a lesser degree in the other six states (Guerrero, Campeche, Hidalgo, Puebla, San Luis Potosí and Veracruz) where 80% to 90% of households have TVs. The areas with fewer TVs are the worst off in terms of communications because they also have fewer telephones, internet users and newspaper readers. These isolated areas are not well integrated with the mainstream Mexican society or economy and therefore have a difficult time competing economically.

Mexico's first geostationary satellite was placed in orbit in 1985. *Satélites Mexicanos* (Satmex) currently operates three satellites providing voice, data, internet and video services to Mexico, South America and the continental USA.

Telenovelas and historietas

The highest rating programs on TV are televised novels, *telenovelas*. A *telenovela* is a limited-run television serial melodrama, somewhat like a soap opera but normally lasting less than a year, and where the eventual ending has already been scripted.

The first global *telenovela* was *Los ricos también lloran* (*The rich cry too*), originally shown in 1979. Telenovelas are now a $200 million market. Some critics claim they are effective promoters of social change, others deride them as being nothing more than mass escapism.[12] Whichever view is more accurate, their portrayals reflect society's values and institutions.

Advocates of *telenovelas* point to their role in challenging some traditional Mexican media taboos by including story lines about urban violence, racism, homosexuality, birth control, physical handicaps, political corruption, immigration and drug smuggling. Early *telenovelas* tended to be shallow romantic tales. The form subsequently evolved to include social commentaries and historical romances, some applauded for their attention to historical detail.

Some were used for attempts at social engineering. An early government-sponsored *telenovela* promoted adult literacy programs. Several others openly advocated family planning and have been credited with contributing to Mexico's dramatic decline in fertility rates (chapter 9). Other *telenovelas* have targeted younger audiences, focusing on issues connected to pop music, sex and drugs.

Besides the shallowness of the plot lines in most telenovelas, the other common criticism is that their stars are almost always white-skinned, blue-eyed blondes. Sadly, all too often, actors with indigenous looks are relegated to roles portraying menial workers such as home help or janitors.

Telenovelas have been extraordinarily successful commercially. They have become immensely popular not only in Latin America and among the US Hispanic population but also in more than 100 other countries, mainly in Eastern Europe and Asia.

In print media, a similar role to the *telenovela* has been played by *historietas* (comic books), the best of which have tackled all manner of social, political and environmental issues well before such topics made the main-stream press. *Historietas* helped educate millions of Mexicans and were also a commercial success. Their circulation peaked in the 1980s but has since declined due to competition from television and, more recently, the internet. The most influential creator of *historietas* is the cartoonist and writer Eduardo del Río (Rius) whose work earned him a 1991 United Nations Environment Programme prize.

Cultural diffusion

The process of cultural diffusion (the spread of knowledge, skills and cultural traits from one society to another) could not occur in the absence of communications and transportation networks. It is often claimed that Mexico is being invaded by US culture. The claim is made that this invasion is gradually resulting in the homogenization of Mexican culture to the point where many aspects are, or may become, indistinguishable in the future from US culture.

Advertising for US products is everywhere in Mexico. US music and movies play in every major city. Christmas Day is now celebrated at least as widely as Three Kings' Day (6 January), the traditional day in Mexico for children to receive gifts. Young Mexicans know as much about Halloween (an import from north of the border) as they do about their own festival for Day of the Dead. Household shopping is as likely to be purchased in the nearest Wal-Mart as in the longer-established corner store.

The long-term effect of these changes is a degree of placelessness. Shopping malls either side of the border

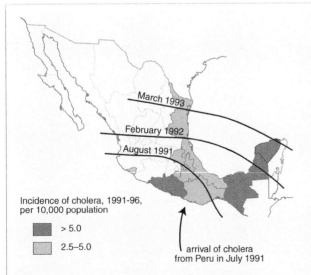

Incidence of cholera, 1991-96, per 10,000 population

- ▨ > 5.0
- ▨ 2.5–5.0

March 1993
February 1992
August 1991

arrival of cholera from Peru in July 1991

Cholera in Mexico, 1991–1996

The 1991-96 cholera epidemic in Mexico began in Peru in January 1991. It quickly spread northwards, reaching Central America by March and Mexico by July (Figure 18.5). The cholera epidemic then spread slowly across Mexico before abating.

The incidence of cholera was much higher in the Gulf coast states than either inland or along the Pacific coast. By the time the epidemic was over in 1996, more than 43,500 cases had been reported in Mexico and 524 people had died.[14]

Figure 18.5 Diffusion of a disease: the spread of cholera, 1991–1996[13]

already house many of the same transnational store chains and brand name goods. This convergence makes it increasingly difficult to distinguish between countries. However, in our opinion, this view is over simplistic.

Even as these trends are taking place, many aspects of Mexican culture are sweeping northwards. The spread of the Spanish language in the USA has long been documented. Hispanic purchasing power and voting power are potent forces of change. Mexican *telenovelas* and some genres of Mexican music are also invading the USA. Mexican food is gaining widespread popularity. More salsa is now sold in the USA than ketchup. The celebrations of *Cinco de Mayo* (5 May), commemorating the day in 1862 when the Mexican army defeated the French army at the Battle of Puebla, are far more elaborate now north of the border than south.

Cultural diffusion is a complex process and often operates in both directions simultaneously. Even assuming that cultural homogenization is a viable concept, the homogenization of Mexican culture remains a very long way off.

The annihilation of distance through the development of such technologies as e-mails, instant messaging and internet telephony has forever changed many aspects of everyday life. Many young people now enjoy social interactions via online social networking sites such as Facebook with friends and acquaintances all over the world. In some cases, they are unlikely ever to meet face to face. Theirs is a new virtual "water fountain" somewhere in cyberspace.

Do the rules of geography apply to such virtual spaces?[15] Some of the principles developed by geographers to describe and analyze spatial interactions and patterns will perhaps no longer apply, but this will not prevent geographers from exploring the new and exciting world comprised of cyberspaces and cyber-networks. The techniques they use may well be derived from those used by earlier geographers in studying the imaginary spaces of the physical, social, economic and human landscapes found in literature.

19

Tourism and development

Most UN World Tourism Organization (WTO) statistics define tourists as those who spend at least one night (and less than a year) away from their usual home. The WTO ignores the precise reasons for travel. To the WTO, tourists include those visiting friends or family as well as those on trips for business, professional, religious or health reasons. In reading this chapter, it is important to remember this very broad definition.

In our discussion, we distinguish between tourists (as defined by the WTO) and day-trippers (who undertake excursions lasting less than 24 hours). We end the chapter by examining the special case of foreign retirees, many of whom live year-round in Mexico.

In a spatial sense, at both the national and international scale, flows of tourists operate in both directions simultaneously. For example, while many tourists head for nearby large urban centers, favoring those with multiple attractions such as state capitals or Mexico City, many urban residents move in the opposite direction, away from the cities, primarily to coastal resorts but also to mountainous regions or rural areas in the economic periphery.

Because tourism brings foreign funds into the national economy, it is often termed an 'invisible' export. However, the overall tourism balance of payments is not quite as favorable as it first seems since many Mexicans travel outside the country and their spending constitutes an invisible import.

An economic multiplier applies to all tourism activities. The World Travel and Tourism Council estimates that the total direct and indirect effects of tourism on an economy are about three times more than the direct effects alone. The economic multiplier for employment is 3.24. The tourist industry not only benefits hotels and restaurants but also many forms of transportation, cultural, commercial, leisure, sports and entertainment activities.

The development of tourism in Mexico

International tourism began at the end of the 19th century as railways were built (see chapter 17) and Mexican destinations were promoted in the USA. The first generation of US travelers, sometimes hiring private rail cars, undertook the Mexican equivalent of the European Grand Tour, taking in all the major cities on the rail network. Early on, Mexican authorities actively promoted cultural and historical attractions such as the pyramids at Teotihuacan, close to Mexico City, restored and opened to the public in 1910 to commemorate the centenary of independence.

The pace of tourism development quickened with the advent of motor vehicles and became especially frenetic after successive governments, beginning in the 1930s, emphasized highway building and improvements. Between 1939 and 1950, aided by promotional campaigns (Mexico had tourism offices in four US cities by 1945), the number of tourists tripled from 139,000 to 390,000, and tourism receipts increased five-fold. By 1955, Mexico attracted 500,000 tourists. The main attractions were obvious: climate, captivating scenery, friendly people, bargain prices and proximity to the USA.

Trains were gradually replaced by first motor vehicles and then air travel. For example, the percentage of travelers entering Mexico by road rose from 30% in the 1940s to 59% in 1950, before declining to 27% in 1955 as air travel began to acquire more importance.

Acapulco was Mexico's first major resort. Overlooking the Pacific, Acapulco had been fashionable among wealthy Mexicans since the 1920s. The first road from Mexico City to Acapulco opened in 1927; this became a four-lane highway in the 1955 and is now a toll super-highway.

The development of Acapulco during the 1940s and 1950s, with new roads, hotels and an airport, provided alternative employment for peasants who had left their land, and helped to reduce the flow of migrants out of the poverty-stricken state of Guerrero. Some viewed Acapulco as a growth pole for further coastal development, but most other coastal towns continued to lag behind for decades. By the 1950s, it had become the playground for Hollywood's jet set, the world's first major resort to rely mainly on tourists arriving by air. In the 1960s, Acapulco's city center was redeveloped and a new airport was built inland.

Acapulco began a prolonged period of stagnation during the 1970s, struggling to cope with urban growth, the provision of adequate urban services and air and water pollution. In the past decade, it has turned things around based on a series of major gated hotel developments that overcome visitors' security concerns.

From the 1940s, tourism was being diversified elsewhere in Mexico by placing more focus on local customs and traditions, by building spas such as Ixtapan de la Sal and San José Purua, and by restoring more archeological and historic sites (see Table 30.1). In addition, Mexico has hosted numerous major sports events, including the Olympics in 1968 and the World Cup soccer tournament in both 1970 and 1986.

Domestic tourism and day trippers

Though most attention is focused on international tourism, domestic tourism accounts for about 80% of total tourism revenues in Mexico. Including business travel, Mexicans make about 160 million domestic tourism trips each year. A 2005 study found that slightly over a third of families took a summer vacation away from home. Each traveling group averaged four persons and had visited their chosen destination on an average of nine previous occasions. About 40% stayed in hotels, 38% with friends, 6% used second homes and 4% camped. The average ex-

penditure was $45 daily a person, mainly on food and transport. About 55% traveled by private vehicle, 38% by bus and 6% by plane. Preferred destinations were Acapulco (13%), Puerto Vallarta (6%), Cuernavaca (5%), Veracruz and Cancún (4% each) and Guayabitos, Manzanillo, Puebla and Tampico (3% each).[1]

Domestic day-trip flows are focussed on Mexico City, where weekend traffic patterns reflect the multitude of city dwellers who want some respite from urban stress. However, if the relative sizes of places is taken into account, the most significant flow of day trippers is probably that occurring on weekends and holidays between Mexico's second city Guadalajara and the small communities on the north shore of Lake Chapala, about 50 km (30 mi) to the south.

Elsewhere, there are seasonal flows of day-trippers from central Mexico to specific attractions such as the Monarch butterfly overwintering reserves in eastern Michoacán (January, February and March). Throughout Mexico, there are also some very significant periodic one-day flows to religious shrines and festivals. The economies of many towns, including San Juan de los Lagos and Talpa (both in Jalisco), Cubilete and Atotonilco (both in Guanajuato), Chalma (Mexico State) and Ocotlán (Oaxaca), are heavily dependent on this "pilgrimage" traffic.

How important is international tourism to Mexico?

Mexico has been one of the world's top ten international destinations for the past 15 years[2] (Figures 19.1 and 19.2). Tourism is a major money earner, accounting for about 8% of Mexico's GDP, and is the nation's fourth largest source of foreign currency after oil, remittances sent home by Mexicans working in the USA and foreign direct investment. Foreign revenue from tourism reached $13 billion in 2008 when almost 23 million tourists visited Mexico, 11 million of them arriving by air.[3] In the opposite direction, Mexicans took more than 14.4 million foreign trips in 2008, 92% of them to the USA or Canada, spending a combined total of $5 billion. Many of these trips were focused on shopping or visiting family.

Mexico is the most popular destination in Latin America, the 3rd most popular in emerging markets after China and Ukraine and the 10th most visited destination worldwide[4] (Figure 19.2). In terms of revenue from international tourism, Mexico fares less well, placing 14th worldwide with $12.9 billion, a paltry figure compared to the USA ($96.7 billion),

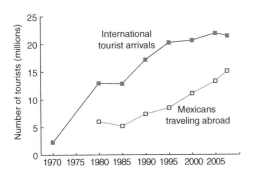

Figure 19.1 Trends in Mexican tourism[5]

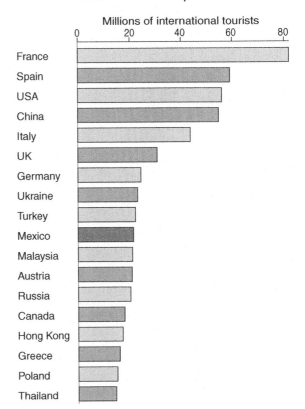

Figure 19.2 International tourist arrivals[8]

Spain ($57.8 billion) and France ($54.2 billion) and exceeded even by Canada ($15.5 billion).

About 9 out of every 10 international tourists in Mexico come from either the USA or Canada. Numbers rose sharply (19%) in 1995, the year after NAFTA was signed. Mexico is the second most important destination for Canadians after the USA. Most of Mexico's other tourists come from Europe and Asia; only a small number of tourists originate in Latin American countries.[6]

The average expenditure per international tourist was about $400 a day in 2008 and the average trip length 2.1 days. Salaries in tourism average about 30% higher than the national average.[7] The expenditure per tourist figure is lower than most other countries in the region and elsewhere in the world, suggesting that Mexican tourism activities have great potential for further development.

For statistical purposes, Mexico's Tourism Secretariat (Sectur) does not count visitors who spend between 24 and 72 hours in border towns as fully-fledged tourists, but instead labels them border tourists, excluding them from international comparisons. Border towns accommodated about 9 million border tourists in 2008, a number which pales beside the 70 million trans-border day trippers (see below) who visited Mexico in that year (Figure 19.3). Since 1996, a dip in the number of border tourists has been compensated by a marked increase in the number of tourists staying in the interior (Figure 19.4).

International day trippers

In 2008, international day trippers brought about $2.5 billion into the economy; 71% drove across the border, 20% walked and 9% arrived on cruise ships. The largest day trip flows are those for work, shopping or family visits in places such as Tijuana.

Cruise ship passengers (Figure 19.3) count as day-trippers since they generally spend less than 24 hours in port. Each cruise ship passenger spends more than twice as much per visit as those who drive or walk across the border.

Mexico recorded 6.4 million cruise ship passenger arrivals in 2008.[9] The number of passengers doubled between 2000 and 2005; since then, it has fluctuated between 6.2 and 6.5 million. The island of Cozumel (Quintana Roo) accounts for 41% of all cruise ship passenger arrivals in Mexico. In 2008 Cozumel received 1008 cruise ships carrying a total of 2.6 million passengers, placing it firmly in the world's top ten. Other important cruise ship ports include Cabo San Lucas (13% of all cruise ship arrivals), Ensenada (11%), Puerto Vallarta (10%), Mazatlán (9%), Progreso (6%) and Acapulco (3%).[10] Traffic to destinations on the Pacific coast has been increasing much more rapidly than traffic to the Caribbean coast.

Premium tourism

In addition to beach destinations (see below), heavy investments have occurred in recent years in amenities for the niche markets related to premium tourism.

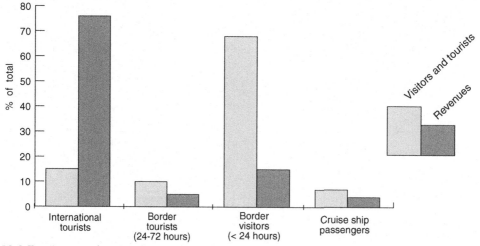

Figure 19.3 Tourism numbers and expenditures[11]

These include nautical facilities, golf courses, spas, haciendas and boutique hotels.

The US marina and private yacht market is worth $17 billion a year. Despite Mexico's proximity to the USA, ideal climate, extraordinary scenic beauty and abundant fish, the country has only about 30 marinas with 3,000 berths, compared to the 10,000 marinas and over 2 million berths in the USA. Sectur estimates that each yacht visiting Mexico results in a net $10,000 inflow. The major, fully-equipped marinas are in La Paz, San Carlos (near Guaymas), Mazatlán, Puerto Vallarta, Manzanillo, Ixtapa, Acapulco, Huatulco, Cancún and Puerto Aventuras (Quintana Roo). There is a long-term plan to build additional marinas in the sheltered waters along both coasts of the Sea of Cortés.[13]

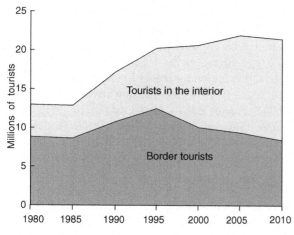

Figure 19.4 Border tourists and interior tourists[12]

Mexico has more than 200 golf courses; this number is increasing by about 15 courses each year. The three main golfing areas are Los Cabos and the southern part of Baja California Sur, the Maya Riviera (including Cancún) and Puerto Vallarta. The Los Cabos area alone has about a dozen courses, half of them of championship standard. Los Cabos is poised to become an exclusive world-class golfing center, somewhat like Palm Springs but with the added attractions of a coastal location and marina facilities. The popularity of golf in Mexico has boomed since Guadalajara-born Lorena Ochoa became the leading female golfer in the world and a superstar on the US LPGA tour. Ochoa's success has led to Mexico hosting several LPGA events, in Mexico City, Morelia and Guadalajara. On the men's side, several US PGA men's events have been held in Cancún.

Mexico's dozens of hot-springs (spas) are vestiges of its volcanic history and are concentrated in the Volcanic Axis (see chapters 2 and 3). Mexico's spas range from rustic open-air swimming holes to plush super-luxury retreats. Spa tourism is focused in towns such as Ixtapan de la Sal (Mexico State) and Tequisquiapan (Querétaro).

Purpose-built resorts

Mexico's mass tourism industry in the past forty years has been dominated by large-scale, purpose-built developments partially funded by federal funds. In 1967, responding to bullish predictions of US demand for beach vacations, Mexico's central bank identified the five best places for completely new, purpose-built tourist resorts. Top of the list, as part of a 30-year plan, was the uninhabited barrier island now known as Cancún. The other choice locations were Ixtapa, Los Cabos, Loreto and Huatulco.

The National Fund for Tourism Infrastructure (renamed the National Tourism Development Fund, Fonatur, in 1974) began building Cancún in 1970 and Ixtapa in 1971. Besides the original five places, Fonatur has begun to develop several other sites for tourism, including the Costa Maya and Riviera Maya in Quintana Roo, and a section of the Copper Canyon (Chihuahua). Fonatur's latest mega-project is the Riviera Nayarit stretch of coastline north of Puerto Vallarta.

Cancún has become Mexico's foremost tourist resort. Factors considered in the choice of Cancún included water temperatures, the quality of beaches, varied attractions, sunshine hours and travel distances from the main markets. The stated benefits were thousands of new jobs, increased revenues, the development of a previously peripheral region and the diversification of the national economy. Public funds were used to purchase land, improve it by fumigation and drainage, and install all necessary basic infrastructure (airport, highways, potable water, electricity, telephone lines, convention center, golf course, harbors). Private sector investors developed hotels, a shopping center and supporting services.

By 1975, Cancún had 1769 rooms in service; by 2008, it boasted about 150 hotels and more than 27,000 rooms. Second only to Mexico City, Cancún airport now handles 200 flights a day. The influx of people to Cancún has been especially dramatic. The city has had to cope with unprecedented growth rates as its population shot up from 30,000 in 1980 to about 600,000 today (Figure 19.5). The number of tourists in Cancún dipped slightly in 2001–2002 due, in part, to the 2001 9/11 tragedy in the USA. Hurricane Wilma (2005) put many hotel rooms temporarily out of commission. Cancún is only one focus of an extensive tourist corridor along the Quintana Roo coast, stretching as far south as Tulum.

Huatulco's site on the coast of Oaxaca had been initially identified in 1969 but the area lacked adequate transportation infrastructure until the regional highways were improved in 1982. Legal land expropriations followed; by 1984 Fonatur controlled more than 21,000 hectares (50,000 acres). In 1985 Fonatur began construction of an airport and a service town, La Crucecita, a few kilometers back from the coast. In 1986 the villagers of the coastal community of Santa

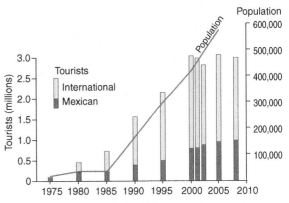

Figure 19.5 The growth of Cancún

Cruz were resettled in La Crucecita. Most of Huatulco's nine bays were linked by paved road by 1987.

Fonatur took a number of steps to help the original residents adapt to the massive changes taking place around them. It built schools, held public meetings, provided medical and police services, and offered job training programs. Most people gradually adapted; some are employed in Huatulco hotels and some started their own small businesses. By 1994 Huatulco had 1905 hotel rooms and attracted 170,000 tourists, 26% of them foreign. The average length of stay was 4.22 days.

Huatulco's growth has not been as rapid as Cancún's. By 2006, Huatulco had 2506 rooms and played host to 312,000 tourists (15% foreign). While Cancún first attracted Mexican tourists and then foreign tourists followed (and now dominate), in Huatulco the proportion of foreign tourists has fallen as the resort has developed. The master plan for Huatulco foresees 30,000 hotel rooms and a city with an eventual population of 600,000.

Fonatur's construction of La Crucecita established a clear spatial and visual divide between the tourist areas on the coast and the residential areas for tourism employees on the inland side of some low hills. This had also been the case in Cancún where the luxury hotel zone is only a few kilometers from overcrowded and squalid shanty settlements. Fonatur developments have been characterized by the creation of tourist enclaves. In the case of Ixtapa, the hotel zone is on a formerly secluded bay only five kilometers west of the long-established fishing village of Zihuatanejo, the main source of labor. Despite their proximity, the settlements of Ixtapa and Zihuatanejo are not intervisible, since they are separated by a 300-m-high (1000-ft-high) ridge.

Table 19.1 Tourist capacity and numbers[14]

	Rooms[a]	Total tourists (x 1000)	% foreign
Planned resorts			
Cancún	21 776	2 432	65
Huatulco	2 506	312	17
Ixtapa-Zihuatanejo	4 740	687	23
Loreto	521	174	33
Los Cabos	8 145	1 073	78
Traditional resorts			
Acapulco	16 329	4 163	2
Cozumel	4 313	447	60
La Paz	1 703	239	23
Manzanillo	3 541	742	9
Mazatlán	8 122	1 254	21
Puerto Vallarta	10 664	1 493	43
Tuxtla Gutierrez	2 749	541	2
Veracruz	8 743	1 774	4
Villahermosa	3 154	664	4
Large cities			
Guadalajara	13 822	2 305	10
Mexico DF	45 717	10 296	27
Monterrey	10 377	1 596	18
Puebla	4 695	1 005	10
Interior cities			
Cuernavaca	2 612	526	10
Guanajuato	1 980	413	8
Hermosillo	2 240	428	1
Mérida	4 453	860	23
Morelia	3 283	742	7
Oaxaca	4 799	647	17
Querétaro	3 341	763	11
San Luis Potosí	1 184	162	22
Zacatecas	2 741	501	13
Border cities			
Ciudad Juárez	3 139	539	19
Tijuana	4 841	1 087	22

[a] 1-star to 5+ star hotels inclusive

Where is tourism in Mexico?

Figure 19.6 and Table 19.1 show that vacation tourism predominates along the Caribbean and Pacific coasts whereas business tourism is more important in the large inland cities. Excluding Mexico City, the resort city of Acapulco draws most tourists, almost all of them national. Cancún is the next most popular destination, but two-thirds of its visitors are international. On the Pacific coast, international tourists are much more important to Puerto Vallarta than they are to Mazatlán, Manzanillo or Huatulco. Very few international tourists visit the Gulf coast.

Mexico has more than 14,000 hotels with 600,000 hotel rooms, including 26% categorized as 5-star or better and 19% 4-star. The 5-star+ category has risen since 1990 when it was only 15%.[15] More than half of all Mexico's hotel rooms are in one of the 80 main tourist centers in the country.

Mexico's tourist capacity (Table 19.1) masks the fact that hotels are rarely full. In 2007, the national occupancy rate was 54.8%. Traditional beach resorts such as Acapulco, Mazatlán and Puerto Vallarta had an occupancy rate of 52.2%, compared to 68.1% for modern, planned mega-resorts like Cancún and Los Cabos. The occupancy rate in the large cities—Guadalajara, Mexico City and Monterrey—was 55.0%, well ahead of the 47.2% for other interior cities.

Is tourism a sound development strategy?

The positive aspects of tourism, as evidenced by Fonatur's planned resorts, are well documented: thousands of new jobs, often in areas where few alternatives exist; inflows of tourist dollars (and pesos); economic multiplier effects; increased tax revenues; reduced economic and social differences between the country's periphery areas and its core; and a more globalized society and economy. The prospects of attracting more tourists also encourage institutional support for protecting local cultures and environments.

Between them, Fonatur resorts, with their relatively high occupancy rates, receive 40% of all foreign tourists and attract 54% of all foreign currency from tourism. They also provide $2.765 billion in commerce and contribute more than $300 million in tax revenue, just from value-added tax and lodging tax.[16]

Critics of tourism as a means of development point to pollution, crime, demeaning jobs, poor wage rates, the 'leakage' resulting from the repatriation of profits by multi-national corporations which minimizes

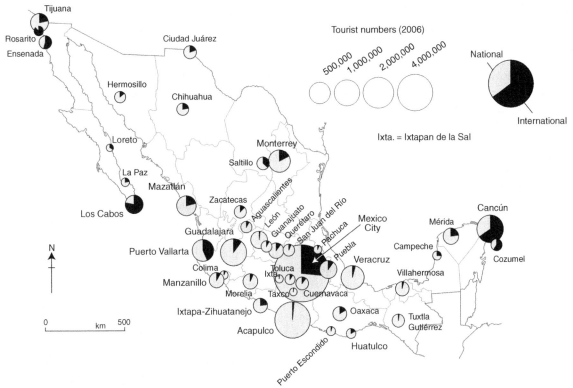

Figure 19.6 National and international tourist volumes, 2006

local economic benefits, and the uncertainties associated with demand for tourism.

It is often claimed that a gradual diffusion of wealth into the undeveloped hinterland will occur around major tourist centers, with multiplier effects extending inland, creating new employment options. This may be true in the case of Huatulco, where La Crucecita was built as a support town a short distance inland, but is certainly hard to see in most cases, even around relatively long-established resorts such as Acapulco and Puerto Vallarta.

In most locations, tourism is a highly seasonal occupation. Mexico's tourism peaks are in the second half of December (Christmas-New Year) and the summer months (June, July, August) with lesser peaks coinciding with Easter and the US spring break when thousands of college students flock to coastal resorts. Many hotel and restaurant workers have to find alternative jobs for the off-season.

As tourism takes off, land speculation raises land and property prices, often to the point where local residents are unable to participate in the real estate boom or even purchase their own home.

Major hotels often import a very high percentage of the goods they consume, from food to manufac-

tured items. This can further hurt the local economy and reduce the prospects for local or regional suppliers. Investments in tourism are sometimes focused on short-term gains rather than long-term benefits. Upgrades to such services as waste treatment and disposal systems may well be considered a low priority.

Besides these economic implications, there are also a number of potential cultural and social drawbacks. Proposed tourism projects may be completely out-of-keeping with the social and cultural norms of existing communities. Resort construction leads to high rates of in-migration, putting great pressure on local housing and essential services. Uncontrolled urban growth brings its own health and sanitation risks as well as possible increases in delinquency and crime. Several studies of ethnic tourism in Chiapas have compared the benefits derived from tourism—such as greater empowerment for women in the local community—with the drawbacks it has brought such as an increased homogenization of culture, as expressed in language, dress and architecture.[17]

Environmental changes are also virtually inevitable when a new resort is built. Habitats are damaged or destroyed and biodiversity is reduced. Mangroves and coral reefs are particularly vulnerable. Local topography is remodeled and natural sediment flows offshore are disturbed. Wastes are generated. The air, soil, ground water, lakes, streams and the ocean may be contaminated. Water usage may reach unsustainable levels. Exotic (non-native) species may be introduced with unknown consequences. Tourism may also lead to increased illegal trafficking of rare species.

Even if tourist developments are well managed, minimizing the economic, social and environmental impacts, there is still a massive risk associated with adopting tourism as a development strategy, especially if the focus is on foreign tourists. The number of tourists choosing to take holidays in Mexico is dependent on conditions in the USA and Canada which are beyond Mexico's control. Adverse natural hazards such as hurricanes and earthquakes are also beyond Mexico's control. News media play an important role. Press reports of insecurity or health risks invariably have a negative impact on tourist numbers.

Hurricanes (see chapter 4) can wreak havoc on tourist resorts. Hurricane Wilma (2005) was especially destructive. Under normal conditions, waves rolling onto the Caribbean coast of Quintana Roo average 2 m (6.5 ft) in height, and wind velocity av-

erages 4 m/s (9 mph). Wilma brought 30 m/s winds (67 mph) and 10 m (33 ft) waves.[18] Quintana Roo attracts more than 3 million visitors a year; the state's annual tourism revenue exceeds $3.2 billion. Wilma caused over $2.0 billion in damages to roads, ports and hotels. Tourism revenue fell by $160 million a month. Beaches were heavily eroded, but restored by an ambitious $20 million public works campaign which involved pumping offshore sand to the shore to create new beaches, twice as wide as the old ones. Coastal areas were reforested with thousands of mature palm trees and tourists soon flocked back to enjoy the resort's turquoise waters and fine, golden sand.[19]

Perhaps the greatest single risk is that associated with changing fashions. While Huatulco may be the 'in-place' this year, perhaps it will somewhere in Jamaica or elsewhere next year. While golfing or yachting holidays may be popular choices this year, perhaps cultural or ecotours are next...

Major resorts face a real challenge reinventing themselves to meet changing demand, though in recent years Acapulco has done just that, emerging from a prolonged period when it was far-from-fashionable into a period of rejuvenation (see Figure 19.7).

Butler's resort cycle model

Butler's model (Figure 19.7) describes the evolution of a tourist resort. His model, similar to a product life cycle model, is quite a good fit with the evolution of Acapulco, a traditional resort which evolved over several decades.

The model would not be expected to work as well with resorts such as Cancún and Huatulco,

which were planned from the start and developed rapidly with the infusion of millions of dollars of federal funds.

In the case of planned resorts, the stages of exploration and involvement are unlikely to apply. The adapted model for such places might perhaps start at the development phase.[20]

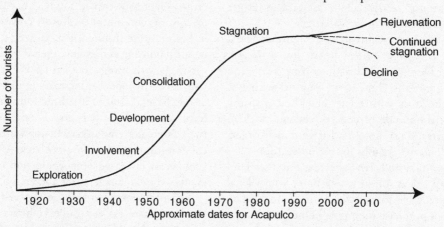

Figure 19.7 Butler's resort cycle model applied to Acapulco

How ecological is ecotourism?

Ecotourism is often touted as one solution to many of these potential woes. Mexico's biodiversity (see chapter 5) is phenomenal; it is one of the five most important countries in the world in terms of biodiversity.

To be ecologically successful, ecotourism probably has to be small-scale. Constructing the infrastructure necessary for large-scale coastal ecotourism projects often involves the destruction of highly-productive (in ecological terms) wetlands, including tropical mangroves. These ecosystems play a vital role in helping preserve biodiversity and their destruction has serious long-term economic implications for fishing, port and marina access, coastline preservation and beach-based tourism.

Mangroves are especially vulnerable, with an undeserved reputation for being impenetrable thickets harboring noxious insects and reptiles. Mangroves sequester carbon and help reduce the organic content of water. Their roots bind unstable coasts, preventing erosion and acting as a natural barrier against hurricanes. They are important breeding, shelter and feeding places for fish, crustaceans and birds as well as being a source of charcoal, firewood, wood and roofing materials. They offer economic opportunities of fishing for shrimp, mollusk, fish and crustaceans.

In the year 2000, the total area of mangroves along Mexican coasts was estimated at 880,000 hectares (2.2 million acres), approximately two-thirds on the Atlantic and Caribbean coasts, and one-third on the Pacific. The annual loss of mangroves is estimated to be between 2.5% and 5% of this area. Even with the lower rate of loss, by 2025 mangroves will occupy only half of their 2000 area. In 2007 Mexico enacted federal legislation to protect existing mangroves.[21]

The unique habitats of coral reefs are also at risk. Mexico has important zones of coral from the Baja California Peninsula and Sea of Cortés in the north to Cozumel Island and Chinchorro Bank in the south. The latter area is the northernmost extension of the Meso-American Barrier Reef system which is the world's second largest reef system after Australia's Barrier Reef. Marine pollution, overfishing and tourism have all hastened the decline of coral reefs, though many areas are now protected.[22]

Even animal migrations are considered at risk. Some studies have shown that the number of tourists viewing the whale migrations off the coast of Baja California, for instance, is already having an adverse effect on the whales' breeding habits.

Is tourism sustainable?

How can we assess the long-term viability and likely impacts of tourism? The relationships between the number of tourists and their impacts are complex. They depend on natural resources and existing infrastructure, as well as management and impact mitigation strategies.[23] One way of trying to quantify environmental indicators in order to determine the limit of tourist flows that can be supported by a given area without long-term degradation is by assessing tourist carrying capacities. There are several distinct tourist carrying capacities.

The physical carrying capacity is the maximum number of visitors that can access a given site each day. It is a function of the total space available, opening times, average length of visit and each individual's need for personal space. The ecological carrying capacity is the maximum number of visitors that a site can support before environmental damage, such as loss of biodiversity, occurs. The perceptual carrying capacity is the maximum number of visitors a site can sustain before one specific group of users (such as youths or the elderly) decides that the location is overused and therefore chooses to avoid it, on account of its noise, congestion or perceived danger.

The effective carrying capacity is the maximum number of visitors that should be allowed for any given site. This is a function of physical carrying capacity, adjusted for environmental and management factors which vary from site to site, including budget, legal limits, national policies, infrastructure and susceptibility to erosion.

For tourism to be sustainable, it must be within either the effective carrying capacity or the ecological carrying capacity. Tourist carrying capacity applies only to a specific site or place and is likely to vary seasonally. In addition, it depends on the profile of the typical visitor.

An alternative to looking at the impacts of tourism and managing visitor numbers based on carrying capacities is to consider how to manage the impacts themselves. This idea assesses the "limits of acceptable change" for an area. This assumes that recreational use of landscapes will always cause changes, but provides a means of judging if these changes are acceptable given the potential gains (economic, social, environmental) deriving from that use.[24]

A more quantitative way of evaluating the environmental impacts of tourism is by considering its ecological footprint[25] (see also chapter 30). This is the theoretical amount of land and water required to produce the resources consumed by tourism and to absorb its waste, given prevailing technology. Tourism's ecological footprint includes the effects of airline travel, air pollution, carbon emissions, energy consumption, habitat destruction (for roads, airports, hotels, recreational facilities), water consumption and solid waste generation.

A recent study using 2006 data[26] suggests that US and Canadian tourists visiting Cancún had a positive economic impact of $1.894 billion (assuming an average daily expenditure of $124 dollars and average length of stay of 6 nights). The annual impact in environmental terms was calculated as being 8.82 billion liters of water, 235 million KwH of power, 38,000 tons of solid waste and 2.63 tons of CO_2 from air transport.

Can the Tarahumara Indians survive?

The remote Copper Canyon region in northern Mexico is the home of 50,000 Tarahumara Indians who have preserved much of their distinctive culture (language, dress, customs, beliefs) into this century, partly because of their extreme remoteness (see chapter 17). Many live untouched by the trappings of modern civilization, moving between caves just below the canyon rim and winter shelters at lower altitude near the Urique River. Their radically different lifestyle and extreme isolation beg many questions. Their ancestral homelands are already being invaded by marijuana growers, and trampled on by outside developers who have very different notions of property rights and very different customs.

Are the Tarahumara Indians really in any position to make informed decisions about their future? Should we leave them entirely alone and let them decide entirely for themselves? Should we offer education about what we would consider the benefits of the modern world? Should we improve their access to health services and hospitals? Should we encourage them to acquire computers and internet access? Or might these progressive elements destroy their existing lifestyle, break down their social and political structures and ultimately wipe them out?

The total dollar value of these environmental impacts was estimated at $50 million dollars (76% of it attributable to US tourists), leaving a positive economic balance overall of $1.844 billion. The greatest impact was CO_2 emissions, which were higher for Canadians ($28/person) than US tourists ($18/person) due to differences in flight distances. However, there are a lot of assumptions in this study and it is only one of several possible ways of quantifying the various impacts.

Mexico's National Tourism Plan 2001-2006, which promoted sustainable tourism development, introduced a tourism sustainability index based on 27 key indicators. These indicators included water (availability, consumption, treatment); energy; air quality; waste management; environmental education plans; economic benefits (employment, contribution to local economy, land tax); social impacts (demographic pressure, safety); tourism demand (tourist satisfaction, tourist expenditures, seasonality, return visit rates); supply of tourism services (quality, price, tourist guides, attractions); urban and environmental planning; urban infrastructure (housing, water, drainage, energy, paving) and architectural and landscape conservation.

Is sustainable tourism really possible? Sustainability must not only ensure economic success but must also meet various ecological and social criteria. The economic dimension of sustainability requires the employment of local residents, a rise in local incomes, ensuring profitability and matching the enterprise to regional priorities. It also suggests the desirability of a more equitable distribution of tourism revenues. Unfortunately, most evidence suggests that in areas such as Quintana Roo, where tourism has taken off, the gap between the "haves" and the "have-nots" has widened significantly.

The associated changes in society may be less noticeable in the short term, but far more significant over the long term. The social or socio-cultural dimension of sustainability requires that respect be maintained for local people, their customs, culture and traditions. Some of Mexico's tourism hotspots are in the poorest regions of the country such as Chiapas or the Copper Canyon region (Chihuahua). Ideally, tourism will reduce out-migration from these areas and result in greater social equity. The counter-argument is that tourism developments threaten native peoples. Further developing the Copper Canyon region, for example, may destroy the life-style of the indigenous

Tarahumara Indians (see box). Some indigenous communities have much greater control over local tourism. In the state of Michoacán, P'urepecha Indians near Paricutín Volcano operate their own tourist cabins, originally built by the state government. They are determined to ensure that their language and customs not only survive this collision with tourists but form the basis for a healthy cultural tourism program, with little or no dilution for foreign tastes. Originally somewhat reluctant to embrace tourism, they now see its potential to drive development.

The environmental dimension of sustainability requires natural resources to be preserved rather than destroyed. For example, instead of felling its trees for firewood, a community may decide to target tourists and promote the observation of woodland flora or fauna. Management plans try to ensure that effective conservation strategies are in place and that visitors are informed about their role in maintaining the area's environmental capital and biodiversity.[27] In some regions tourism is a particular threat to already scarce water resources (chapters 6 and 7).

Retirees and "residential tourism": a case study of Chapala-Ajijic

Retirees, mainly from the USA and Canada, form a special subgroup of tourists. About 1 million US visitors to Mexico each year are over the age of 60. Their total expenditure is about $500 million a year.[28] Three-quarters arrive by air; half of these stay 4-8 days and almost one in ten stays 30 days or longer. Half stay in hotels, and one-third in time-shares; the remainder either stay with family or friends, or own their own second home. Of the 25% arriving by land, almost one in three stays 30 days or more. For Canadians, the patterns are broadly similar except that a higher percentage arrive by air.

The number of retiree tourists is relatively easy to quantify. However, it is extremely difficult to place accurate figures on the number of non-working, non-Mexicans who have chosen to relocate full-time to Mexico. Technically, these "residential tourists" are not really tourists at all but longer-term migrants holding residency visas. They form a very distinct group in several Mexican towns and cities, with lifestyle needs and spending patterns that are very different from those of tourists. Their additional economic impact is believed to exceed $500 million a year.

The largest single US retirement community outside the USA is the Guadalajara-Chapala region in

> ### A sustainable resort?
>
> Loreto Bay, a 3-billion-dollar development in Baja California Sur, utilizes infrastructure originally built by Fonatur. Its planners claim that their interlinked series of villages will be fully sustainable. Eventually, all Loreto Bay's electricity will be generated from wind turbines. Almost all waste is recycled. Water is the big issue. To avoid any further stress on the local San Juan Londó aquifer, a combination of water conservation, watershed restoration and desalination will ensure self-sufficiency. Landscaping utilizes native plants, well adapted to the warm, semi-desert environment. But questions remain. For example, will sufficient low income homes be provided for the workforce required to service the resort?

Jalisco, according to state officials. The metropolitan area of Guadalajara, Mexico's second city, has a population of about 4 million. The villages of Chapala and Ajijic (combined population about 40,000) sit on the north shore of Lake Chapala some 50 km (30 mi) to the south. Historically, Chapala was the first lakeshore settlement to attract foreign settlers, as early as the start of the 20th century.[29] Today the area is home to a mix of foreign artists, intellectuals, escapees (of various non-judicial kinds), pensioners and ex-servicemen. In the last 40 years, Ajijic has become the focal point of the sizeable non-Mexican community living on the lakeshore. Depending on how they are defined, there are probably between 6000 and 10,000 foreign residents in the Chapala-Ajijic area, the higher number reflecting the peak winter season. About 60% of retirees in the area own their own homes or condos, though many still own property in the USA or Canada as well, and many make regular trips north of the border.

The main pull factors for residential tourists are an amenable climate; reasonable property prices; access to stores, restaurants and high quality medical service; an attractive natural environment; a diversity of social activities; proximity to airports; tax advantages, and relatively inexpensive living costs.[30]

David Truly has suggested that conventional tourist typologies do not work well with Ajijic retirees.[31] He identified migrant clusters with similar likes and dislikes. Retirees vary in education, travel experience and how they make decisions about relocation. Early migrants tended to dislike the USA and Canada and adapted to life in Mexico. They were generally content with anonymity unlike many more recent migrants. Traditional migrants appreciate all three countries, but have chosen Mexico as their place of permanent residence. Many new migrants do not especially like the USA or Canada but are not particularly interested in Mexico either. They seek familiar pastimes and social settings and are content to have relatively little interaction with Mexicans.

The large influx of residential tourists into small lakeside communities like Ajijic inevitably generates a range of reactions among the local populace. From empirical studies of regular tourism elsewhere, George Doxey developed an "irritation index" describing how the attitudes of host communities change as tourist numbers increase.[32] His model applies equally well to residential tourists. In the initial stage the host community experiences euphoria (all visitors are welcome, no special planning occurs). As numbers increase, host attitudes change to apathy (visitors are taken for granted) and then annoyance (misgivings about tourism are expressed, carrying capacities are exceeded, additional infrastructure is planned). If numbers continue to grow, hosts may reach the stage of antagonism, where irritations are openly expressed and incomers are perceived as the cause of significant problems.

Residential tourism in the Chapala-Ajijic area has certainly wrought great changes on the landscape. Residential tourists have created a distinct cultural landscape in terms of architectural styles, street architecture and the functions of settlements.[33] Gated communities have been tacked on to the original villages. Subdivisions, two around golf courses, have sprawled up the hillsides. Swimming pools are common. Much of the signage is in English. Even the central plazas have been remodeled to reflect foreign tastes. Traditional village homes have been gentrified, some in an alien "New Mexico" style.

On the plus side, many retirees, as a substitute for the family they left behind, engage in philanthropic activities, with a particular focus on children and the elderly. Retiree expenditures also boost the local economy. Areas benefiting from retirees include medical, legal and personal services, real estate, supermarkets, restaurants, gardening and housecleaning. Employ-ment is boosted, both directly and indirectly, which improves average local living standards.

On the minus side, decades of land speculation have had a dramatic impact on local society. Land and property prices have risen dramatically. Many local people have become landless domestic servants, gardeners and shop-keepers with a sense that the area is no longer theirs.[34] Crime levels have risen and some local traditions have suffered.[35] The abuse of water supplies has resulted in declining well levels. Over zealous applications of fertilizers and pesticides have contaminated local water sources.

Other locations besides Chapala-Ajijic where a similar influence of non-Mexican retirees on the landscape can be observed include San Miguel de Allende (Guanajuato), Cuernavaca (Morelos), Mazatlán (Sinaloa), Puerto Peñasco (Sonara), Rosarito (Baja California) and Todos Santos (Baja California Sur). The most preferred locations are all on the Pacific coast side of Mexico.

As more baby-boomers reach retirement age, residential tourism offers many Mexican towns and cities a way of overcoming the seasonality of conventional tourism. Lesser-developed regions have an opportunity to cash in on their cultural and natural heritage and improve their basic infrastructure.[36]

Future trends

Mexico's share of world tourism has remained largely unchanged in recent years. The World Tourism Organization's Tourism 2020 Vision posits a significant increase in international tourism by 2020. If Mexico maintains its current 16% share of arrivals in the Americas, the number of international tourists visiting Mexico will more than double from current figures to more than 44 million in 2020.[37]

However, these predictions do not take climate change into account. Global climate change is predicted to result in a 0.3-0.7°C rise in Mexico's average temperature each decade, a slight increase in annual rainfall, and an increased incidence of thunderstorms and hurricane activity, particularly on the Pacific coast.[38] Research elsewhere suggests that Mexico would experience a slight increase in tourism between now and 2025 if no climatic change were to occur, or a modest decrease in tourism in the event of a 1°C rise in average temperature by 2025.[39]

20
Mexico and the world economy

Mexico, like all countries, is not economically independent. It must import all the goods and services it needs or wants but does not produce.

Where does Mexico get the money needed to pay for imports? To obtain the needed funds, Mexico must sell goods, such as petroleum or automobiles, or services to the world. In order to export such goods and services, Mexico should be able to supply them more efficiently than the importing country. This is based on the concept of comparative advantage which, very briefly, holds that countries should focus on the goods and services that they can supply efficiently and trade these for the goods and services that they cannot produce efficiently. Compared to the USA, Mexico has a comparative advantage in assembling automobiles, while the USA has a comparative advantage in producing wheat. Both countries are better off if they focus on what they do best and trade for things they are less good at producing. Thus, trade can result in a "win-win" situation.

This chapter looks at Mexico's economic interactions with other countries of the world. The concept of economic base facilitates our understanding of Mexico's economy and its economic interactions.

Economic base

What does economic base involve? Why is it important? The economic base of an area relates to the goods and services it exports, i.e. produces and sells to markets outside the area. Such exports may include mineral, agricultural or manufactured products as well as services, including labor. The economic base is everything that brings outside money into an area. It therefore includes the money spent when tourists come into the area and pay for hotels, meals and activities. It also includes remittances sent into the area from workers who have moved away to find employment.

The economic base of an area is crucially important to its economic health. It brings in the funds needed to pay for imports as well as for non-base or local-market-serving economic activities such as retailing, personal services, construction, housing, food and transportation. If an area's economic base is heavily dependent on only one or two items, then the economy suffers enormously if the market for those items declines.

The economic base of some areas in Mexico is rather obvious. The economy of Quintana Roo, for example, is almost entirely dependent upon tourism services. Likewise, many areas in Campeche are entirely dependent on the petroleum industry. The economic specialization of different states is discussed in chapter 16.

In many cases, the economic base of an area is either not at all obvious or is very complex, involving a wide range of goods or services. For example, Guadalajara obtains money from the outside world from visitors, retirees and the export of manufactured goods (shoes, clothing, electronics) as well as administrative, educational and health services, among other things. Money from outside flows into Guadalajara for these things and gives the city funds for the items it must import such as food, automobiles, gasoline, electricity and construction materials.

If the economic base of an area grows rapidly, then the whole economy of the area grows rapidly, more workers are hired, people migrate in to fill new job openings, and the population expands rapidly. If the economic base shrinks, the impacts ripple through the economy in reverse; workers are laid off, families migrate out, and the place deteriorates.

Mexico's economic base

Mexico's economic base generates about $340 billion in foreign revenue each year and is quite diverse, which enhances economic stability. The major components of Mexico's economic base are briefly discussed below.

Oil

As we saw in chapter 15, Mexico is a major oil producer, producing about 3 million barrels a day (b/d) of oil in 2008. At $60 a barrel, oil exports of 1.8 million b/d generate about $40 billion a year, roughly 14.5% of Mexico's total exports.

Remittances

There are millions of Mexican workers in the USA who send a sizable portion of their wages back to their families in Mexico. A later chapter focuses explicitly on international migration. On a per person basis, Mexico receives more worker remittances than any other major country in the world. An estimated 20% of Mexican residents regularly receive some financial support from workers abroad. Such remittances are the mainstay of the economies of many Mexican communities, such as many rural areas in Durango, Zacatecas, Guanajuato, Jalisco and Michoacán. In 2008, they exceeded $25 billion. Studies suggest that the funds sent as remittances are mostly spent on housing, food, clothing and durable consumer goods. A growing portion is being invested in education and small businesses. The corollary is that only a small percentage goes towards savings.[1]

Tourism

Mexico's marvelous beaches and rich cultural history draw millions of tourists each year. These tourists spend a great deal, adding about $5 billion a year in "invisible exports" to Mexico's economic base. Tourism was examined in more detail in chapter 19.

Foreign direct investment

Many foreign individuals and corporations view Mexico as an attractive place for investment. Each year, foreigners spend about $20 billion to buy Mexi-can enterprises, or to build factories or resorts in Mexico. Of course, Mexicans also invest abroad, but far more foreigners invest in Mexico than vice-versa. Many USA transnational corporations have built factories in Mexico to produce their products for sale in the Mexican market (as well as for export). Mexican supermarkets sell "made in Mexico" versions of Campbell's soups, Kellogg's cereals, Wonder bread, McCormick's spices, Hershey's candies, Kleenex, Ajax, and dozens of other foreign brands, including the omnipresent Coca-Cola and Pepsi.

The importance of foreign direct investment is shown by the fact that many of the biggest private sector enterprises in Mexico are linked to foreign corporations such as Wal-Mart, General Motors, Ford and Delphi Automotive (USA). It is worth noting that almost all foreign subsidiaries must be at least 51% owned by Mexicans. Part of Mexico's success in attracting foreign investment is due to the advantageous trading conditions enjoyed by exporters as a result of Mexico's numerous free-trade agreements.

These four major sources (oil, remittances, tourism, and foreign direct investment) account for about $95 billion a year. However, this is only about 30% of all the foreign exchange Mexico earns each year. Where does the rest come from?

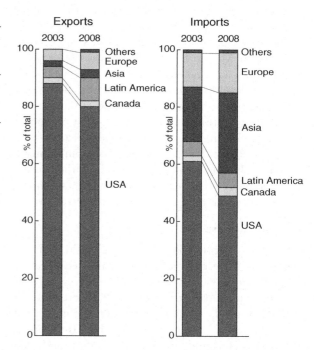

Figure 20.1 Exports and imports, 2003 and 2008[2]

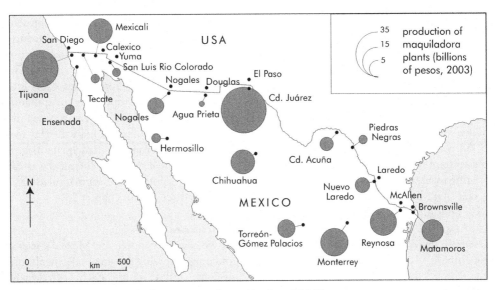

Figure 20.2 Production of maquiladoras in northern Mexico, 2003[3]

Manufacturing

Manufacturing is the mainstay of Mexico's economic base. Exports of a very wide variety of manufactured goods bring in $230 billion a year, more than five times as much as oil exports. For example, exports of textiles, clothing, and shoes alone account for $8 billion a year, significantly more than the net amount earned from tourism.

Over one million cars, about 70% of the cars produced in Mexico, are exported each year earning over $50 billion. Of course, this is not all pure income because Mexico assembles cars from a mix of domestic and imported components. In 2008, Mexico was the 10th largest vehicle producer in the world, behind Japan, China, USA, Germany, South Korea, Brazil, France, Spain and India.

Maquiladoras

Many of Mexico's exports are assembled in the country from imported pieces. Maquiladoras are assembly plants in Export Processing Zones which import raw materials and components duty free, and produce goods for export, mainly to the USA. There were only 12 maquiladora plants in Mexico in 1965. But with NAFTA and Mexico's free trade policy, the number of plants shot up in the 1990s and they now number over 5000. These plants are mostly located in border cities such as Tijuana, Mexicali, Ciudad Juárez, Reyonosa and Matamoros (Figure 20.2).

Manufacturing and assembly plants were attracted across the border because of favorable wage rates, less stringent enforcement of environmental laws and the large pool of non-unionized workers. In international terms, wages in Mexico decreased markedly after currency devaluations in the 1980s, and the country became highly competitive in comparison to its potential competitors in Asia. In the early 1990s, the border region became one of the lowest cost manufacturing locations in the world and the number of maquiladora plants mushroomed. Employment in maquiladoras peaked in the year 2000 when they employed more than 1.3 million workers.

Since then, Mexico's wage rates have become far less competitive than they once were and some firms have moved to Asia where labor costs are now lower (see box). The falling value of the US dollar and the slow-down in the economies on both sides of the border have also adversely affected the operations of maquiladoras, resulting in a reduction in the number of plants and workers.

What kinds of things are assembled in maquiladoras? The range is very wide, including consumer electronics, household appliances, power tools, clothing and shoes. Many shoppers in the USA probably do not realize how many of the items they buy are made in Mexico. Many of the products made in Mexican maquiladoras are not marketed in Mexico, or are only available in Mexico if they are specifically re-imported by a Mexican retailer.

While most of the capital for maquiladoras comes from US investors or Mexico–USA joint ventures, foreign companies eager to export to the USA under

Globalization and industrial relocation: competition from China

In recent years, Mexico has faced increased competition in world markets from China and other Asian countries. Mexico's contribution to US imports peaked at about 12% in 2003 but has since fallen to around 10%. Chinese imports to the USA overtook Mexican imports in 2003 and now account for 15% of the total market.

According to Mexico's central bank, Mexico's lost market share between 2001 and 2005 was worth $27 billion,[4] equivalent to 15% of all non-petroleum exports. Some multinationals closed their assembly facilities in Mexico and moved them to China.

What are China's advantages?

The two most important ones are wage rates and the much larger local market. The average hourly wage for manufacturing in China is $0.66, compared to $2.13 in Mexico.[5] China also offers more incentives for foreign investment. The companies that have moved are manufacturers of textiles, electronic items and auto-parts[6]; these footloose industries do not have complex and expensive plants (unlike steelworks and chemical plants for example) and can therefore relocate relatively easily. While most have relocated in China, some have preferred South Korea or India.

What are Mexico's comparative advantages over China?

Mexico's major advantage is proximity to the US market. Shipping a standard 40-foot container from Mexico to the USA costs less than half the cost from China. Mexico also has a more educated workforce, with about one-quarter of the population having completed secondary education, compared to less than 17% in China. The productivity of Mexico's workforce is slightly higher than in China, and the country also retains a slight edge over China in terms of its legal system. In an effort to stem the outflow of jobs, the Mexican government has opened several high-tech industrial parks, such as Silicon Border in Mexicali, and these appear to be having some success.

the rules of NAFTA are also well represented. As an example, the three biggest manufacturing employers in Tijuana are Samsung, Sony and Panasonic.

Maquiladoras led an export boom, but at what environmental cost? Some researchers estimate that transnational firms operating maquiladoras are responsible for 85% of all environmental pollution in El Paso and Ciudad Juárez.[7] The most serious problems arise from the inadequate disposal of toxic wastes and the leaching of chemical wastes into water systems. Air pollution from maquiladoras in Ciudad Juárez is discussed in chapter 23.

Agriculture

As we saw in chapter 15, Mexico's varied climates and long growing season make it almost ideal for growing certain crops. Each year, Mexico exports about $8 billion worth of fruits, vegetables, coffee and other crops, as well as honey and a range of processed agricultural goods such as tequila and beer.

Mexico is fortunate that its economic base is very diversified. In theory, this should make it relatively stable and cushion it from external shocks. However, most of its economic base is linked to the USA, which purchases 80% of Mexico's exports (Figure 20.1). Canada is second with 2.5%. The USA is also the source of virtually 100% of remittances as well as most tourists and foreign investment. These very close links with the USA make the Mexican economy especially vulnerable to changing economic conditions in the USA (see box on effects of US economic recessions).

Mexico's imports

What do Mexicans buy from other countries and how much do they spend? Mexico is the world's 11th largest importer.[8] It pays out about $300 billion a year for the goods and services it imports, or about $2800 per person. Imports have grown at over 10% per year since 1993, considerably faster than the overall economy. As a result, imports are gaining a larger and larger share of the Mexican market. About half of all imports come from the USA; this figure has declined sharply since 2003 (Figure 20.1), while imports from Asia have increased over the same period. China now supplies 11% of imports, Japan 5%, Germany and South Korea 4% each, and Canada 3%.

What does Mexico import? Many of Mexico's imports are rather obvious, even to the casual observer.

The major provisions of the North American Free Trade Agreement (NAFTA)[9]

- **Agriculture**: Tariffs on all farm products are to be eliminated over 15 years (by 2009). Domestic price support systems may continue provided they do not distort trade.

- **Automobiles**: After 2002, at least 62.5% of an automobile's value must be produced in North America for it to qualify for duty free status. Tariffs are to be phased out by 2005.

- **Banking**: US and Canadian banks may acquire Mexican commercial banks accounting for as much as 8% of the industry's capital. All limits on ownership end in 2004.

- **Disputes**: Special judges have jurisdiction to resolve disagreements within strict timetables.

- **Energy**: Mexico continues to bar foreign ownership of its oil fields but, starting in 2004, US and Canadian firms can bid on contracts offered by Mexican oil and electrical monopolies.

- **Environment**: The trade agreement cannot be used to overrule national and state environmental, health, or safety laws.

- **Immigration**: All three countries must ease restrictions on the movement of executives and professionals.

- **Jobs**: Barriers to Mexican migration to the USA remain.

- **Patent and copyright protection**: Mexico to strengthen laws protecting intellectual property.

- **Tariffs**: Tariffs on 10,000 custom goods are to be eliminated over 15 years (by 2009). One-half of US exports to Mexico are to be considered duty-free by 1999.

- **Textiles**: A "rule-of-origin" provision requires most garments to be made of yarn and fabric that has been produced in North America; most tariffs to be phased out by 1999.

- **Trucking**: Trucks were to have free access to cross-border routes and throughout the three countries by 1999. However, the USA has continued to impose restrictions on Mexican trucks.

These include commercial airplanes, some vehicle parts, foreign TV programming, Hollywood films, selected foods and many consumer items, mainly from Asia, such as toys, plastic goods, shoes, electrical tools, small appliances and consumer electronics. However, these readily observable imports represent a relatively small portion of total imports.

Most imports are not obvious. The majority of imports are industrial machines such as those for making and shaping metal, generating electricity, making cement, processing raw materials, facilitating construction, extracting and refining petroleum, assembling cars or manufacturing consumer products. Other not so obvious imports include car parts for assembly, agricultural machinery, and some bulk foods such as corn, wheat, beef, and pork. One surprise is that even though Mexico is the world's 4th largest corn producer, it is also 3rd in corn imports, behind only Japan and South Korea.[11]

Mexican multinationals

While the majority of multinationals in the world are US or European in origin, many Mexican firms have also become successful global players in an ever more globalized world. Pre-NAFTA (1994) success stories include Cemex, the world's third largest cement maker; Gruma, the world's largest producer of corn flour, and glass-maker Grupo Vitro.

Immediately post-NAFTA successes include Grupo Bimbo, the largest bread-maker in the western hemisphere; Grupo Savia (seeds and food distribution); Grupo IUSA (construction items), and IMSA (steel and plastics). Companies that have joined the ranks of multinational firms more recently include Corporación Durango (paper and packaging), Grupo Alfa (diversified products from petrochemicals to steel and frozen food) and Grupo México (copper)[10]

Figure 20.3 Mexico's trading agreements

There are also "invisible imports", which involve expenditure in foreign currency, even though no good or service is actually imported. For example, each year, millions of Mexicans travel abroad and spend about $8 billion in other countries.

In addition, Mexico pays out about $15 billion each year on its foreign debt of $150 billion. In terms of external debt, Mexico ranks well outside the world's top twenty.[12] Mexico's per person external debt of about $1400 is only one-twentieth that of the USA and half that of Argentina. Though substantial, external debt is therefore not such a serious problem for Mexico as it is for Argentina.

Trade strategy

Mexico has staked its economic future on interactions with the world economy. This started when the North American Free Trade Agreement (NAFTA, see box) took effect on 1 January 1994. Since then, trade between the three signatories (Mexico, USA and Canada) has more than doubled and intra-regional foreign investment has tripled, leading to considerable growth in manufacturing industries and commerce. Mexico's exports and imports have risen rapidly since 1994.

Has NAFTA been a success or a failure? On the one hand, it is credited with creating half a million new manufacturing jobs in Mexico. On the other, imports of cheap, often subsidized, agricultural goods under NAFTA may have resulted in the loss of well over one million agricultural jobs.

From a geographical perspective, NAFTA successes have occurred mainly in central and northern Mexico, and have therefore only served to increase the divide between the relatively prosperous north of the country and the poorer south. In addition, despite NAFTA, trade disputes continue between Mexico and USA with regard to several products, including sugar and steel.[13]

Since NAFTA, an aggressive policy of seeking free trade agreements with a large number of countries has transformed Mexico into the 7th largest player in the world (if EU countries are combined) in terms of value of trade. Currently, more than 90% of all Mexico's trade is under free trade agreements.

Mexico has fully embraced free trade, export promotion and globalization to the point that by 2006 it had free trade agreements in place with 30 countries (Figure 20.3), more than any other nation on the globe, and was the only country with major free trade agreements covering both North America and Europe.

Where do US economic recessions hit Mexico the hardest?[14]

Recessions in the USA have severe impacts on Mexico's economy. The deep recession of 2008–2009 hit all parts of the economy, but the sectors most affected were those most closely linked to the US economy, namely motor vehicle manufacturing, maquiladoras and other assembly plants, tourism and remittances. These are tied to US business cycles and, except for remittances, are particularly dependent on foreign direct investment which dries up significantly during recessions.

The earliest and hardest hit was the auto industry. During the first half of 2009, production and exports were down 40%–50% and sales down 30% compared to a year earlier. The state most affected was Chihuahua (30% of its GDP is auto manufacturing), followed by Puebla, Nuevo León, Guanajuato and Mexico. Maquiladoras and other non-vehicle assembly plants were also hit hard, with serious impacts on the border economies of Baja California, Chihuahua, Nuevo León and Tamaulipas.

Recession-related declines in the numbers of US tourists were felt the most by Baja California Sur and Quintana Roo, and to a much lesser extent by Jalisco and Nayarit. The states most affected through remittances were Zacatecas and Michoacán as well as Durango, Guanajuato and Jalisco. Interestingly, while the gross amount of dollar remittances declined by about 5% in 2009, this was more than offset by a 25% depreciation in the value of the peso. As a result, states dependent on remittances actually did relatively well during the 2008–2009 recession.

Combining these sectors, which state economies were most affected by the 2008–2009 US recession? The worst hit were the tourist states of Quintana Roo and Baja California Sur. The Federal District was third because, in addition to being an important tourist destination and assembly center for vehicles and other goods, most foreign direct investment comes through the capital. Other states closely linked to the US business cycle include Michoacán (remittances), Chihuahua (motor vehicles and assembly plants), Baja California (assembly plants), Nayarit (remittances and tourism), Nuevo León (assembly plants) and Zacatecas (remittances).

The two least affected state economies were Tabasco and Campeche, which are dependent on oil extraction. Other less affected states are Yucatán, Veracruz, Tlaxcala, Colima, Oaxaca and Chiapas. All states are impacted to some extent because a US recession usually causes a recession in Mexico with adverse multiplier impacts in all states.

What exactly is globalization?

Globalization can be defined in simple terms as "the process by which events, activities and decisions in one part of the world can have significant consequences for communities in distant parts of the globe."[15] Though globalization began centuries ago with colonial conquests and trade, it has only gained widespread attention in the past few decades.

Globalization is a highly contentious issue. There are major debates as to whether globalization brings more benefits than problems. While many international organizations such as the International Monetary Fund and World Bank are pro-globalization, many individuals and sectors of society remain deeply skeptical, and a powerful anti-globalization movement has arisen in some parts of the world.

How globalized is Mexico?

Several attempts have been made to quantify globalization. In this section we compare two indices which look at how globalized Mexico is compared to other countries.

The KOF Index of Globalization[16] measures three main dimensions of globalization: economic, social and political. Economic globalization considers the long distance flows (exports, imports) of goods, capital and services, as well as political restrictions (tariffs, taxes) to these flows. Social globalization measures the international spread of ideas, information (telephone traffic, internet access) and people (migration, tourism). Several small European countries score well on these first two measures. Political globalization examines the number of embassies a country has, as well as its membership of international organizations and participation in UN peace missions. European countries occupy the first seven places on this dimension. Based on the indices for these three dimensions, an overall index of globalization is calculated.

The 2009 KOF Index used data from 2006 to rank 208 countries. Mexico placed 65th overall, with rankings of 79th for economic, 69th for social,

The geography of drug trafficking

Illegal drug trafficking brings somewhere between $10 and $20 billion into Mexico each year, mainly from the USA where demand for drugs, including heroin, cocaine, methamphetamines and marijuana, is enormous. Drug growing and trafficking are both highly profitable. Peasant farmers can make as much from a single crop of marijuana as they can from several years of traditional crops.

The major cartels try to control the entire supply chain from production to final distribution. Competition between cartels is fierce. They pay off corrupt officials, have powerful paramilitary units, armed with weapons primarily bought in the USA, and employ increasingly sophisticated methods of transportation, including unmanned mini-submersibles.

The geography of the drug trade has changed significantly in recent years. Prior to the 1980s, Colombian cartels were the link between South American producers and US markets, using clandestine aircraft, or boats via the Caribbean. In the 1980s, Colombian and US drug eradication efforts forced Colombian cartels to shift their supply routes to Mexico, where they needed the support of Mexican gangs. These gangs soon gained control and became powerful cartels, each with its own major region of operations. Historically, for example, the Gulf Cartel, based in Matamoros, controlled supply routes along the Gulf coast, while the Juárez Cartel, based in Ciudad Juárez, focused on northern Chihuahua together with parts of Nuevo León and Sonora.

As a result of turf battles among cartels, and President Calderon's massive crackdown involving 40,000 military troops, about 5,000 people were killed in Mexico's drug war in 2008.

Is Mexico's current offensive against drug cartels being successful? Closer monitoring of airports and air traffic in southern Mexico reduced airborne shipments of cocaine from Columbia by up to 95%, pushing up the street price in many US cities.[17] Mexican drug gangs are now extending their influence into Central America in an effort to control land-based routes more effectively, and into parts of South America in their attempt to control supply. They are also diversifying their markets, with an increased presence in Europe. As it becomes harder for drug cartels to operate, some have diversified into other criminal activities such as kidnapping and the smuggling of Cubans and Central Americans to the USA.

Drug trafficking may bring as much as $20 billion into the Mexican economy each year but the costs, in terms of deaths and in lost foreign investment and decreased tourism, greatly outweigh any benefits.

and 80th for political globalization. By comparison, Russia ranked 61st, Argentina 63rd, Brazil 79th, China 91st, Indonesia 100th and India 122nd.

The A.T. Kearney Globalization Index has four main components: economic integration (trade, foreign direct investment), personal contact (telecommunications, travel, remittances), technological connectivity (internet) and political engagement (international treaties, organizations and peacekeeping). The 2006 index ranked 62 countries.[18] Mexico placed 42nd overall, with ranks of between 36 and 41 for each of the four components. For comparison, Russia ranked 47th, Argentina 43rd, Brazil 52nd, China 51st, Indonesia 60th and India 61st.

In Mexico's case, these two globalization indices give broadly similar results. The data suggest that Mexico is relatively globalized compared to other large emerging countries. However, in the case of the USA, the different methodologies of the two indices produce very different results. The KOF index ranks the USA as 38th out of 208, with rankings of 59th for economic, 56th for social and 9th for political globalization respectively. The A.T. Kearney index places the USA 3rd out of 62 countries, despite its ranks for separate components of 58th for economic, 40th for personal, 1st for technological and 41st for political globalization. The differences between the indices indicate the difficulty of quantifying globalization.

21

500-year transition to an urban society

Mexico is an urban society, but it has not always been so. During the last one hundred years, the proportion of Mexicans living in urban areas (localities with more than 2500 inhabitants) increased from 30% to 75%. Almost half of the population now lives in cities of over 100,000 and over one quarter lives in urban centers of over 500,000. This chapter describes the evolution of urbanization in Mexico.[1]

Pre-Columbian period

The beginnings of urbanization in Mesoamerica started around 2500BC. Agriculture had developed to the point where sufficient surpluses were available to support permanent quasi-urban settlements. Small centers emerged and died depending on levels of agricultural surplus as well as politics and wars. Ceremonial centers also emerged, but there is some disagreement concerning whether these should be considered truly urban. As interregional trade became more important, trade centers came into existence.

The earliest truly urban center in the Americas was Monte Alban in Oaxaca which dates back to 500-300BC. Teotihuacan, the great city in the Valley of Mexico started in about 300BC when the use of irrigation and improved agricultural technology produced the sizeable surplus needed to support a significant urban population, a professional army, and grand infrastructure projects. Teotihuacan, located about 50 km (30 mi) northeast of Mexico City, controlled a large empire with links to most of southern Mexico. At its peak in the 6th century, its population approached 200,000 making it one of the world's largest cities. Teotihuacan was Mexico's

dominant urban center for over 500 years, but in the 7th century, its control weakened, perhaps as a result of population pressures and the overexploitation of its environmental base. Within decades it was defeated by enemies, burned, plundered and abandoned.

The Classic Maya period, AD250 to 900, coexisted with Teotihuacan for several hundred years. The Maya civilization is best known for its magnificent ceremonial centers, such as Palenque and Chichen Itza. The influence of the Maya covered southern Mexico, the Yucatán, and extended south into Guatemala, El Salvador and Honduras. However, there was not a Maya Empire as such, but rather a large number of rival "city-states" such as existed in ancient Greece. As a result, there was no single dominant Maya capital comparable to Teotihuacan or Rome. Instead, there were numerous small cities serving political, military, trade and ceremonial functions. In the 10th century, the Maya civilization collapsed, probably as a result of internal conflict, overpopulation and severe environmental overexploitation.

Subsequent urbanization was characterized by more dispersed centers in most regions of Mesoamerica. The centers were less concerned with spiritual and ceremonial activities and more with military and trade issues amongst various "states" and alliances. Irrigated agriculture expanded and populations grew.

Northern groups began to dominate. The Toltecs from northern Mexico moved into the Valley of Mexico and established an expansive empire that controlled central Mexico. At about the time of the Maya collapse, they established their capital at Tula, about 65 km (40 mi) north of Mexico City. Tula arguably was Mexico's most important urban center for 250 to 300 years. Its population eventually grew to between 30,000 and 40,000. However, Tula was abandoned early in the 13th century after being overrun by invaders from the north.

The Aztecs were another group that came from the north to settle in the Valley of Mexico. In the 15th century, they established a hegemonic militaristic empire that stretched from the Gulf of Mexico to the Pacific. Their capital, the island city of Tenochtitlan, grew to about 200,000 by the time the Spaniards arrived in 1519.

Mexico's current urban concentration is directly linked to the three very important empires, Teotihuacano, Toltec and Aztec, which were centered in the Valley of Mexico. Each succeeding empire tended to locate its capital near the capital of earlier empires. The Spanish chose to locate their capital on the same spot as the magnificent Aztec capital, Tenochtitlan, and Mexico became a clear exception to the general rule that colonial empires established their colonial capitals on the coast to facilitate communications with the European colonial power.

Colonial period: 1519–1821

Tenochtitlan was one of the largest and grandest urban centers on Earth when the Spaniards arrived in 1519. For the next three hundred years, the Spaniards built an urban system designed to control and exploit Mexican resources while shipping her riches back to Spain. Mexico City was the administrative and religious center, while Veracruz was the main port.

The area of New Spain was far too large to administer from a single capital city. It stretched from Guatemala all the way north to Texas, Colorado and California. A system of cities developed to reflect the exploitive goals of the colonial regime. The resulting urban system was not well integrated in that there were few transportation and communications lines between the urban centers. Instead, these lines generally ran from each center back to Spain. The urban system was oriented toward achieving the colonial goal of exploitation.

Within this system, a number of different types of urban centers emerged. There were administrative–military cities focused on controlling the colony. Cities serving this function included Mexico City, Guadalajara, and Mérida. A step below these were secondary administrative–economic centers which extended colonial control further into the hinterland.

Centers in this group were Puebla, Oaxaca, Querétaro, Guanajuato, and Zamora. Port cities, such as Veracruz, Acapulco, and Mazatlán, facilitated trade and exportation of colonial riches to Spain. Mining centers such as Guanajuato, Pachuca, Zacatecas, San Luis Potosí, and Taxco focused on extracting and processing mineral riches. Some of these cities fit into more than one category.

In terms of population size, the colonial hierarchy of cities tended to reflect a close fit to the empirical rank-size rule, which relates the size of a city to its national ranking. According to the rank-size rule, in a well-balanced hierarchy, the population of the largest center is twice that of the second largest center, three times that of the third largest center, four times that of the fourth largest, and so on. In 1790, Mexico City had a population of about 105,000 (see Table 21.1), followed by Puebla with 57,000 and Guanajuato with 32,000.

Of course, a hierarchy of cities is not static. The population of cities in the hierarchy changes with fluctuations in their economic base as well as with political and military events. For instance, Guanajuato's population rose from 32,000 in 1790 to more than 41,000 in 1803. By 1827, in the aftermath of the struggle for independence, its population had fallen back to just 35,000. The important thing to remember is that the urban structure during the colonial period in Mexico reflected and facilitated the goals of the Spanish government, namely to control and exploit the area for the Spanish Crown.

Independence: 1821–1877

During the War of Independence, 1810 to 1821, the fierce fighting had significant consequences for the colonial urban system. Mining and agricultural production declined sharply, throwing the entire economic system into disarray. Many mestizos and Indians abandoned their villages and towns feeling that they were unsafe. Their massive migrations temporarily swelled the populations of Mexico City, Querétaro, and Guadalajara. Querétaro's population swelled to almost 40,000 in 1826, some 10,000 more than a decade earlier.

New port cities blossomed as the loyalists struggled to keep their ties with Spain and the insurgents sought to get clandestine supplies from abroad. Although the decade of violence involved great economic disorganization and considerable cityward migration, it did not result in the precipitous population decline

Table 21.1 Mexico's urban growth, 1790–2000[2]

Year	% urban	Urban population (millions)	Population of largest urban areas ('000s)			
			Mexico City	2nd city	3rd city	4th city
1790	8	0.3	105	57	32	22
1870	15	1.2	225	65	65	37
1910	29	4.4	471	119	96	79
1921	31	4.5	615	143	96	88
1930	34	5.5	1 029	180	133	115
1940	35	6.9	1 803	275	206	149
1950	43	11.0	3 138	380	375	235
1960	51	17.7	5 252	851	708	297
1970	59	28.3	8 800	1 491	1 246	546
1980	66	44.3	13 354	2 193	1 913	773
1990	71	57.9	15 048	2 987	2 604	1 330
2000	74	72.8	18 519	3 787	3 364	1 942
2008	77	79.0	19 827	4 299	3 929	2 606

associated with the conquest. Mexico's population grew from 6.1 million in 1810 to 6.8 million in 1823.

Independence from Spain did not promote rapid urban growth. The new ruling class was composed mainly of criollos, Spaniards born in Mexico. The conservative criollos, who were more interested in their landed rural estates, were opposed by urban liberals focused on developing commerce or industry. This dialectic continued for about 60 years while the structure of urbanization changed very little.

A few years after winning independence, the new country was involved in wars, first with rebels in Texas in the 1830s and then with the USA in the 1840s. These wars and Mexico's role in the US Civil War brought Mexico into direct and constant confrontation with the USA. Mexico lost half its territory, but the lost lands were sparsely populated at the time and not well integrated with the rest of the country. The Civil War in the USA stimulated some urban growth in the northeast as smuggling became important.

Throughout the period, Mexico was saddled with a highly regionalized, weakly-linked urban system in which the cities were consumers rather than producers. Urban and overall population growth rates were low, with cities often growing more slowly than rural areas. Mexico City remained the locus of politi-

cal and economic power, not so much because of its own dynamism, but because all urban centers were rather stagnant. By 1862, the population of Mexico City had grown to about 210,000, roughly the size of Tenochtitlan when the Spanish arrived, or of Teotihuacan in the 6th century.

Mexico City was growing faster than other cities, causing Mexico to move away from the rank-size rule towards urban primacy. Urban primacy is the situation when one very large primate city dominates the urban structure, as well as the country as a whole. Cities and countries with this pattern now include: London, UK; Paris, France; Buenos Aires, Argentina; Cairo, Egypt; and Bangkok, Thailand. Such a pattern is associated with strong central government control, countries which in the past had large colonial empires, and countries where the political and economic power are both centered in one city.

By 1870, Puebla, the second city in the hierarchy, was replaced by Guadalajara, a prosperous regional center in the western highlands. With a population of 65,000, Guadalajara was only about one quarter the size of Mexico City. Meanwhile, Guanajuato, Querétaro and other cities in the Bajío region, between Guadalajara and Mexico City, began to suffer a gradual decline in relative importance. By the 1860s Guanajuato, located in a rather isolated mountainous area, was a dying city. Its population was down to 37,000 because its silver mines were essentially mined out.

Another important development was the effort to spread trade to ports other than Veracruz. Tampico, about 450 km north of Veracruz, became a major port and prospered through the efforts of foreign merchants who provided goods and services to the interior as far west as Zacatecas and San Luis Potosí.

The Mexican economy and urban system was relatively stagnant in the middle years of the century. The economy was experiencing severe problems and Mexico was heavily indebted to Britain, France, and Spain. The three countries sent armed forces to Mexico in an effort to collect their debt. The French succeeded in occupying Mexico City and installing Maximilian of Hapsburg as the Emperor of Mexico in 1864. Mexican forces under Benito Juárez retreated, but regained power in 1867. These political changes had limited impact on the urban hierarchy and the economy, which were relatively dormant throughout the period.

Porfirio Díaz regime: 1877–1910

The economy didn't get rolling until Porfirio Díaz came to power in 1877. Díaz focused on establishing a stable environment to attract foreign industrial investment. He paid little attention to the harsh realities of Mexico's largely rural underclass which made up about 85% of the nation's population.

In this period of dependent capitalism, the government granted numerous concessions to encourage industrialization. This shifted the economy away from subsistence agriculture and accelerated the process of urbanization. Peace, industrialization, renewed mining activity, a growing railroad system and increased exports, stimulated urbanization as the poor from rural areas moved toward cities and industrial jobs.

The expansion of the railroad network greatly enhanced growth of some cities while diverting it from others. Mexico City, Guadalajara, Toluca, and Aguascalientes grew rapidly as diversified centers of commerce and manufacturing. Veracruz regained its position as the country's major port city with completion of its rail link to Mexico City in 1872. Cities bypassed by major rail lines, such as Puebla, Morelia, Tlaxcala, León, and Guanajuato, declined in importance. Perhaps the clearest example of the impact of the railroad is Torreón, Coahuila, which went from a *rancho* of 200 inhabitants in 1892 to a thriving cotton production center of 34,000 in 1910.

With the railroads and increased industrialization, the largest cities began to assert their dominance. In 1884, Mexico City with 300,000 inhabitants was followed by Guadalajara with 80,000, Puebla with 75,000, and Monterrey with 42,000. Mexico City was clearly the dominant primate city, but it was still smaller than six or seven cities in the USA. By 1900, Mexico City had grown to 350,000 inhabitants and became even more dominant. Guadalajara had grown to about 100,000 and solidified its position as the second leading city.

By the first decade of the twentieth century, Mexico City had become even stronger politically, economically, and demographically. Its rapid growth resulted from the orientation of the railroad system, strict governmental control of public finances, and ready access to foreign capital. The impact of foreign and local investments in urban and industrial projects created an urban system which began to differ significantly from that of fifty years earlier.

Between 1900 and 1910, Mexico City's population grew by 3% annually and reached 471,000. In contrast, Mexico's other major cities grew by less than 2% per year. By 1910 Guadalajara had 119,000 inhabitants; Puebla had 96,000; and Monterrey had 79,000. The urban primacy of Mexico City was firmly established; it had four times the population of Guadalajara (Table 21.1).

During the decade several of the older cities declined in relative importance. León, the nation's fourth largest city in 1900, dropped to seventh in 1910. Guanajuato dropped from 8th to 14th. Querétaro fell from 13th to 18th. During this period, Monterrey and other cities outside the central region moved up the urban hierarchy.

By the end of the Porfirio Díaz regime in 1910, certain tendencies of twentieth century urbanization were already established. Mexico City was the dominant primate city. Veracruz was the principal foreign port. The economy was heavily dependent on foreign capital. A multifunctional system of cities was developing in the Bajío Region. Monterrey was becoming an increasingly important industrial city. The Pacific ports were declining in importance and becoming relatively isolated.

The Revolution and its aftermath: 1910–1939

Unlike the War of Independence a century earlier, the Mexican Revolution had a dramatic impact on the nation's population structure and urban system.

The total population fell from 15.2 million in 1910 to 14.3 million in 1921. The destruction of many small communities and the general insecurity in the countryside stimulated urban migration. This influx swelled some cities far more than others. Mexico City's growth accelerated to almost 3.5% per year; the population reached 662,000 by 1921. Several older cities in central Mexico continued their relative decline. Guanajuato dropped from 14th in 1910 to 27th in 1921.

The revolution and its aftermath reversed the Porfirio Díaz policy of promoting foreign investments to stimulate urban industrialization. The new revolutionary regime focused attention on long-standing rural problems and discouraged US and other foreign intervention in Mexican affairs.

The urban situation in Mexico did not change significantly in the immediate post-revolutionary period. Governments tried to put the pieces back together and restore stability. The real turning point of Mexico's Revolution came with the election of Lázaro Cárdenas in 1934. Cárdenas, from rural Michoacán, was determined to use state funds to achieve social justice, especially in the rural sector. He dramatically increased social and economic expenditures.

The worldwide depression of the 1930s provided Cárdenas with the opportunity to turn the political revolution of 1910 into a true social revolution. His determination to lessen Mexico's dependence on the USA and other foreign powers, is demonstrated by his nationalization of petroleum properties in 1938. His aggressive agrarian reform programs broke up the large rural estates (*latifundios*) and created communal land ownership in the form of *ejidos*. In the process, he turned his administration away from urban and industrial challenges and reaffirmed his concern for the countryside where the bulk of the population lived.

The revolution, worldwide depression, and Cardenas' agrarian reforms significantly slowed rural to urban migration during the 1930s. The depression disrupted urban life more than it hurt rural areas. In addition, large-scale governmental irrigation projects in the northwest created alternative destinations for many potential urban migrants. Thus the pace of urbanization that had accelerated under Díaz once again stagnated.

In sum, the 1910-1940 period was an era of "revolution and rural reform," characterized by relatively slow rates of urban population growth, with considerable variation among different regions. Mexico City continued as the nation's primary city, its population reached about 1.8 million in 1940.

Explosive urbanization: 1940–1969

The decade of the 1940s marks a clear turning point in urbanization as rural to urban migration accelerated rapidly. A variety of events, programs, and policies worked together to accelerate urban growth, particularly in Mexico City. The end of the worldwide depression gave cities an opportunity to recover and even prosper. The creation of the Bracero migrant labor program resulted in millions of rural Mexicans migrating to the USA. The program enabled Mexicans to alleviate the severe USA labor shortage during the second world war. When they returned to Mexico, many of these migrants settled in cities.

Mexico pursued new policies fostering industrial development. Several major hydroelectric river-basin projects promoted industrialization by providing relatively cheap electric power. The spread of government-sponsored health and education programs enabled many educated rural youth to migrate to cities to seek jobs that paid far better than agricultural work. While the government continued many of the agrarian reform schemes initiated by Cardenas, this did little to stem the flow of migrants to cities.[3]

Rapid urbanization after 1940 did not occur in isolation from the broader transformations of Mexican society. The concentration of population and industries in a few metropolitan centers resulted from specific governmental policies and private sector forces. Mexico City was the primary beneficiary (or victim) of these centralization policies. In commerce, education, labor, banking, telecommunications, housing, and so on, the forces of centralization created a pattern of "primacy" even more powerful than that evidenced by mere population numbers.

Beginning in the 1950s, the Mexican Government followed a policy of import substitution industrialization. This approach encouraged and provided incentives for industries that produced items that previously were imported, such as consumer goods and motor vehicles. Import substitution industries tended to locate near their main market, which was Mexico City with its very large population of relatively high income consumers. Mexico City was also the clear center of political power and financial capital. Industrial entrepreneurs wanted to be close to government, so they could easily lobby for government subsidies and incentives. The Mexico City bankers also preferred to loan to industrialists who were building near the capital.

The policy of import substitution concentrated growth in large cities, particularly Mexico City, at the expense of the rest of the country. Government infrastructural and other investments were heavily concentrated in the capital, while other areas received very little. The resulting pattern of urbanization, sometimes called "dependent urbanization," is characterized by dynamic growth of a few large cities and vast backward regions of relative poverty. There was a net flow of people and wealth from the relatively poor periphery to the dominant urban core. Rapid industrial growth in Mexico City contributed to environmental problems of air and water pollution, traffic congestion, overcrowding, as well as flooding and sewage problems. Early attempts to combat these included additional infrastructure investments in Mexico City, which attracted even more rural labor.

About the only countervailing force to rapid urbanization, was the continuation of Lázaro Cárdenas' agrarian reform programs for establishing small ejidos. After an initial burst of activity in the late 1930s, the government continued to create *ejidos*, albeit it more slowly, in the underdeveloped countryside. The focus shifted to some of the most remote areas, such as colonization programs in Quintana Roo and Chiapas. Despite these policies to encourage peasants to stay in rural areas, migration to cities continued.

By 1950, Mexico City had over 3 million residents and had become one of the most dominant primate cities in the world. Its population was more than eight times that of the next largest cities, Guadalajara (380,000) and Monterey (375,000).

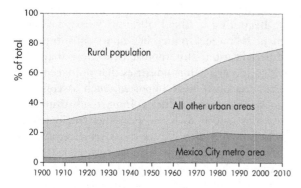

Figure 21.1 From rural to urban[4]

Between 1950 and 1970, Mexico experienced unprecedented urban growth. The population shifted rather rapidly from majority rural to majority urban. (Figure 21.1) The proportion of Mexicans living in urban localities of over 2500 inhabitants went from 43% up to 59%. The greatest growth was in large urban areas. Mexico's urban population grew by over 150% from 11 million to 28 million. In contrast, rural population inched up by only about 38%, going from just under 14 million to a bit over 20 million.

Mexico City was the focus of urban growth. From 1950 to 1970 the population of the Federal District increased 125% to 6.9 million. However, this was nothing compared to the growth just beyond the Federal District boundaries. The population of this urban periphery exploded from only 86,000 in 1950 to 1.9 million by 1970. This periphery area, together with the Federal District, comprises the Mexico City Metropolitan Area (ZMCM),[5] which reached 8.8 million by 1970. Some Mexicans began boasting that by the year 2000 it would reach 30 million and be the world's largest city.

Other large cities in Mexico grew even faster than the capital. From 1950 to 1970, Guadalajara grew by 295% to 1.5 million. Northern cities also grew rapidly. Monterrey grew by 232%, to 1.25 million. Ciudad Juárez grew by 245% to 424,000. Tijuana grew by an amazing 420% from 65,000 to 341,000. Secondary cities in central Mexico also grew rapidly, but nowhere near as fast as the northern cities. Puebla grew by 135%, Toluca by 115%, León by 168%, and San Luis Potosí by 86%.

De-concentration: 1970–1989

By 1970, Mexico City appeared to be on its way to becoming the world's largest city. The government was beginning to recognize that rapid growth was associated with even faster growing urban problems of pollution, traffic congestion, and diseconomies of scale.

In 1978 the government issued a National Plan for Urban Development. The purpose of the plan was to shift growth away from Mexico City by decentralizing industries, jobs and population. A number of state-owned enterprises like Pemex were to be moved from the capital to other regions of the country. Several hundred other "dirty" industries were to be transferred out of the metropolitan area.

The plan also called for shifting federal government spending away from the Federal District and toward other regions. Particular attention was focused on the problems of the northern borderlands. At that time, the budget for the Federal District was larger than those of all the other states combined. Obviously, this type of budget allocation greatly favored the growth of Mexico City over other areas of the country.

The Government's de-concentration efforts did not really begin to work until the 1980s. During the 1970s the Federal District grew by almost two million reaching 8.8 million by 1980. However, its growth rate during the decade of 2.5% per year was less than the national average of 3.3% per year. The outlying urban areas in the ZMCM more than doubled to about 4.6 million, growing at 10% per year. The total population of the sprawling metropolitan area reached 13.4 million in 1980 or about 20% of the country's total population.

During the 1980s, the government started serious implementation of the plan to shift growth away from Mexico City. It was relatively successful in this effort. From 1980 to 1990, the population of the Federal District declined from 8.8 million to 8.2 million. The ZMCM population increased to about 15 million, but its growth rate during the 1980s was significantly less than one third that of other urban areas in Mexico and less than half that of the country as a whole.

During the 20 year period between 1970 and 1990, Mexico's secondary cities grew considerably faster than the capital. Interestingly, the population of cities in central Mexico increased faster than northern cities. Guadalajara grew by 4.67% per year and surpassed Monterrey which increased by 3.75% per year. The Puebla-Tlaxcala metro area and León grew faster than Tijuana and Ciudad Juárez in the north. Smaller cities in the north like Mexicali and Chihuahua also grew relatively slowly.

From 1970 to 1990, Mexico's smaller cities grew considerably faster than the largest cities. Which cities grew the fastest? Interestingly, the most rapid growth was in Toluca and Cuernavaca, two cities relatively near Mexico City. Toluca, the capital of the State of Mexico is only about 60 km west of the capital. Cuernavaca is only about 65 km south. Querétaro, about 180 km northwest of the capital also grew very rapidly. Much of the potential growth of the capital was diverted to the nearby urban areas of Toluca, Cuernavaca, Querétaro, as well as Pachuca, 80 km (50 mi) northeast, and Puebla-Tlaxcala, 100

km (60 mi) east. The other fast growing city was Villahermosa in Tabasco which benefited from expanding petroleum activities.

The data indicate that government efforts to shift growth away from Mexico City have been relatively successful. The ZMCM's share of total manufacturing fell from 47% in 1980 to only 26% in 2000.[6] The trend toward greater de-concentration is expected to continue in the years ahead.

Fertility decline and NAFTA: 1990–present

During the second half of the 1990s, two strong forces influenced Mexico's urbanization: rapid fertility decline and the implementation of NAFTA (the North American Free Trade Agreement).

From 1990 to 2004, Mexico's fertility rate dropped rather dramatically from 3.6 to 2.5 children per woman (see chapter 9). As a result, the overall population growth rate and the urban growth rate both declined. Still the ZMCM grew 1.7% per year during the 1990s. This is considerably faster than the previous decade, but much of the growth resulted from the addition of nine new municipalities with 650,000 residents to the ZMCM. It reached 18.5 million by 2000; far less than the 30 million figures that was forecast in 1970. Other urban areas grew faster than the ZMCM, but slower than they had during the 1980s.

The signing of NAFTA in 1994 had a significant impact on the pattern of urbanization in Mexico. When NAFTA removed tariffs on imported corn and beans, small Mexican producers could not compete with the cheap imports. As a result, an estimated 1.3 million agricultural jobs in Mexico were lost.[7] On the other hand, NAFTA created an estimated 5.3 million jobs in Mexico, including about 500,000 in manufacturing and roughly 1.9 million in the informal sector. Virtually all of the jobs created were in urban areas. Overall, NAFTA impact has strongly stimulated urban growth while fostering rural decline and out-migration.

Many Mexican and foreign firms built maquiladora manufacturing plants near the northern border to take advantage of the US market. These investments stimulated urban growth in border cities, particularly Ciudad Juárez, Tijuana, Mexicali, Matamoros, Nuevo Laredo, and Reynosa. Later, maquiladora plants were also built in areas distant from the border like Mérida and Aguascalientes. Largely as a result of NAFTA, border cities grew faster during

Table 21.2 Mexico's thirty largest urban centers, 2009–2030[8]

Rank		Eco-nomic base	Population (x 1000)	
			2009	2030*
1	Mexico City Metro	Diverse	19 982	22 636
2	Guadalajara	Diverse	4 365	4 773
3	Monterrey	Diverse	3 986	4 869
4	Puebla	Industrial	2 647	2 528
5	Tijuana	Industrial	1 784	2 553
6	Toluca	Industrial	1 775	1 896
7	León	Industrial	1 555	1 443
8	Cuidad Juárez	Industrial	1 408	2 368
9	Torreón	Industrial	1 187	1 284
10	San Luis Potosí	Diverse	1 037	1 075
11	Querétaro	Diverse	1 036	1 373
12	Mérida	Diverse	955	1 234
13	Mexicali	Industrial	926	1 050
14	Aguascalientes	Diverse	910	1 094
15	Cuernavaca	Diverse	850	1 111
16	Chihuahua	Industrial	839	865
17	Tampico	Transport	835	931
18	Saltillo	Industrial	793	948
19	Veracruz	Transport	786	540
20	Morelia	Diverse	783	733
21	Acapulco	Tourism	776	651
22	Hermosillo	Diverse	703	817
23	Reynosa	Industrial	702	852
24	Cancún	Tourism	693	984
25	Villahermosa	Industrial	671	887
26	Tuxtla Gutierrez	Diverse	623	766
27	Culiacan	Diverse	622	712
28	Oaxaca	Diverse	560	621
29	Matamoros	Industrial	493	716
30	Xalapa	Diverse	423	408

* population estimate (2030)

the 1990s than most other Mexican cities, essentially reversing the trend that existed during the 1980s. Consistent with this reversal, Toluca and Cuernavaca, the two fastest growing urban areas in the 1980s, were amongst the slowest in the 1990s. On the other hand, Querétaro continued its rapid 1980s growth through the 1990s. Puebla-Tlaxcala also grew relatively rapidly in both decades.

Mexico's current urban hierarchy

The Mexico urban hierarchy is still very dominated by its primate capital city. Even though the Mexico City urban area (ZMCM) has grown relatively slowly during the past 30 years, by 2000 it had a population of 17.8 million, making it the world's second largest urban area, behind Tokyo-Yokohama and just ahead of Sao Paulo, New York, and Mumbai. Of course, such comparisons are largely dependent on how one defines an urban area. One could argue that the ZMCM could include Toluca, Cuernavaca, Pachuca and Puebla-Tlaxcala, all within 100 km (60 mi) of the capital. This would increase its population to about 23 million. Even without these periphery urban areas, the ZMCM is almost five times larger than Guadalajara, instead of twice as large as expected from the rank size rule.

The concept of urban hierarchy is more complicated than the rank-size rule, which is based solely on population size. Urban hierarchy is based more on the functions served by urban centers and their relationships with their hinterlands. An urban hierarchy is conceptually similar to an organization chart or layered pyramid. At the top is the largest center, the dominant financial, economic, and often political center of the country. It has the widest range and most complex set of urban functions and services such as international banking, stock exchanges, trade organizations, and major media and communications centers. It is the center of power of the country: the place where the most important decisions are made.

At the second level are a few regional cities that are the centers of power in their region or hinterland. They provide high level services that are not available elsewhere in the region. Such services might include investment banking, an important international airport, as well as sophisticated business, legal and medical centers. At the third level are a larger number of subregional centers which are the focus of economic activity in their subregion. At each succeeding lower level, there are a greater number of centers serving as the economic foci of their smaller hinterlands.

Often a center's population is a guide to its level in the hierarchy, but not always. Some centers may have a large population, but do not provide a wide range of key economic functions to surrounding areas. For example, Puebla is Mexico's fourth largest urban area, but does not serve as a real center for a national region because it is so close to Mexico City. In other words, Mexico City is so economically dominant in central Mexico that Puebla has been unable to carve out a substantial hinterland of its own. The same can be said for Toluca, Mexico's fifth largest urban area. As a result, some geographers argue that Mexico City is now the center of a megalopolis, a super-sized conurbation, stretching from Toluca in the west to Puebla and Tlaxcala in the east, and from Cuernavaca in the south towards Pachuca in the north.

Tourist centers like Cancún and Acapulco are other examples of cities that have a reduced regional importance despite their relatively large populations. They provide vacation and recreation services for visitors from around the world. However, neither is a state capital, and they are not necessarily the key functional center in their respective regions.

Given their complexity, the specific delineation of urban hierarchies has often been as much art as science. So far, no uniformly accepted, easy to use criteria have been developed for this purpose. Efforts to delineate urban hierarchies have traditionally used information on the range of services provided; financial, communication and transportation flows; as well as a center's location, its surrounding hinterland, and the distance to competing centers.

Mexico City is at the apex on the Mexican urban hierarchy; Guadalajara and Monterrey are key second level cities. Beyond these three centers, there is less agreement concerning the appropriate levels of other urban centers. Some think there are only two real level two cities, while others have argued that Toluca, Tijuana and Ciudad Juárez should also be considered level two cities.[9] There is even less agreement when it comes to specifying cities in levels three and four. The exact delineation of the levels is less important than understanding the basic concepts of urban hierarchy and realizing that a city's level is related to the range of functions it provides to its surrounding hinterland.

A suggested current urban hierarchy of Mexico is shown in Table 21.3. This hierarchy, mapped in

Figure 21.2 Mexico's urban hierarchy

Table 21.3 Mexico's urban hierarchy

Level	City or cities
I	Mexico City Metro
II	Guadalajara, Monterrey
III	Cuidad Juárez, Puebla, Tijuana, Toluca
IV	Aguascalientes, Chihuahua, Cuernavaca, León, Mérida, Mexicali, Querétaro, San Luis Potosí, Tampico, Torreón-Gómez Palacio
V	Acapulco, Cancún, Culiacán, Durango, Hermosillo, Matamoros, Morelia, Nuevo Laredo, Oaxaca, Poza Rica, Reynosa, Saltillo, Tuxtla Gutierrez, Veracruz, Villahermosa, Xalapa

Figure 21.2, is based on objective and subjective information on the urban center itself, as well as the population in its hinterland and its distance from a competing urban center. This hierarchy is only suggestive. Intermediate levels could be added indicating centers that could arguably be included in either the level above or level below.

The suggested hierarchy above is very different from the urban system of the pre-Colombian era, or Colonial era, or even of the 19th century. The one constant is that the Mexico City has always been at the apex of the hierarchy. The point here is that urban systems change with the economic and political changes.

The process of urbanization was very slow following independence, accelerated under Porfirio Díaz, stagnated again after the revolution and then exploded following the second world war. The positions of individual cities may change drastically with changing economic and political conditions. For example, Guanajuato was once an important level two city, but with the decline of its silver mines, it dropped to level five or lower.

Projected changes in large cities and the urban hierarchy

During the next thirty to fifty years, the current Mexican urban hierarchy is expected to change, perhaps dramatically[10] (Table 21.2). Urbanization is expected to continue. The most rapid rate of urbanization is predicted to be in Quintana Roo, where the number living in cities will more than double, from 600,000 in 2000 to 1.7 million by 2030. Half of the total will live in either Cancún or Playa del Carmen.

Interestingly, the thirty largest cities in 2000 are also expected to be the thirty largest in 2030, though their order will have changed. At the top of the hierarchy, Mexico City will remain dominant, and will need to house, feed and employ an additional four million inhabitants. It is expected that by 2025, Monterrey will have vaulted over Guadalajara in population size to become the nation's second largest city. Four years later, Tijuana will overtake Puebla to become the fourth largest city.

By 2030, another six cities will have passed the one million mark: Mexicali, Cuernavaca, Aguascalientes, Mérida, San Luis Potosí and Torreón. The most rapid rise has been, and will continue to be that of Cancún, the planned resort city. From a population well below 10,000 in 1970, it is now over half a million, and by 2030 is confidently predicted to approach (some even say exceed) one million (see Figure 19.3).

The rapid rate of growth of Cancún is mirrored in several other smaller tourist resorts. Two other places in Quintana Roo—Playa del Carmen and Tulum—are each expected to increase their populations five fold by 2030, and three locations in Baja California Sur—Cabo San Lucas, San José del Cabo and Colonia del Sur—are each expected to triple between 2000 and 2030. These towns and cities are the fastest growing in the nation.

On the other hand, a few cities are expected to actually decline in population between 2000 and 2030. The largest city in this category is Veracruz, which will see its population fall from its current level of about 620,000 to around 540,000. Other cities where population will decline include Guanajuato, Poza Rica and Minatitlán.

22

The internal geography of Mexico's cities

The last chapter discussed the growth of urbanization in Mexico. It investigated the growth and functions of cities and Mexico's urban hierarchy. This
chapter focuses on the activities which take place
within urban areas. How does an urban area evolve
during its lifetime? Why and how do urban areas
expand spatially? Why do some areas evolve into industrial zones while others are commercial and still
others are high status residential neighborhoods or
low income districts?

Mexico's cities have a very long history. Mexico
City was originally founded in 1325, Oaxaca in 1532,
Guadalajara in 1542, Mérida in 1558 and Monterrey in 1596. In this chapter we trace the evolution
of Mexico City and compare it with a general model
of Latin American urban development (see box and
Figure 22.1). The final section discusses the spatial
structure of Guadalajara and Monterrey.

Mexico City in colonial times: 1530–1820

The internal geography of cities is closely related to
transportation technology. Pre-Columbian cities in
Mexico were walking cities; the wheel had not been
developed and animals were not used for transport.
Human power moved people and goods, but not very
quickly or efficiently. As a result, cities were relatively
compact and congested; densities were high. Despite
these transport restrictions, at least one urban center
in pre-Columbian Mexico had a population estimated to exceed 200,000.

The Aztec capital Tenochtitlan was built on an
island in the middle of a lake, and was a thriving
city when Hernán Cortés arrived. After the conquest,
the Spaniards built their colonial city directly on top

of Tenochititlan's main buildings and large central
plaza or Zócalo. Spanish colonial urban centers were
explicitly patterned after cities in Spain, with a grand
central square or plaza at the center (large enough
for displays of horsemanship). The streets were laid
out following a north-south, east-west grid. In larger
cities, smaller plazas might be planned every four
blocks or so.

Colonial Mexico City conformed closely to the
Latin American city model (Figure 22.1). Important
government, commercial, and religious buildings,
such as the Cathedral, faced onto the square. Status
was largely correlated with distance from the main
plaza, the hub of all activity. Wealthy and important
colonial officials had large homes in a zone surrounding the main square. This zone tended to be square
or rectangular given the grid pattern of streets. Less
important, middle income families lived in smaller
houses farther from the main plaza; lower status
groups lived even farther from the main square. The
lowest status mestizos and Indians lived around the
outside of the city. The city was very compact and
congested. The wealthiest residents in the center
lived relatively close to the poorest families on the
periphery. With the very high densities, there was
considerable noise and congestion, as well as sanitation problems and other health issues.

As Mexico City and other major Latin American
cities grew throughout the 300-year colonial period,
they tended to maintain a roughly concentric pattern; however, the growth of important government
and business activities as well as wealthy residential
neighborhoods usually favored one side of the city.
As these high status activities expanded they slowly

took over middle status areas, which in turn expanded into poorer neighborhoods. The poorest groups were pushed to the periphery or to undesirable steep hillsides or low areas prone to flooding. The rate of spatial expansion never managed to keep pace with the growth of population and economic activity. Densities and congestion increased.

From the very beginning in Mexico City, a high status sector extended west of the Zócalo. The Aztecs considered Chapultepec Hill, six kilometers (3.6 mi) west of Tenochtitlan, a royal retreat. They built a castle there, connected to their island capital by a

long causeway. Spanish King Charles V declared the zone a nature reserve in 1537. Early colonial Viceroys built palacial residences there. In 1592, Viceroy Luis de Velasco constructed an impressive park, the 90-hectare (216-acre) Alameda Central about a kilometer west of the Zócalo. The area between the Alameda and the Zócalo became the city's highest status area. The development decisions made during the 16th century solidified the west as the preferred direction and set the pattern of growth for the next 400 years. Similar high status sectors evolved in virtually all Latin American colonial cities.

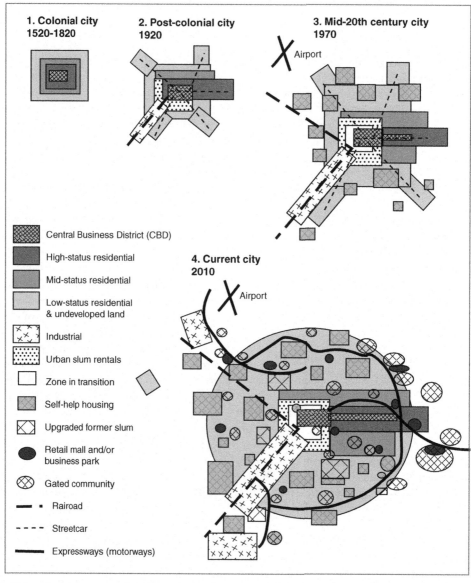

Figure 22.1 Urban land use model for large cities in Latin America[1]

Mexico City after independence: 1820–1920

During the first fifty years after independence, the rate of Mexico City's population and spatial growth was relatively slow, but it picked up after 1870. Gradually, the concentric square geography of the colonial period evolved into a less symmetric pattern, largely because of investments in high status commercial and residential construction west of the Zócalo, increased industrialization, and new transportation technologies. Transportation developments stimulated spatial expansion and set in motion forces that are still shaping the city.

Railroads and trams reached the city in the late 1850s. The railroad to the northeast set the stage for industrial development in that direction. The first horse-drawn and steam powered trams ran in different routes west from the center to Chapultepec Park and Tacubaya, about 7 km southwest of the Zócalo.[3] New residential areas developed as residents could relatively easily travel considerable distances to places of employment. During the next forty years, numerous new street railway lines were added opening new areas for development on southern and western sides of the city. However, the privately owned street railway system did not build lines deep into the lower status sectors to the north and east of the center.

In the 1860s, Emperor Maximilian ordered the construction of broad Parisian-style tree-lined boulevards in Mexico City. The biggest and most impressive, connecting the Alameda Central to Chapultepec Castle (Maximilian's residence) became Paseo de la Reforma, which remains one of Mexico City's most famous and highest status boulevards. As higher income families gravitated towards the west side, the other three sides of the center experienced a gradual influx of lower income groups.

Rapid industrialization and railroad expansion during the regime of Porfirio Díaz (1877–1910) stimulated both population growth and expansion of the industrial zone to the north and northwest. These industries initially were relatively near the city center, but as the city grew, the industrial zone expanded out along the rail lines into the areas now known as Azcapotzalco and Gustavo A. Madero. Entrepreneurs also established lighter industries within the industrial zone and throughout the city, though the dirtier of these industries were largely kept out of the high status western sector. The city's population increased from about 225,000 in 1870 to over 470,000 by 1910. During the Revolution, refugees from rural area violence streamed into the city raising the population to 662,000 by 1921.

As the city expanded, the upper classes sold or abandoned their colonial homes near the city center and moved to areas further west, deliberately avoiding noisy and polluted industrial areas. Their former residences were converted into *vecindades*, cheap tenements with individual rooms rented to families. *Vecindades*, with a shared central court, kitchen and latrines, became Mexico City's first slums. As these

---

Urban land use models

During the 20th century, several generalized models were developed to describe and explain the internal geography of cities. The first models sought to explain the patterns of various urban land uses in cities in the USA and Canada. Later, models were developed for Latin American cities, which had very different characteristics.

The model shown in Figure 22.1, based on that suggested by Janoschka, starts with the colonial period and traces the changes that have occurred during the last 500 years. These changes were driven by population growth, housing segregation by income level, development of urban transportation technologies, and industrialization.

Models of urban growth are based on theory and generalized empirical observations. As a result, the details in numerous specific instances do not exactly fit the model. For example, the concentric squares with social status declining with distance from the main plaza (Figure 22.1) were often irregularly shaped and by no means homogeneous. Generally, the growth of the high status zone out from the main square was biased towards a particular direction giving rise to a higher status sector.

The concentric square model of colonial Latin American cities is almost the inverse of the well-known Burgess concentric zone model of early 20th century cities in the USA.[2] The Burgess model has the lowest income groups in slums surrounding the Central Business District. Beyond the slums are working class neighborhoods, with high income residential areas at the urban periphery.

became overcrowded, incoming migrants moved into cheap, undesirable housing in the industrial zone or on the urban periphery. Still, the urbanized area remained relatively small, confined to about 25 km² (10 mi²) (Figure 22.2).

The clear distinction between industrial zones on one side of the city and high status residential areas on a different side (Figure 22.1) adheres to the general Latin American city model and is strikingly similar to Hoyt's well known sector model of urban development.[4]

By 1910, an efficient electric streetcar system enabled greater expansion. The lines stretched 25 km to the south and southwest, but largely neglected the areas to the east, north, and northwest. Interestingly, the steam and horse-drawn trams continued to operate in areas between streetcar lines for decades after the arrival of streetcars. The last horse-drawn line, just east of the Zócalo, finally closed in 1932. Streetcars enabled many employees to easily travel up to 15 km (10 mi) to and from work and thus greatly stimulated housing development on the outskirts of the city.

As the city expanded, old established middle income residential areas north and east of the Zócalo were taken over by industrial activities or tenements. Housing near industries and their pollution were less attractive, but were convenient residences for low income industrial workers. Middle income residential areas on the west side were taken over by higher status commercial and residential activities.

Marginal groups on the urban periphery were pushed farther and farther from the city center as the city expanded. On the high status side of the city they were often replaced by wealthy suburbs; on the industrial side, they were often overtaken by industrial developments.

Mexico City in the mid-20th century: 1920–1970

Mexico City's population grew slowly in the 1920s and 1930s but more than doubled during the 1940s. It almost doubled again during the 1950s reaching 5.6 million by 1960. This explosive growth was a function of two basic factors: natural population growth was rapid as urban birth rates far exceeded urban death rates, and massive rural-urban migration. The new migrants were drawn by employment opportunities stimulated by rapid expansion of import substitution industrialization. New factories were built along the railroads and spread north into Ecatepec, Tlalnepantla, and Naucalpan, municipalities in the State of Mexico (Figure 22.2).

Urban bus services started operating in the 1920s and expanded throughout the fifty year period. After about 1950, bus and minibus service became a dominant force. Private automobiles and trucks were also becoming a major force shaping the city, especially late in the period. They were very flexible and enabled rapid spatial expansion of residential areas as well as commercial and light industrial developments. Expansion was more rapid along major thoroughfares and urban expressways. Automobile ownership more than tripled in the 1960s, reaching nearly 600,000 by 1970. Traffic congestion and air pollution became serious problems.

The enormous influx of mostly poor immigrants created a very severe housing shortage. These immigrants initially headed for the low income *vecindades* which eventually ringed the center on all sides except the west, forming the so-called *herradura de tugurios* (horseshoe of hovels).[5]

These areas had expanded as developers built cheap new tenements using the old *vecindades* as a model. Following government-mandated rent control during the second world war, investors often abandoned the *vecindades*, depleting an already poor housing stock. Affordable housing became the major concern of low-income residents.

With Mexico City's inner city neighborhoods deteriorating severely, so-called "irregular" housing or *colonias populares* emerged as the only viable option. Irregular housing schemes were initiated by developers who claimed the ownership of large tracts of contiguous land on the periphery.

The land would be subdivided into numerous small lots and sold on an installment plan to low-income families, who would construct low cost one room shacks which they called "home." These neighborhoods were called irregular because many residents lacked legal deeds to their lots, their houses did not meet building codes, and they usually lacked important urban services.

In some cases, the developers illegally obtained *ejido* properties of dubious agricultural worth. Whether *ejido* or not, the tracts usually consisted of marginal lands, either prone to seasonal flooding or on very steep hillsides.

Legally, investors could not sell lots without services such as water, drainage, paved streets, electricity and other basic infrastructure. Frequently, however, investors did little more than mark the lots for sale; and provide "paper" services.

Lots with services were considerably more expensive and beyond the reach of most of the urban poor. In general, local government tolerated these unserviced and thus illegal developments, because they helped relieve the low income housing crisis.

Developers could make fortunes with these housing schemes. In a two km by two km piece of land (1.5 mi²), they could sell up to 50,000 lots. At $200

a lot, this brought them $10 million. Developers often reneged on their promises to provide services, though their plans did at least provide vacant strips of land between plots, which became known as "paper streets". In the beginning, such "irregular" communities had no running water, no sewers, no drainage, no electricity, and no form of public transport. (See box below about how such shanty towns changed with time into suburbs).

Colonias populares were established throughout the metropolitan area, except for the high status

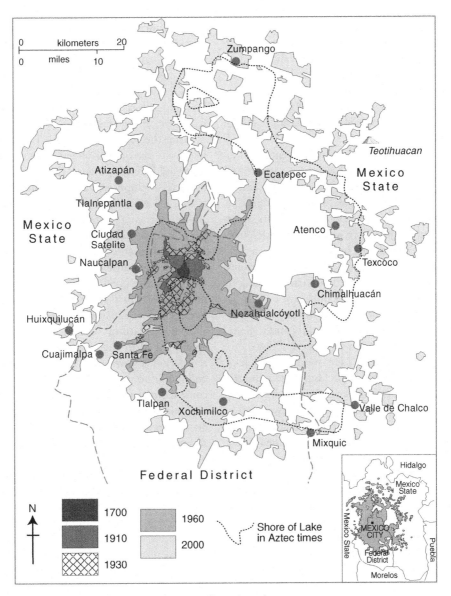

Figure 22.2 Spatial growth of Mexico City Metropolitan Area[6]

western sector. The highest concentrations were in the industrial zones, at the periphery, and in undesirable areas, such as Lake Texcoco lakebed and other low areas that were prone to flooding.

In the 1950s, the Federal District government started to oppose these housing developments. In contrast, the neighboring State of Mexico tolerated and even encouraged the development of such communities, explaining why numerous *colonias populares* were established just beyond the Federal District boundary in Naucalpan, Tlalnepantla, Ecatepec, Chimalhuacán, and Nezahualcóyotl municipalities. These grew very rapidly (See box and Figure 22.2). For example, Chimalhuacán, on the Texcoco lakebed just north of Nezahualcóyotl, grew from 20,000 in 1970 to 525,000 in 2005. Similarly, Valle de Chalco Solidaridad, on the lakebed of the drained Lake Chalco, and alongside the main road to Puebla, went from 44,000 in 1970 to 332,000 in 2005. Currently, about 60% of the Metro Area's population lives in *colonias populares*.

All large Latin American cities experienced widespread irregular housing which went by a variety of names: shanty towns, squatter settlements, or *favelas*. In cities where building regulations were rigorous and vigorously enforced, the poor resorted to squatting and land invasions. They would erect shacks, often no more than crude tents on any vacant land they could find, be it private or publicly owned. At times great invasions were implemented. Virtually overnight, thousands would occupy a piece of vacant land.

Removing these instant communities was a difficult task for government both physically and socially. From time to time, officials would use bulldozers to clear such areas, but within a few weeks, the shacks and tents would reappear. The bulldozers might destroy squatter settlements several times, but each time the land would be reoccupied and new squatter settlements would appear. Such settlements absorbed millions of poor urban Latin American residents and appeared throughout urban areas wherever there was vacant land (see Figure 22.1).

Attempts were also made to improve the housing situation by building public housing in either apartment complexes or high density duplexes and row houses. However, even at heavily subsidized prices, this "acceptable" housing was way beyond what the urban poor could afford and often was occupied by families with higher incomes. For example, the 12,000-unit 1960s Nonoalco-Tlatelolco housing

project just north of the center mostly benefited public employees. Sometimes, public housing units were purchased by enterprising, sometimes corrupt, businessmen with close ties to urban officials.

Upper and middle class housing development spread in the direction of the high income sector (Figure 22.1). Polanco, just north of Chapultepec Park, was developed in the early 20th century as a high income residential area. It experienced a construction boom in the 1950s when mansions and luxury apartment complexes were built. Polanco has remained one of Mexico City's most prestigious areas.

With limited new land available in Polanco, new high status residential and commercial activities began locating further west. Most of the developments included, as part of their name, Las Lomas ("The Hills", used here collectively for the numerous high-end developments stretching west from Polanco). Developers built these in the 1930s to house Mexico City's wealthiest residents.

After the 1950s, automobile transport opened up relatively distant periphery areas to higher income residential development. The residential and commercial developments of Las Lomas expanded rapidly to the west taking over undeveloped wooded hills as well as the city's main garbage dump. Eventually they expanded all the way into the State of Mexico.

Ciudad Satélite (Figure 22.2) was founded in the 1950s as a genuine satellite city, separated from the city proper by green space. However, its population mushroomed in the 1970s and Satellite City is now entrenched well inside the urban zone.

Major retailing in Mexico City was relatively concentrated in the city center at the beginning of the period. However, it spread along streetcar lines and major boulevards, especially toward the high income sector. In addition, as surrounding small towns were absorbed into the expanding metropolis, they became retail nodes. Late in this period, the first suburban retail malls started to appear in the high income sector.

Government and private offices continued to be concentrated near the center. The degree of concentration was greatly facilitated by the electric elevator, a very important and often overlooked form of urban transportation. It enabled people and goods to move up or down numerous floors quickly. The elevator made it practical to build office buildings higher than six stories. The prestigious 44-story Torre Latino America became the tallest building

From shanty to suburb

Residents of irregular settlements quickly learned to fend for themselves, sometimes using cooperative self-help approaches and at other times relying on their local community entrepreneurs to provide basic services. For electricity, enterprising individuals ran power lines into the areas and started selling electricity to neighbors. Others scaled nearby power poles and illegally (and dangerously) tapped into existing lines. Communities would periodically petition utility companies until they brought power lines (and telephones) into the community. Even if only a few houses connected, neighbors could then be connected.

Water is especially crucial. Residents first used carts to haul in water; later, water trucks sold water for storage in improvised tanks. Some residents resold water to neighbors by the bucket. Others hoisted 55-gallon drums onto their rooftop and installed pipes to bring water to sinks. Eventually, municipal water serve was obtained.

The public health risks of not having sewers or drainage are particularly serious. Open creeks rapidly became open sewers. Some residents cooperated to install sewer and drainage lines from their street to the creek. Others applied whatever political pressure they could to persuade municipal governments to install sewer trunk lines; in most cases, such efforts were eventually successful.

Unlike renters in inner city slums, people in these settlements invested whatever they could spare in their homes. Cooking over fires gave way to stoves using bottled gas. Cardboard and plywood walls were replaced with brick. Houses gradually acquired glass windows. Dirt floors were replaced by concrete; corrugated iron roofs were replaced with tiles. Two-story houses started to appear.

Eventually such squatter settlements gained a degree of permanence and the residents could petition for title to their small plots of land. With time, municipal governments had to accept the reality that these communities were permanent and required public services, not only water, sewerage, and electricity, but also garbage collection, paved streets, schools, health centers and policing. United, the residents of some of these low income areas became a surprisingly powerful political force.

Entrepreneurial spirit also led to improvements. The first to get gas stoves opened small eateries. Tiny stores sold a wide range of convenience foods and other goods, often through the front window of a small house. Gradually, some stores expanded to several rooms. Before long, communities had such services as beauty salons, barber's shops, bars, music stores, money lenders, dressmakers, laundries, tortillerías, bakeries and hardware stores.

Eventually, doctors and dentists opened offices, as did cabinet makers, upholsterers, welders, funeral homes, and auto and appliance repair. After a decade or two, some of these areas had cinemas, department stores, office buildings, hospitals, hotels, and small factories. They had been transformed from a shanty to a suburb.

---

in Latin America when it was built near Alameda Central in 1956. Other skyscrapers followed. This greatly increased the density of office space in the city center, though this density greatly exacerbated surface congestion. In addition to expanding upwards, office space also expanded outwards, both into slum areas and out into the high income sector.

Fragmentation after 1970

After 1970, Mexico City, like most Latin American cities, began to change. During the proceeding period, rapid population growth and the increasing demand for low income housing were the dominant forces resulting in a preponderance of irregular communities. Starting in the 1970s population growth declined considerably, as fertility rates dropped and the stream of poor rural immigrants slowed significantly. Furthermore, the largest cities started to experience substantial out-migration to other parts of the country. This was also the decade when the government announced a plan to decentralize urban growth. Federal spending was shifted away from the capital as were a number of state-owned enterprises like a large Pemex refinery, near the city center. Several hundred other polluting industries were transferred out of the metropolitan area. The impact of the plan became evident in 1980s as the population in the Federal District declined during the decade.

Growth in the periphery of the metropolitan area in the State of Mexico also slowed from 10% per year in the 1970s to 3% per year in the 1980s.

Two new transportation options became important in the last third of the 20th century: the metro (subway), which opened in 1968, and *colectivos*. The metro eased congestion, but did not stimulate sprawl because it did not reach beyond the Federal District boundary. The system was one of the world's largest, with over 200 km of track and about four million passengers a day. Even though fares are subsidized, use of the metro peaked about 1990 at about 4.7 million passengers a day. In 2000 about one-sixth of passenger trips in Greater Mexico City were made on the metro.

Colectivos or *peseros* (because the standard fare was originally one peso) started as Volkswagen Combi minivans that picked up passengers who flagged them down. They were informally operated, a bit faster, more comfortable, and costlier than buses, but cheaper than shared taxis, which they essentially replaced. *Colectivos* could profitably serve lower density areas, such as those at the urban periphery. By 2000, almost half of all trips were made by *colectivo*.

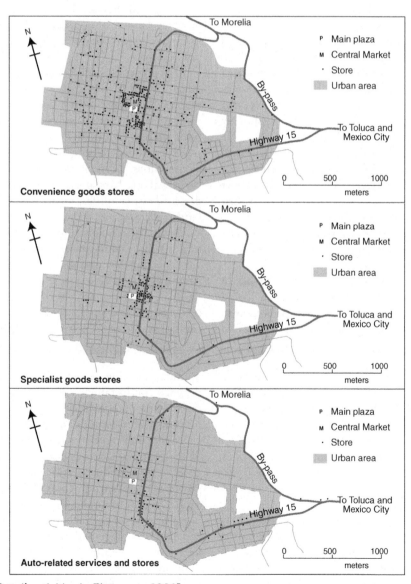

Figure 22.3 Retail activities in Zitácuaro, 1980[7]

In recent years, 20 passenger minibuses have largely replaced the eight passenger VW Combis. In Mexico City, full sized buses were relatively unimportant, accounting for only about 5% of all trips.

Private investment and individually owned automobiles grew to become dominant forces shaping the spatial expansion of the city. By the 1970s, a sizeable portion of urban families could afford cars. Given that car owners had higher incomes and created more demand, private urban developers responded accordingly. Public transportation, mostly by *colectivos* or buses, but also by tram and subway, continued to be extremely important for commuters and low income groups. Expressways were built to serve newly developed areas and the opening of a new expressway in turn stimulated rapid development.

Between 1960 and 2000, private car ownership in Mexico City increased from about 165,000 to roughly 2.7 million. By 2000, private automobiles accounted for about one-third of all trips; nearly half of all households had access to a car. Automobiles greatly increased congestion as well as air pollution. To meet demand, the government improved the road system which stimulated additional use of private automobiles as well as housing development on the urban periphery.

During the 1990s most new housing developments were in gated communities, with neighborhood associations providing urban services such as water, sewerage, garbage collection, street maintenance and lighting, as well as security. A number of previously open neighborhoods were converted to gated communities by building protective walls. Most gated communities were relatively homogeneous. Residents could largely avoid direct contact with lower income groups, except of course for their household help, gardeners, and drivers. Suburban gated communities usually had between 50 and 500 detached single family dwellings. Some of them had common facilities such as sports clubs with pools and eateries. Inner city gated communities often took the form of high rise condos.

Other suburban developments, such as shopping malls, focused primarily on commercial activites. The first malls were opened in the high status sector, but with gated communities throughout urban areas and the growing ownership of private cars, malls began appearing wherever there was sufficient demand and easy access by private automobile. Shopping centers ranged in size from perhaps ten stores to mega malls with hundreds of stores as well as restaurants, cinema complexes, and even hotels. Access via major thoroughfares or expressways was a crucial location factor and ample parking was always required. Public transportation was available for retail workers. Suburban industrial parks were also a key component of the new urban form. Their location largely depended upon access to expressways and a suitably

The distribution of retail activities in a mid-sized city

Figure 22.3 shows the distribution in 1980 of three distinct types of commercial establishments in the mid-sized city of Zitácuaro in Michoacán.[8] Founded hundreds of years earlier, the city grew spontaneously, almost organically, with little planning; its population by 1980 was 100,000.

Cars were not a necessity. The residents of Zitácuaro did not have to walk far to purchase their basic daily shopping needs. Convenience stores (top map) existed in every neighborhood. Many (145 out of 393) were genuine "corner stores", strategically located at street intersections. On average, each convenience store served about 250 residents.

More specialist stores (middle map), selling so-called "shopping goods" such as clothes and furniture, had a very different distribution. A few were located in residential areas, but most were concentrated in the heavily trafficked central area of the city, in the narrow streets close to the main plaza or zócalo, west of the main highway.

By 1980, a bypass had been opened enabling through traffic to avoid the main congested highway through the center of the city. However, the distribution of specialist stores does not appear to show any close connection to either the old highway or the new bypass.

This contrasts with the distribution of stores connected to auto services (gas stations, auto parts, tire repairs, mechanics) where the preferred locations in 1980 were close to the main highway (bottom map). In the succeeding years, this distribution has changed somewhat. Many of these services have now relocated to the by-pass to better serve the passing traffic.

qualified labor force. Sometimes access to railroads and airports was also important.

As urban areas expanded spatially (Figure 22.2), they surrounded and absorbed existing smaller urban centers, which originally were distant from the urban periphery. During the expansion process, these smaller centers became nodes for various types of development including residential, commercial, industrial, and recreational. This process, combined with the expansion of gated communities, malls, suburban office complexes, and industrial parks, resulted in a metropolis with numerous growth nodes or centers, giving a land use pattern that is quite similar to the well known multi-nuclei model.[10]

In conclusion, Mexico City's development since 1520 closely resembles the general development model of Latin American cities presented earlier in this chapter. It started as a concentric colonial city where status declined with distance from the city center. Its spatial development, enabled by improvements in urban transportation, exhibited a high status sector in one direction and lower income and industrial development in other directions. The population explosion in the mid 20th century led first to inner city slums and then to expansive low-income irregular housing wherever land was accessible, generally on the periphery. In the 1990s it became more fragmented when private automobiles allowed gated communities, and suburban commercial and industrial centers.

Does the general urban model work equally well for Mexico's two next largest cities, Guadalajara and Monterrey? In the next sections, we first look specifically at the pattern of socio-economic areas in Guadalajara, and then examine the way in which Monterrey has developed.

Social divisions in Guadalajara

Guadalajara, the state capital of Jalisco, started as a typical colonial city in the mid 16th century, with the highest status activities surrounding the center. Horse-drawn trams were established in the 1870s facilitating spatial expansion. The high status sector

---

Ciudad Nezahualcóyotl

Ciudad Nezahualcóyotl, just east of the Federal District, burst onto the national scene during the 1960s. During the late 1950s, speculators gained de facto possession by questionable means of roughly 50 km^2 (20 mi^2) of Lake Texcoco which had been drained in 1900 and had become an uninhabited salty marsh in the rainy season and a dust bowl in the dry season. They sold nearly 200,000 plots cheaply and on credit, perhaps a few dollars down and a about a dollar a month for ten years.

The families who acquired the plots immediately started to erect shacks. Aside from electricity, which was provided by the national utility, the plots lacked basic services (water, drainage, pavement, schools, etc.) and therefore were illegal under State of Mexico law; but the government tolerated this situation. The community became an immediate boom town.

By 1963, a new municipality, Nezahualcóyotl, was legally carved from surrounding municipalities. By 1970, the population was over 600,000, but still over half the area was without paved streets, water supply and drainage. This meant it severely flooded every summer and was a dust bowl the rest of the year. Residents became frustrated

with the broken promises of the developers, demanded that they be jailed for fraud, and stopped their monthly payments. The feud lasted for years and some developers were actually jailed. Eventually most of the area was "regularized" in that residents got legal deeds and basic services.

By 1980, the population reached about 1.3 million making it one of the largest and most densely populated municipalities in the country. Since then it has declined to about 1.1 million, as many families moved to newer, more distant *colonias populares*. By 2000, the community was quite mixed. About 20% of families were renters, nearly all had electricity and TVs, over 80% had refrigerators, 60% had telephones, nearly one in three had an automobile, and almost one in five had a computer.[9]

Ciudad Nezahualcóyotl now has trees, parks, a zoo, banks, shopping centers, offices, libraries, universities, cinemas, *vecindades*, apartment buildings, as well as a cathedral and Olympic sports stadium, which hosted some 1986 FIFA World Cup matches. Currently, it is a vital part of Mexico City and provides jobs for almost 250,000.

expanded west along the tram line to Los Colomos and northwest toward Zapopan. The city also expanded along tram lines in the southeast to Tlaquepaque, where some wealthy residents also lived, as well as north to Atemajac, where there were many textile factories, and northeast to Oblatos.

The national railroad reached the southern portion of Guadalajara by 1888, stimulating industrial growth and warehousing activities in that part of the city. During the Porfirio Díaz regime, industrial growth favored the south side and attracted rural immigrants who settled south, east, and north of the center.

The first electric streetcars connected the city center to Tlaquepaque in 1908. Soon lines ran to the high status areas in the west along Vallarta Avenue and northwest to Zapopan, opening these areas to more extensive development. Streetcars also ran to the southern industrial areas as well as to La Experiencia, a textile manufacturing area to the north.

As mortality rates dropped, population, industrial development, and spatial growth accelerated rapidly after 1950. The population went from about 380,000 in 1950 to 1.25 million in 1970, and to 3.7 million by 2000. Natural increase accounted for about 40% of the population increase, and migration 60%. Of the migrants, one-third came from elsewhere in the state of Jalisco and two thirds from elsewhere in Mexico, principally from Zacatecas, Aguascalientes, Michoacán, Colima and Mexico City. By the mid-1970s, the urbanized metro area had expanded and merged with the cities of Zapopan, Tlaquepaque, and Tonalá.

With a severe limit on affordable rental housing in the tenements near the city center, developers established numerous irregular housing schemes in vacant areas within and surrounding the city, though there were significantly fewer on the higher status west side.

Between 1970 and 1986, home ownership became increasingly difficult. In 1970, a typical low-income home cost the equivalent of 1525 times the daily minimum wage; by 1986, the same home cost 4155 times the minimum wage. By 2000 neighborhoods originally initiated as irregular housing contained over 40% of the current population (Figure 22.4).

By 2000 private automobile ownership had facilitated the sprawl of the metro area out along major thoroughfares running southeast and southwest and into several surrounding municipalities. Investors established new industrial facilities along the south *periférico* (ring road) as well as southeast toward the airport and beyond.

Developers built numerous gated communities, mostly on the west side for higher income groups. In addition, entrepreneurs constructed numerous large suburban shopping malls on the west side (Gran Plaza, Plaza del Sol, Centro Magno, Plaza México, Galerías, and Plaza Patria) catering to clients with private automobiles. Smaller, less elegant, shopping malls were also built throughout the urban area.

Like Mexico City, Guadalajara generally adheres to the Latin American urban model. By 1990 (Figure 22.4) higher status areas were mostly in the west. The lower income and marginal areas were largely on the north, east and south periphery of the metro area. With the development of gated communities in the years since 1990, the urban area had become somewhat more fragmented, consistent with the model.

Monterrey, an exception to the general model

Monterrey only emerged as a real city after the colonial period. The relatively small city did not experience real growth until late in the 19th century when it became connected by railroad and started to attract industrial development. Early in the 20th century, investors built the largest iron and steel works in Latin America a few kilometers east of the city center. Many related industries located nearby. These industries and the railroad, which ran east–west about four kilometers (2.5 mi) north of the city center, stimulated early industrial development in these directions. Developers established low income housing tracts for industrial and other workers on the east, north and west periphery of the city. Neighborhoods for the wealthier classes were developed south of the city center.

The city experienced another surge of industrialization and immigration in the 1950s and 1960s. Industrial development continued after 1970 when the national government implemented policies to shift development away from Mexico City. Monterrey became a major producer of steel, metal fabrication, cement, beverages, petrochemicals, food, telecommunications, auto parts, glass, and house furnishings. It also developed into a major financial center and one of the wealthiest and most progressive cities in the country.

Low income housing became a serious problem after the 1960s as the inner city tenements became

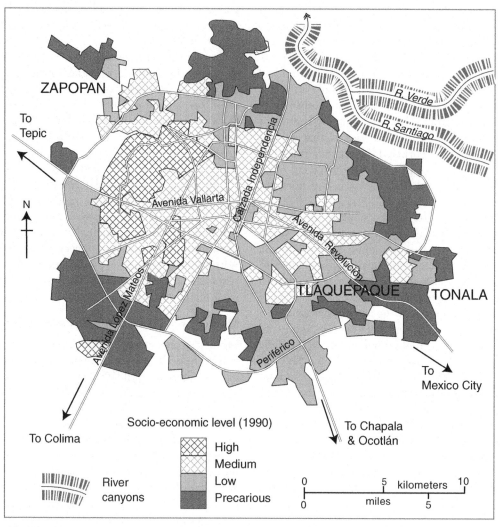

Figure 22.4 Socio-economic areas in Guadalajara, 1990[11]

extremely crowded. The government was not sympathetic to irregular housing schemes, so low income groups established numerous illegal squatter settlements on vacant land near the industrial zone. Government made a few efforts to remove these, but most survived and eventually became regularized.

The high status sector expanded south into San Pedro Garza García, which became one of the wealthiest municipalities in the country. The high overall income and wages in the city meant that many workers could afford private automobiles and owning their own home.

As a result, many large and small gated communities and suburban shopping malls were built around

the urban periphery. The urban area became relatively fragmented with many low income residential zones located near high income areas.

Monterrey does not fit the general Latin American urban model as well as Mexico City or Guadalajara. Firstly, it never really existed as a colonial city. Secondly, its development was more heavily dependent on industry. Thirdly, its relative wealth and progressive leadership in some ways make it more similar to a North American city than a Latin American city. It fits the model only in that it developed a definite high status sector in contrast to lower status industrial sectors, and eventually became spatially fragmented.

23

Urban issues, problems and trends

The last chapter investigated the evolution of the internal geography within large Mexican cities from the 16th through the 20th century. This chapter focuses on urban trends in the 21st century, current problems and issues, and the future of Mexican cities.

Urban sprawl

The rapid spatial expansion of Mexican cities from 1970–2000 is accelerating in the 21st century. The main stimulus of this sprawl is income growth, leading to widespread ownership of private automobiles and the desire of Mexican families to own homes. The number of automobiles in Metropolitan Mexico City is about 10 million, almost double the number in 2000. Over half of households have a private car, many have several cars. Automobiles are responsible for nearly half of all trips. Expanded car ownership also is contributing to urban sprawl in Guadalajara, Monterrey, Puebla and other large urban areas.

Automobiles are greatly increasing congestion as well as air pollution. To cope with mounting traffic problems, government is investing in new expressways, overpasses, road widening and parking infrastructure. These are stimulating additional car purchases and even more traffic. While the 2008–2009 economic downturn dramatically reduced new car purchases, it only delayed the inevitable expansion of automobile ownership.

New suburban residential developments now stretch up to 40 km (25 mi) from the centers of major cities. Some developers sell undeveloped lots; others build family homes. Most of these new developments are in gated communities. Security has become a paramount concern as the media gives greater attention to crime, kidnapping and drug wars. Newly built gated communities have protective walls and private security forces. In recent years a number of previously open neighborhoods have become gated by building protective walls.

While the new higher status gated communities in Metropolitan Mexico City usually favor the western suburbs, they are now being built throughout the metropolitan area. Lower income gated communities are being built mostly to the north, east and south. Many upscale gated communities are immediately adjacent to areas of poverty, separated only by a high wall, perhaps topped with barbed wire. As a result, the urban pattern is breaking from the tradition of upper income groups concentrated in the high status sector and becoming very fragmented, consistent with the general model of Latin American urban development presented in chapter 22.

The original high status sector surrounding the Mexico City Zócalo stretches westward into the State of Mexico and is by no means homogeneous. The rich living in these areas actually live rather close to low income groups.[1] For example, half of the nearly one million people living in the three delegations (Miguel Hidalgo, Benito Juárez and Cuauhtémoc) surrounding the Zócalo live in neighborhoods that are classified either in the highest income category (234,000 very well-off people) or in the absolute lowest (245,000 very poor people).

The municipality of Huixquilucán just west of the Federal District (Figure 22.2) demonstrates the changes which are occurring at the urban periphery. Its predominately rural population of 33,500 in 1970 increased to 224,000 by 2005. Initially, much of this growth was from lower income groups, but in recent years the area is being absorbed by the expanding high status Las Lomas developments. Many new gated communities are being established as well as golf courses and country clubs. The municipality is now considered one of the wealthiest in the metro area. However, in this so-called "wealthy" municipality, 22 out of 46 *colonias* (neighborhoods) are categorized as "poor" and two are "very poor". The other 22 are considered to be "rich;" there were no *colonias* in the middle. Just to the north of Huixquilucán is Naucalpan, a very industrial municipality with a very large low income population.

Even modest Mexican families without automobiles are contributing to urban sprawl. New lower income housing developments are being built on the periphery of Mexico City, Guadalajara, Monterrey and other metropolitan areas (see box). Though most working families can afford the down payment

---

Low income housing on the urban periphery[2]

Carlos Hernández, his spouse, mother-in-law and two daughters are happy with their house in a new housing development in Zumpango, about 40 km (25 mi) north of Mexico City's zócalo. The government-backed mortgage on the tiny (30 m² –about the size of a two-car garage), $15,700, one bedroom house is $100 a month. Hernández must spend another $110 a month for his daily five hour commute by *colectivo*, bus and metro to his $350 a month maintenance job in the capital. This leaves only $140 a month for all other expenses such as food, utilities, installment payments on furniture and appliances, health care, clothing, schooling, etc.

To help make ends meet, his spouse, Edith, runs an informal convenience store out of the front of the house. The house is very crowded; the kitchen table is brought inside only at mealtimes. Carlos and Edith sleep on a foldout couch in the living room. Edith's mother, Lucía, has the bedroom and the two daughters take turns sleeping with their parents or grandmother. Hernandez is glad he finally owns a house and no longer has to pay rent. His story is repeated tens of thousands of times as hundreds of low-income housing developments are being built on the urban periphery.

---

and monthly payments for these subsidized housing units, these expenses leave little extra for food, clothing, utility bills, commuting and health care. Even these subsidized housing units provide a car parking place because virtually all Mexican families aspire to own their own automobile.

The west-east divide separating Guadalajara's social classes has become even more marked in recent years and has numerous implications for effective city planning. For instance, car ownership rates are many times higher in the western half of the city, while public transport links are focused more on the eastern half. The concentration of the city's 1.6 million cars (2006) in wealthy western areas brings daily gridlock at peak times, despite a central computerized system for controlling more than 1500 traffic light intersections.

The largest new gated residential communities have commercial sections with retail outlets selling convenience goods as well as fast food restaurants. Many also have supermarkets, fashion boutiques, banks and other higher end retail establishments. A new development is the emergence of planned mega suburban centers which have the full range of urban amenities including single family dwellings, apartment and office towers, giant shopping malls, recreational and entertainment centers, and even universities, research centers, large medical facilities and clean light industry. The best example of this type of development is the Santa Fe complex on the western edge of the Federal District (see box). Another example is Puerta de Hierro on the northern edge of Guadalajara.

The development of suburban industrial parks has accelerated in recent years. For example, numerous new suburban industries now stretch all the way to Guadalajara's airport and many kilometers beyond. More and more workers have cars and many industries provide cheap transportation for their workers.

Is Mexico City becoming a megalopolis?

A strong case can be made that Mexico City is now merging with surrounding urban areas (Figure 23.1) into a 'super city' or megalopolis, stretching from Toluca in the west to Puebla-Tlaxcala in the east, and from Pachuca in the north to Cuernavaca in the south. The city of Toluca is only 60 km west of the Zócalo. The eastern border of the Toluca Metropolitan Area (population 1.8 million) is the Federal District. The Cuernavaca urban area (population 850,000) is only

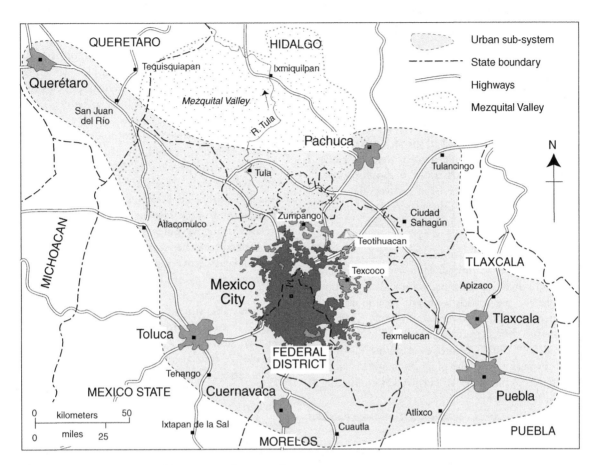

Figure 23.1 Mexico City and its surrounding area[3]

about 20 minutes south by toll road. The western edge of Metropolitan Puebla-Tlaxcala (population 2.6 million) is about 30 minutes from the eastern edge of Greater Mexico City. Pachuca (population 278,000) is only about 30 minutes north. This megalopolis has a total population of about 30 million.

Interactions between cities in this part of central Mexico suggest that this city-region will become even larger in coming years. The patterns of vehicle flows and telephone calls allow the demarcation of an additional area to the north-west that already belongs, in terms of functions, to Mexico City's urban sub-system (Figure 23.1). [4] This area includes the city of Querétaro (population 1.0 million) and the industrial center of San Juan del Río (population 131,000), whose growth started when several manufacturing plants relocated there from Mexico City in the 1980s. It also includes Tulancingo (population 210,000), Tula (population 198,000) with its oil

refinery, and Atlixco (population 84,000). By 2050, the total population within this Mexico City sub-system, defined by functions, is expected to exceed 40 million.[5]

Housing

Decent housing for growing urban populations continues to be a serious issue. The desire for acceptable housing is a main factor contributing to urban sprawl. During the last fifty years numerous government efforts were made to address the urban housing shortfall. While these programs helped the overall housing situation, they rarely reached the poorest urban residents.

Government housing projects currently are found throughout Metropolitan Mexico City, but are more heavily concentrated in two Federal District delegations—Benito Juárez and Coyoacán—south of the center, and in the State of Mexico municipalities of

The Santa Fe complex

The plan for the Santa Fe complex called for private sector financed office towers, a gigantic retail mall, high income housing and park areas as well as schools and universities. Construction was halted briefly by the 1994–95 economic crisis, but soon resumed at full speed. Today, Santa Fe has several skyscraping office towers, over one eighth of the Federal District's total office space, about 70,000 employees, four universities with 13,500 students, over 4300 residents and one of the largest retail malls in Latin America.

Santa Fe (Figure 22.2) is essentially an island that is only accessible by private car; public transport is very limited. Unfortunately, it has not fully lived up to expectations. The preponderance of cars, mostly with a driver and no passengers, has led to severe traffic jams. Perhaps related to this, the vacancy rate of office space is about 25%. Furthermore, even with eight million visiters a year, the gigantic Santa Fe shopping mall is not as heavily utilized as competing malls in the area.

Naucalpan and Atizapán to the northeast. Public housing projects now house roughly 2.75 million people, about 15% of the metro population.

In recent years government efforts have focused primarily on expanding access to mortgages for buyers of new homes. Mortgages for purchase of used homes are considerably more difficult to obtain. Currently, governments programs provide over half of all mortgages, the rest come from private banks.

Federal mortgage incentives and subsidies have stimulated massive low income housing developments at the rural periphery (see box). Some argue that these distant, cheaply built developments with very small dwellings are contributing to rapid sprawl and will deteriorate eventually into suburban/rural slums.

Governance and administration

Urban areas cover many municipalities and thus are difficult to govern and administer. Metropolitan Mexico City involves the governments of the Federal District, the states of Mexico and Hidalgo, as well as 16 Federal District delegations and 42 municipalities in Hidalgo and the State of Mexico. These different entities have different elected officials, priorities and policies concerning public transportation, housing, environmental protection, industrial development, etc. For example, the Federal District policies subsidize public transport and attempt to reduce sprawl; while public policies in the State of Mexico tend to stimulate sprawl. Given this complexity, the federal government is often called upon to take the lead.

Adding to the problem is the law that state and municipal officials are elected for only three year terms and cannot be re-elected. Exacerbating the situation is the limited revenue generating capacity of state and local governments, which must rely heavily on transfers from the federal government.

Guadalajara (covering eight municipalities) and Monterrey (involving 13 municipal governments) have related, but less complicated administrative problems. The situation is more complex for the Puebla-Tlaxcala Metropolitan Area, which spreads over two states and 25 municipalities. Getting all these elected officials and bureaucracies on the same page is extremely difficult.

Efficient urban public transport requires common carriers to cross municipal, and sometimes state, boundaries. This can be a real problem because the different administrations have different and sometimes conflicting laws governing public transport. Fortunately many urban trips are by informal *colectivos*, which operate fairly efficiently, partially because they do not rigorously adhere to all the often conflicting laws. Lack of efficient, cheap public transport and other forces are leading a growing number of Mexicans to commute by private automobile. As a result, traffic congestion is a growing problem in all Mexican cities.

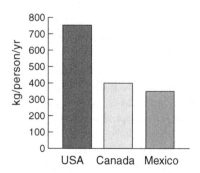

Figure 23.2 Urban waste per person in USA, Canada and Mexico, 2008[7]

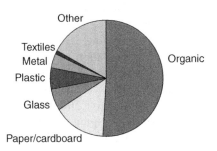

Figure 23.3 The composition of Mexico's urban waste, 2008[8]

Solid waste

Figure 23.2 shows the urban waste produced per person in each of the three NAFTA countries. On a per person basis, Mexicans dispose of about 330 kg (726 lb) each per year[6]. Despite the favorable per person comparisons, Mexico produces three times as much total waste each year as Canada because of its greater population. Residents of Mexico City and urbanized centers in the state of Mexico, Baja California and Nuevo León produce more waste on a per person basis (about 1.0 kg/person/day) than those living in more rural, poorer states like Oaxaca, Chiapas, Hidalgo, Zacatecas and Tlaxcala (0.5–0.7 kg/person/day).[7]

In 2008 only 1.2% of the total urban waste in Mexico was recycled. Given the composition of this waste (Figure 23.3), the successful implementation of relatively simple waste management strategies, including recycling and composting, could greatly reduce the urban waste that is sent to landfills.

Services and poverty

Even though urban growth has slowed, services have not yet caught up, especially in low income areas. Even in the Federal District, which is the wealthiest entity in the nation, services are still lagging even though its population has been essentially stable for the past 20 years. Currently, one in ten does not have safe drinking water, one in seven is without sanitation, 1/3rd lacks proper drainage, 1/6th lacks access to secondary school and 1/8th lacks access to a public health clinic. The situation is worse in most other urban areas. Of course, middle and upper income neighborhoods have far better access to services. Mexico's poverty and unequal distribution of income is a particular problem in urban areas because the gap between the rich and poor is so enor-

mous. Much needs to be done to bring the urban poor up to a minimum acceptable standard of living. The *Oportunidades* program (chapter 29) is making significant strides to close this gap.

Water

An old joke relates how engineers initially rejoiced at successfully draining the former lake on which Mexico City was built (something the Aztecs had tried, but failed to achieve), only to discover that the city now lacked any reliable source of fresh water for its inhabitants (something the Aztecs had successfully managed by building a system of aqueducts).

Water has been a major issue for Mexico City since it was founded almost 700 years ago.[10] Civil engineering works by the Aztecs included causeways and aqueducts connecting their island capital to the mainland as well as lengthy dikes separating the fresh water lakes from the brackish Lake Texcoco which surrounded the city.

The Spaniards did not maintain the Aztec civil works, deforested the surrounding hillsides, and started filling Lake Texcoco. This contributed to major flooding in 1555, 1580, 1604. The city was actually underwater from 1629–1634. During this period the Spaniards invested in several flood control efforts, but they were not successful. In 1788 they started construction of a massive canal to connect the basin to rivers north of the city flowing to the Gulf of Mexico. The open canal, which was up to 30 m (100 ft) deep in places, provided flood relief, but did not completely solve the problem and flooding continued.

In the mid-1850s the government approved another massive flood relief scheme. Construction of the Gran Canal was delayed by numerous political and financial problems; it was not completed until 1900. The 58 km (36 mi) long canal included a 10 km tunnel, and carried lake water, storm water and sewage north to the Río Salado and eventually to the Gulf of Mexico. The scheme successfully drained most of the basin lakes, but summer flooding continued to be a problem for decades.

In 1967 work started on a new flood relief scheme which would carry storm water and sewage through tunnels, as deep as 180 m (600 ft), and canals 68 km north to the Río Salto and down through the Río Tula (see Figure 23.1) to the Gulf of Mexico. This scheme, along with the Gran Canal and massive storm water pumps, has finally solved the summer flooding problem.

The storm and sewage water ends up in the Mezquital Valley where it is used for irrigation. Since only about 10% of the city's sewage is treated, the use of raw sewage for irrigation is potentially a serious health problem for the 400,000 residents of the valley. Heavy metals and salts can become concentrated in the soil and find their way into crops. By law no crops can be grown that can be eaten raw; therefore alfalfa and maize are the main crops.

Potable water is another problem that has plagued the city for centuries. Deforestation in the 19th century depleted the springs that had supplied the city with fresh water via aqueducts. The first fresh water well was built in the city center in 1857. By 1900 there were hundreds of wells sucking water from the underground aquifer.

As more and more water was sucked up through the wells, the city began to sink. Some parts have dropped more than seven meters (23 ft) since 1891. Parts of the city center sank more than a meter between 1948 and 1951, and another meter by 1960. The city sank two meters below what remained of Lake Texcoco, posing a serious risk of flooding during the rainy season. In response, engineers sank wells into Lake Texcoco, sucked water from the aquifer, and the lake level dropped below the height of the city center.

Rates of subsidence are very uneven. In places the weight of large buildings has caused them to sink into the dried out mud. The city's Opera House (Palacio de Bellas Artes) sank so far that its original ground floor is now a subterranean basement. To slow down the rate of sinking in the city center, in 1950 new wells were drilled south of the city reducing central city sinking to its current rate of about 10 cm (4 in) a year. Of course, areas in the south started sinking more rapidly.

Elsewhere, buildings have tilted and underground sewers and water pipes have cracked and broken. Furthermore, drains in the city center sank below the large drainage canals and pumps had to be added to lift storm water and sewage up to the drainage canals.

The wells could not provide enough fresh water. In the 1940s a system was built to pump water 80 km from the upper reaches of the Lerma River eastward over the Sierra de Las Cruces Mountains and through a 5 km (3 mi) long tunnel into the city. When even more water was needed, 500 wells were sunk near the town of Lerma, more than doubling the pumping rate. These wells soon depleted the Lerma aquifer, forcing a return to the original pumping rate.

The demand for water more than doubled during the city's 1945–1975 population explosion. To help meet this demand, engineers built the Cutzamala system to get water from the Presa de Colorines and Valle de Bravo reservoirs over 100 km (60 mi) to the west. This required pumping the water up 1100 m (2600 ft) and over a 2700 m (8300 ft) pass. The project, which opened in 1985, involves 440 km of pipelines, 200 storage tanks, and 100 pumping stations. Currently the city obtains about 30% of its water from the Lerma and Cutzamala projects.

The enormous systems to pump fresh water into the city, and storm water and sewage out, use nearly 10% of the total electricity consumed by the Federal District. Water and sewage fees are relatively low and provide limited incentive for conservation. Water consumption per person in the Federal District is about twice that of Paris. The subsidy amounts to about a billion dollars a year. About 25% of the water is lost through wasteful use and leaking pipes, but recent maintenance and conservation efforts are reducing this figure.

At present about 70% of the city's water comes from 4280 wells sunk deep into the underground aquifers. Water is pumped from these aquifers at more than twice the rate of aquifer recharge. The mining of this water drops the water level in the aquifers by almost one meter (3 ft) per year and concomitantly increases the cost of pumping. Eventually, the aquifers may run dry.

In summary, Mexico City's enormous urban water issues are among the most problematic in the world. The water issues of other Mexican urban areas are minor in comparison, though Monterrey continues to draw more water from its aquifer than can be recharged.

Air pollution

In the 1970s Mexico City became widely recognized as having possibly the worst air pollution in the world. Air pollution was one of the reasons for the government's decentralization policy. The city's geography is a major air pollution factor. Natural dispersion is severely limited by the surrounding mountains on the west, south and east and the prevailing winds from the north. The high altitude and strong sun mean warm days and cold nights, perfect conditions for ozone, which forms in Mexico City at only 21°C

(70°F) compared to 30°C (85°F) in Los Angeles. The city's geography also contributes to thermal inversions, which trap warm polluted air under a layer of colder air. The lower oxygen content of the air means that fuel combustion is 23% less efficient than at sea level resulting in significantly more fuel usage and pollution emissions. Adding to the problem are the dry lakebeds, which receive flood water and sewage in the rainy season. In the dry season they contribute tons of fine natural and fecal dust.

An automatic monitoring network set up in the 1980s showed ozone levels three times higher than the air quality standard 40-50 days a year.[11] Begin-

ning in the mid-1980s the government enacted numerous antipollution policies. These included serious industrial emissions inspections (1986); introduction of unleaded gasoline (1989); the "*hoy no circula*" policy which used license plate numbers to ban specific cars from the road one day a week, or two days a week during pollution emergencies (1989), and yearly vehicle emission inspections (1990). Industrial efforts included closing a large oil refinery near the center in 1990, moving polluting industries out of the city, and converting most industries and many commercial vehicles from diesel to natural or propane gas. By 1991 catalytic converters were required

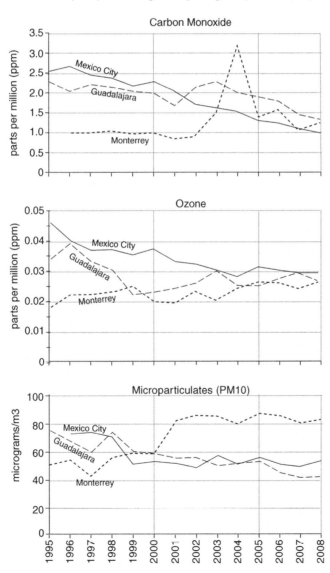

Figure 23.4 Trends in urban air pollution[12]

on all new cars. In recent years these measures have become stricter and more rigorously enforced.

The greatest source of Mexico City's air pollution is transportation; private cars contribute about half, taxis about one fifth, and colectivos about one sixth of the total weight of contaminants added to the atmosphere each year. The rest comes from buses, trucks, light rail, the metro and airplanes. The Metrobus program (see box) which replaced gasoline minibuses with modern diesel buses has been very successful, reducing carbon monoxide, hydrocarbons and particulates by 50%.[13] Emissions of other pollutants, including sulfur dioxide, from the industrial zone north of the center are pushed toward the city center by the prevailing winds. Leaky cooking gas containers are also believed to be a significant source of air pollution.

As a result of aggressive government efforts, the quality of air in Mexico City has improved significantly. Since 1990 the number of hours that air pollution exceeded the city's quality standard has declined by about two-thirds. Ozone continues to be a major problem (Figure 23.4) as do minute particulates under 10 microns (PM10), both of which can have serious health consequences.

2009 International Energy Use Award[14]

In November 2009 Mexico won a prestigious international energy award for its Metrobus program in Mexico City, initiated in 2005. The bus program replaced polluting old buses with efficient low emission new ones. It won the award as a result of the bus program's extremely high environmental and economic effectiveness compared with the investment cost. The new program not only is reducing air pollution, but it is reducing energy use and greenhouse gas emissions as well as providing improved transportation for Mexico City residents.

Mexico was runner-up to Germany in the competition judged by the WWF International and E3G and involving energy initiatives from 22 countries including the USA, Canada, six European Union countries, Japan, South Korea and Australia. The initiatives were judged on their capacity to reduce greenhouse gas emissions, their cost, and their ability to stimulate economic activity.

Mexico City's air quality is now better than that in many world cities and may not even be the worst in Mexico. For example, concentrations of PM10 in Mexico City are very significantly below those of Monterrey and Toluca, as well as Cairo and large Indian and Chinese cities. They are also lower than those in Buenos Aires, Rio de Janeiro, Lima and Montevideo. Monterrey used to have significantly better air quality than either Mexico City or Guadalajara, but its air quality, with the exception of sulfur dioxide levels, has deteriorated since the year 2000.[15]

Does air pollution from maquiladoras in Ciudad Juárez affect people's health?

The worst air pollution along the USA–Mexico border is in Ciudad Juárez in Chihuahua, located across the Río Grande from the city of El Paso in Texas. It is often claimed that this is because of Mexican authorities' poor enforcement of environmental laws and the high number of maquiladora firms operating in the city.

Air pollution does adversely affect the health of Ciudad Juárez's 1.4 million residents, resulting in a higher incidence of respiratory diseases and premature mortality.[16] However, most of the pollutants related to these health issues do not come from the 300 or so maquiladora factories but from family-run brick kilns, dirt roads and vehicles. Industry, including the brick kilns, accounts for only 17% of total sulfur dioxide emissions, and less than 1% of total particulate emissions. Services account for 44% of the sulfur dioxide emissions, and transport a further 38%. Most particulates came from unpaved roads (65% of the total) and from wind-blown soil erosion (31%). Almost all the carbon monoxide (99%) and

Figure 23.5 The elements of a sustainable city[17]

The revitalization of Mexico City's historic downtown

During the 20th century the Historic Center of Mexico City, founded in 1524 atop the ancient Aztec capital of Tenochtitlan, gradually fell into decline. Many wealthy residents moved out to suburbs in the west and southwest of the city. The National University (UNAM) moved to a new purpose-built campus in the south. The city government froze rents in the 1940s. Landlords saw the real value of their incomes plummet; they no longer maintained their properties. The tragic earthquake in September 1985, measuring 8.1 on the Richter scale, hit many badly maintained downtown areas particularly hard. More and more residential buildings were abandoned as insecurity, pollution and decay set in, aided and abetted by the shifting ground levels due to aquifer depletion. The majority of the buildings in good repair were churches, government offices and museums. Even so, in 1987 the center of Mexico City was accorded World Heritage status by UNESCO for its superb

examples of colonial architecture. The 630 blocks that comprise the center boast more than 1000 historic buildings, including the Metropolitan Cathedral (dating from 1573), the 17th century National Palace and the art nouveau Opera House.

At the start of the 21st century, federal and city authorities budgeted $55 million to begin a revitalization of the downtown area. A government-private sector Historic Center Trust was formed to buy and systematically rehabilitate dozens of centuries-old buildings and breathe new life into the city center. Drainage and water systems were replaced. Electric and telephone cables were buried below ground. The facades of more than 500 buildings on 13 streets were carefully restored. Streets were repaved and pedestrianized. Plazas came back to life; new museums sprung up; street vendors were relocated. Cafes and restaurants opened, giving new focal points for residents and tourists alike.

---

nitrogen oxide (92%) added to the air came from transportation.

Socio-economically poor areas are more affected by bad air quality than richer areas, but this is due to the precise location of the small-scale brick kilns, which have no pollution controls, rather than to the locations of maquiladora plants. Most of the city's 350 brick kilns are in densely populated low-income residential neighborhoods such as Anapra, Division del Norte, Fronteriza Baja and Waterfill.

When the kilns were first built, these areas were on the perimeter of the city, but they have since been enveloped by urban sprawl. The health damages arising from the brick kilns are estimated at almost $50 million a year in Ciudad Juárez and an additional $13.4 million a year in El Paso.

A sustainable future?

In the 1970s many believed that by the year 2000 Mexico City would be the world's largest city and have the worst environmental problems. Thanks to declining fertility rates and rigorous governmental efforts, this has not occurred. Population growth and air pollution problems appear to be under control and should not be serious problems in the future,

assuming aggressive air pollution control efforts continue. With increased automobile ownership, sprawl and congestion will be areas of concern in the decades ahead. Water issues are perhaps the most serious. Engineering efforts during the past 400 years have provided considerable relief. In the next decades, current conservation efforts, such as reducing water subsidies, repairing leaks in water lines, and installing water efficient toilets, will be accelerated. Engineers may find methods to recharge the underground aquifers, perhaps by pumping the torrential summer rainfall downward, instead of upward out of the basin.

Figure 23.5 shows the essential components of a sustainable city, based on the International Council for Local Environmental Initiatives' sustainability reports. Mexican cities have made mixed progress so far towards sustainability. In general, most are doing quite well with regards to empowerment and green mobility, but have failing grades for social well-being and ecological integrity.

Mexico City's latest Green Plan (2008) was formulated after extensive public consultations. It provides specific objectives and strategies in seven key areas of sustainability: land conservation, public spaces, water, mobility, air, waste, climate change and energy. It calls for all city-owned vehicles and 5,000 microbuses to be replaced by environmentally friendly vehicles; the building of 300 km (185 mi) of bicycle routes by 2012; the development of green corridors to expand the amount of green space in the city from its current level of about 2 m² per inhabitant to the international norm of 9 m²(100 ft²); and the enforcement of the use of school buses for all private school students by the year 2012.[18]

Effective administration and efficient provision of services will continue to be a problem for Mexican urban areas. The Federal Government may have to take the lead in urban areas that cross state lines such as Mexico City, Puebla-Tlaxcala and Torreón-Gómez Palacio. State governments may need to play a bigger leadership role because with growing automobile ownership, urban areas will continue sprawling across numerous municipalities.

In summary, largely as a result of fertility changes, the growth of Mexican urban areas in the twenty-first century will be far slower and more orderly than in the 20th century. The urban quality of life, which improved tremendously in the 20th century, should continue to improve during the twenty-first. However, the balance between technological innovation, the depletion of world resources, and climate change will affect this.

24

Rural Mexico and rural-urban interactions

In a previous chapter we looked at the historical evolution of Mexico's urban hierarchy and the growth of its largest cities. This chapter focuses on rural Mexico and the small villages and towns at the lowest levels of the urban hierarchy.

Definitions

When discussing urban and rural areas, the first question that arises is "What specifically makes a community rural or urban?" Though we all know what cities are and what "urban" means, this is not a trivial question. When we say that 25% of Mexicans live in rural areas, what does this mean? According to the National Statistics Institute, localities with a population of 2500 or more are considered urban. Localities with fewer than 2500 are considered rural. Localities are recognized spatial communities used by the census agency.

The College of Mexico found the census definition of urban too broad and it developed its own definition. In its view, urban only includes localities of over 15,000 population. Localities with between 10,000 and 15,000 are defined as mixed–urban. Those with between 5000 and 10,000 are defined as mixed–rural, and those with populations of less than 5000 are called rural. This definition may well be better for some research purposes.

The main point here is that the concepts of urban and rural are two ends of a continuum. The defining line between them can be somewhat arbitrary and depends on the reason or purpose for making the distinction. In reality, there are numerous areas that are somewhere between being truly urban or truly rural. Throughout this chapter we use the census agency definition because it is used in most analyses and data sources in Mexico.

Rural areas of Mexico

According to the census of 2000 about 25 million people live in Mexico's 196,157 rural localities. Where are most of these localities? In which parts of Mexico do most rural people live?

There are rural inhabitants in all areas of Mexico. Even the Federal District, Mexico's urban core, has 449 rural localities with a total population of 20,319. Remember that the southern part of the Federal District is quite mountainous and contains several volcanoes.

Veracruz has the largest rural population with over 2.8 million. Chiapas is next with 2.1 million, followed by Oaxaca with 1.9 million. Data on the rural population in each state are provided in Appendix B. Rather than focus on the absolute number of rural residents in various states, it is more useful to look at the rural percentage of state populations (Figure 24.1). This gives a better indication of the rural, versus urban, character of the state.

As we might expect, the less modernized southern states are the most rural. The most rural state is Oaxaca, where 55% of the population live in rural areas. Chiapas is a very close second with 54%. Other southern states which are heavily rural are Guerrero (44%), Tabasco (46%) and Veracruz (41%).

Several central and northern states are also very rural. Just over half of Hidalgo's population is rural. The percentage rural is also relatively high for Zacatecas (47%), San Luis Potosi (41%), Durango (36%) and Nayarit (36%). On the other hand, some states have relatively few rural inhabitants: DF (0.2%), Nuevo Leon (6%), Baja California (8%), Coahuila (11%), State of Mexico (14%), Morelos (15%), Tamaulipas (15%) and Jalisco (15%).

Rural diversity

How similar are Mexico's rural areas? They are all similar in that they lack the characteristics of Mexico's large cities such as tall buildings, traffic congestion, modern shopping malls, bustling streets, heavy industry and the like. While rural areas are all similar in that they lack urban characteristics, Mexico's rural areas are actually quite diverse. There appears to be more diversity among Mexico's rural communities than its cities.

The physical form and architecture of cities are essentially independent from their surrounding natural environments. On the other hand, rural settlements tend to be integrated more closely with the natural environment. For example, villages in the arid central plateau tend to be constructed of locally available adobe, which keep residents relatively cool during the hot afternoons and warm during the colder nights. In the tropical parts of Mexico, rural settlements tend to be built with locally available tropical

materials which keep the rain out, but let air breezes through to mediate the hot tropical climate.

Rural settlements all tend to rely heavily on farming as the basic economic activity. The surrounding natural environment essentially dictates the type of farming that is practiced. Obviously, farmers in the central plateau cannot successfully grow bananas, sugarcane and other tropical products requiring lots of water. However, varieties of corn are grown virtually everywhere in Mexico.

The social characteristics of Mexico's rural areas are also very diverse compared to the cities. In general Mexican cities are quite similar from a social perspective. Social customs and mores, as well as social classes, are relatively constant from one city to the next. Spanish is the overwhelmingly dominant language in the cities. Rural communities in various parts of the country often have different social mores and customs. Communication in some rural areas is largely, if not almost exclusively, in local indigenous languages (see chapter 10). The diversity of Mexico's almost 200,000 rural localities should not be confused with the relative homogeneity within any given rural community. In general there is far more diversity within a Mexican city than within any given rural community.

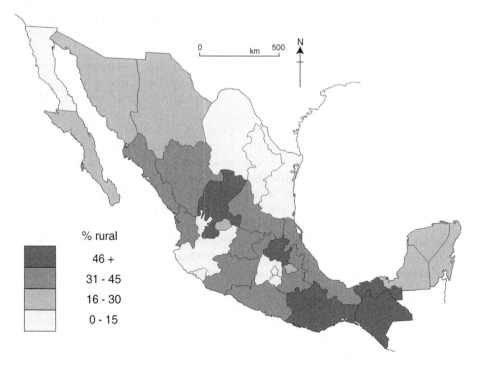

% rural

46 +

31 - 45

16 - 30

0 - 15

Figure 24.1 Rural population, by state[1]

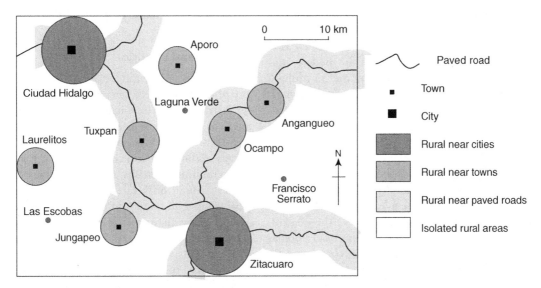

Figure 24.2 CONAPO's four categories of rural area applied to a region of Michoacán

Some rural areas are more rural then others

We all recognize that some cities are more urban than others. For example, Mexico City is considered more urban that a town of 20,000. By the same token, some rural communities are more "rural" than others. For example, a small settlement located near a city or along a main road would be considered less rural than an equally sized settlement in a more isolated area. The National Population Council (CONAPO) classifies rural localities into four groups based on accessibility to cities, towns and roads.[2] The four groups are described below and shown in Figure 24.2. The percentages in these rural groups for each state are given in Appendix B.

Rural localities near cities

This group is defined as localities within five kilometers (3 mi) of cities of at least 15,000 inhabitants. It accounts for 16% of Mexico's rural population, about four million people. About half of the rural populations of Morelos and Tlaxcala fall into this group. Some communities in this category are actually part of the suburbanization or urban sprawl process. People have ready access to many city services and opportunities. If they lack mechanical transportation, they can walk to the city in less than an hour.

What are the socioeconomic characteristics of these localities? The data needed to answer this question often are not readily available. Fortunately, CONAPO has classified rural localities in terms of their degree of marginalization, which provides insights into socioeconomic characteristics. Degree of marginalization is defined using indicators of adult educational attainment, housing quality, and income levels.

About 47% of rural, near city residents live in very marginalized localities.[3] While this is much higher than it is in urban areas, it is significantly less than other rural areas. Rural areas near cities tend to be more similar to urban areas. By way of comparison, in Mexico as a whole about 19% of the population live in municipalities classified as very marginalized.[4]

Representative characteristics of very marginalized communities include adult populations with illiteracy rates of about 25% and completion of primary school rates of only 44%. Roughly 27% of houses lack piped water, 27% lack indoor toilets, 46% have dirt floors and 64% are overcrowded. These housing indicators are closely correlated with significant health risks. About 15% of houses do not have electricity. Roughly 84% of economically active people make less than twice the minimum wage. Communities matching this description are very different from modern urban Mexico.

At the other end of the spectrum, only about 4% of near city residents live in non-marginalized localities, which we will call "modern".[5] For Mexico as a whole, 53% of the population live in modern municipalities. The figure is 100% for the 33 million people who live in Mexico's nine urban areas of over one million inhabitants. Levels of marginalization will be discussed more fully in chapter 29.

Rural localities near towns

This category includes localities within three kilometers of towns with between 2,500 and 15,000 residents. About 2.4 million people, or 10% of the rural population, live in such communities. These localities account for about a quarter of the rural population of Morelos and the State of Mexico.

Communities in this category are more rural than communities near cities. They have easy access to goods and opportunities in towns, but lack ready access to a real urban area. About 66% of this group lives in very marginalized communities compared to 47% for the near cities group. Less than 1% of the near towns group live in modern communities.

Rural localities near roads

This large group includes localities within three kilometers (2 mi) of paved roads. Almost 13 million Mexicans, about 54% of the rural population, fall into this category. It accounts for almost 90% of the rural population in Quintana Roo and over 70% in Zacatecas, Yucatán, Campeche, San Luis Potosí, Nuevo León and Coahuila.

This is a relatively important category because almost 14% of Mexico's total population lives in rural communities near roads. These localities account for 39% of the total population of Zacatecas, and about a third of the total for Hidalgo, Oaxaca and San Luis Potosí. The authors agree to differ as to the reasons for this. One of us believes that the location of paved roads is having an impact on rural settlement patterns. The other believes that rural settlement patterns are having an impact on the location of paved roads! Both viewpoints may be correct with their relative importance depending on the region in question.

While people living in these localities do not have walking access to a city or town, they can relatively easily get to a town or city by bus. Some 69% live in very marginalized communities, while less than 1% live in modern communities. In terms of marginalization, the near roads group is quite similar to the near towns group.

Isolated rural localities

This group includes rural localities that do not fit into any of the other three categories. They are the most rural in that they lack ready access to paved roads, towns or cities. These inaccessible areas are very rarely seen by outsiders. Most urban residents have limited understanding of life in these isolated areas.

Communities in this group are among Mexico's poorest. About 88% of the people in isolated rural localities live in communities classified as very marginalized; less than 1% live in modern communities. Though data are not available, areas that are within 10 km of a city, town or paved road are likely to be less marginalized than those in more remote locations.

Almost five million Mexicans, about 20% of the rural population, live in these communities. Over a million people in Chiapas and about half a million in Oaxaca and Puebla live in isolated localities. The figure for Chiapas represents 29% of the state's total population. About 16% of the people in Nayarit and Oaxaca and 12% of those in Sinaloa and Guerrero live in isolated areas. Providing needed basic services to these rural Mexicans is a major challenge for these state governments as well as the federal government.

Impact of access on education, housing quality, and income levels

The above percentages of localities classified as very marginalized paint a very clear picture. Access is very closely correlated with education levels, quality of housing, and wage levels. The group of rural areas located near cities has a rating of 47% very marginalized, which is two and a half times the national average of 19%. The near towns and near roads group have marginalization rates about three and half times the national figure. The marginalization rate for isolated localities is over four and half times the national average. The main point is that some rural areas are far more rural and isolated than others. Lack of access in isolated areas is clearly detrimental to the quality of life.

Rural access to central place services

The previous section indicates that access to sources of goods, services, markets and opportunities is very important to the economic and social wellbeing of rural and farm communities. Such sources are called central places and may be a village, a small town, a large town or a city.

Farms in rural areas may still grow some of their own food, but they are far less self-sufficient than they were a century or two ago. In Mexico, farm families are definitely part of the cash economy and buy more of their household needs than they produce on the farm. Items purchased from central places include such goods as sugar, clothing, hardware, farm tools, kitchen utensils, fertilizer, pesticides, hybrid seed, oil or kerosene for lamps, matches, paper products, as well as medicines, soft drinks, beer and cigarettes.

Rural areas are also dependent on outside services provided by schools, buses, doctors, dentists, beauticians, mechanics and churches. To pay for these goods and services they are also dependent on markets where they can sell their farm products or their labor to obtain the cash they need to make necessary purchases.

Central place theory

Considerable academic attention has been focused on central places which provide goods and services to their market areas or hinterlands. Walter Christaller analyzed the German rural economy in the 1930s and developed central place theory. The theory provides an idealized description of how goods and services are supplied in rural areas throughout the world. Central place theory describes the spacing and hierarchy of central places by focusing on the threshold demand needed to support specific goods and services, the market areas of central places, and the distances rural people travel to obtain specific goods and services.

According to the theory, every rural region is served by a hierarchy of central places. At the bottom of the hierarchy there are a large number of very small places providing services with very low threshold demands. These very small centers serve the population in the center and a small surrounding rural area.

As one moves up the hierarchy, there are a fewer number of places, providing a wider range of goods and services, and serving a larger market area. This occurs because for a service to be provided efficiently there must be sufficient threshold demand in the center and its surrounding hinterland to support it. For this reason we do not find new car dealers, heart surgeons or ballet schools in every small vil-

lage. These activities can only survive in large centers where there is sufficient demand.

Rural residents must travel varying distances to centers to obtain needed goods or services. The center may be small or may be large depending on the specific good or service that is needed. Rural residents might have to travel less than a few kilometers to a center at the bottom of the hierarchy to buy basic food stables or to attend primary school. They generally have to travel farther to a higher level center to get more specialized items such as clothing, health services, or secondary schooling. They generally have to travel considerably farther to buy a pickup truck, board an airplane or obtain the services of a heart specialist.

The hierarchy of central places in Mexico

How well does central place theory fit the Mexican situation? In terms of the relative numbers of settlements of different size, it fits quite well. The theory suggests that there will be a regular (geometric) progression between the number of settlements of each successive size. As Table 24.1 shows, the hierarchy of central places in Mexico is quite similar to that predicted by the theory.

At the lowest level in Mexico are a large number of very small centers providing a limited range of goods and services. At this level are small convenience stores (*abarrotes* or *bodegas*) selling basic Mexican household goods such as sugar, tortillas, bread, produce, snacks, basic canned goods, candy, eggs, beer, soft drinks, cigarettes, matches and basic toiletries. Other small stores at this lowest level might sell such things as household cooking and lighting

Table 24.1 Number of settlements or municipalities in Mexico, 2005[6]

Population size	Number of localities or municipalities	% national population
<2 500	184 714	23.5
2 500–9 999	2 379	10.6
10 000–49 999	615	12.1
50 000–499 000	162	25.6
500 000–999 000	23	13.9
1 000 000+	11	14.3

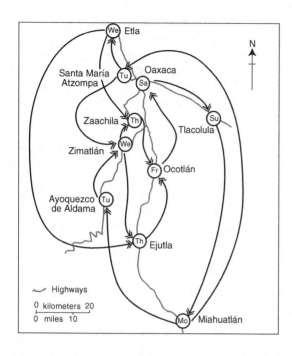

Figure 24.3 The weekly market cycles of central Oaxaca

fuels (wood, gas, or kerosene), seed, animal feed, fertilizer and other basic farm inputs. Other services might include a place that buys agricultural production, auto and tire repair shops, and a bus pick-up point. Some of these small centers might also have *tortillerías* (shops making tortillas), a primary school and a pay phone.

At the next higher level there is enough demand to support everything at the lowest level plus simple bakeries, hardware stores, mini-super markets, electrician/plumbers, welding shops, simple clothiers or dressmakers, beauty salons, basic health care, simple pharmacies, a church, a secondary school, simple eateries, and repair of household electrical items (radios, blenders, TVs). There might be only half or a third as many settlements (places) at this level as at the lowest level.

Central places at this level might also have weekly or periodic markets. Such markets usually occur only one day a week because there is not sufficient threshold demand to support them on a daily basis.

Figure 24.3 shows the major weekly marketing cycles for the Oaxaca area in southern Mexico. With the exception of Oaxaca city (population 480,000)

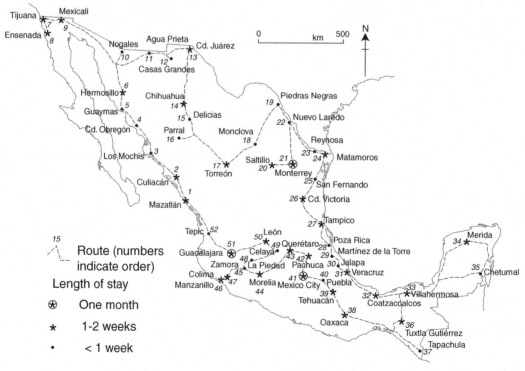

Figure 24.4 The touring route of Hermanos Vázquez circus, 1982–1983[8]

and Miahuatlán (33,000), all the other towns have populations between 13,000 and 20,000. The merchants at such markets generally carry their wares from village to village on the days of their respective markets. Some local farmers also sell their produce at such markets.[7] These markets give villagers access to a much wider range of goods than might otherwise be possible. Simultaneously, traders maximize their opportunities to make a profit.

Depending on the rural population density and economic demand for particular goods and services in the geographic area, periodic or weekly markets may not exist at this level of the hierarchy in some regions and may only appear at higher levels.

A similar principle applies to a circus (figure 24.4), which needs access to an even larger threshold population than a weekly market. This is because each individual visitor will not be prepared to travel far to see the show and has little interest in seeing the same acts more than once. Even a very large city will only house enough people to fill the Big Top for a few weeks. The circus's solution, in central place terms, is to access the combined populations of numerous towns or cities by moving from one to the next, on an annual or biannual itinerary.

As we move up the hierarchy in Mexico, there is enough demand to support everything at the lower levels as well as new services requiring higher levels of threshold demand. These might include doctors, dentists, carpenters, construction supplies, furniture and cabinet makers, bars, restaurants, a Pemex gas station, auto parts stores, and a variety of retail outlets selling such things as stationary and paper products, mobile phones, toys, flowers, plastic ware, and kitchen items. Centers at this level are larger and far fewer in number than the smaller centers at lower levels.

At the next higher level there are even fewer and even larger central places providing such services as appliance sales, jewelry stores, banks, opticians, lawyers, accountants, photographers, preparatory schools, hospitals, hotels, used car and pickup sales, a Coca-Cola bottler, funeral homes, a bus station, a Telmex office, TV and electronics sales, cyber cafes, clothing boutiques and shoe stores.

Further up Mexico's hierarchy there is enough demand to support higher level services such as: new car and truck sales, TV and radio stations, movie theaters, giant supermarkets, printers, bookstores, dry cleaning, real estate offices and office supply

Figure 24.5 The application of central place theory to Uruapan, Michoacán

Key:
- ◉ Central places: population 20,000+
- ● Other towns: population 10,001–20,000
- · "Urban" localities: population 2,501–10,000

stores. Centers at this level would be fewer in number and have larger geographic market areas.

At the top of the hierarchy are places like Mexico City and Guadalajara, where the demand is sufficient to support the highest level goods and services such as giant modern retail malls, international airlines, convention centers, international hotels, live theater, investment banking, TV studios, multimedia advertising agencies, major universities with medical schools, all types of specialized luxury products, and very specialized professional services such as heart and brain surgeons.

The spacing of central places in Mexico

Central place theory may work quite well in Mexico in terms of the relative numbers of settlements of different size, but the theory also suggests that those places on the same level of the urban hierarchy should form a distinctive spatial pattern and be roughly equidistant from one another. In essence, this means that each of these central places will be at the center of an approximately equally sized market area, or sphere of influence, well positioned to serve everyone who lives within its limits.

Figure 24.5 shows the settlements in the western part of the state of Michoacán. The largest city by far is Uruapan (250,000 inhabitants in 2008). Around Uruapan are six fairly large neighboring towns or cities. Each of these settlements has its own corresponding market area. However, even though these six places are roughly equidistant from Uruapan, they turn out to be very different in size. For example, Zamora (240,000) has more than four times the population of Pátzcuaro (53,000). Zamora is bigger because in addition to providing services to a larger, more prosperous, surrounding market area, it also has some manufacturing and is on a railroad line and the original highway between Mexico City and Guadalajara.

In addition, there is no observable regularity in the pattern of settlements of the two smaller sizes—"other towns" and "urban localities"—shown on the map. This is clearly in contradiction to central place theory, but should not really be a surprise. The theory assumes, for the sake of simplicity, that large areas will not have any significant differences in relief or soil fertility and that transport costs will be directly proportional to distance. It also assumes that rural areas have equal population densities and that their residents have similar consumer tastes and purchasing power. In practice, these assumptions are not valid, and some of the anomalies in the pattern of settlements shown on the map can be easily explained. For instance, the areas immediately north of Apatzingán and east of Nueva Italia are very mountainous, far less favorable for farming and settlement than the area north of Uruapan.

The very idea that settlements will be equidistant from one another begs a very important question, pertinent to our earlier discussion of the categories of rural settlements. Should we measure distance only in a spatial sense, in kilometers, or might it be more worthwhile to consider it in terms of the time or monetary cost required to make a particular journey, taking into account the terrain and transportation network?

In summary, central place theory does a good job of explaining the number of central places at each level and the types of services they provide. At the same time, departures from the idealized shape and size of market areas predicted by the theory help to reveal the complexities of Mexico's physical, human and socio-economic geography.

25

Migration within Mexico

In chapter 8 we investigated which areas of Mexico experienced the fastest population growth and which the slowest. Why do some states grow far faster than others? The main reason is migration, though birth and death rates are also a factor. This chapter looks explicitly at migration within Mexico. The next chapter will discuss international migration.

What is migration? In the most basic sense, it is a relatively permanent change of residence from one community to another. It may be a move around the world or to a different neighborhood in the same city. Most migration studies focus on movements across some type of boundary such as municipal border, city limit, state line or international border.

What specifically is a "relatively permanent" change of residence? Traveling to visit a relative, taking a vacation or making a business trip is not normally considered migration. Spending the summer at one's cabin in the mountains is usually not considered migration either. On the other hand, moving to take a summer job harvesting crops or working at a resort may be considered "temporary migration."

While temporary migration is an important field of study, in this chapter we focus on moves of a permanent nature. Given the availability of data, the focus is primarily on people who moved away from their municipality or state of birth, as well as those who moved to a new municipality during the last few years.

Factors affecting migration

Understanding migration requires understanding what factors motivate decisions to move from one area to another. We saw in an earlier chapter that when the economic base of an area increases rapidly, multiplier effects come into play generating growth in supportive enterprises. Such direct and indirect economic growth creates thousands of new jobs, and migrants stream in to take those jobs. Though the search for better economic opportunities is the most obvious factor affecting decisions to migrate, other factors also come into play.

Push and pull factors

We can think of migration in terms of push and pull factors. Factors that push or motivate someone to leave a particular area include such things as poverty, political oppression, climate, personal issues and legal problems. Pull factors draw people to a specific area. They include economic opportunities, attending college, marriage, political or religious freedom, or an attractive environment and climate. Push factors tend to be more influential in decision-making than pull factors since migrants have personal experience of their home area, but have only "acquired knowledge" (via friends and relations) about their intended destination on which to base their decision. In most decisions both push and pull factors are important. In fact they work together to form a complementarity, such as poor economic conditions in rural Mexico pushing people out, and relatively well-paying jobs pulling them into Mexican cities.

Fig 25.1 shows a model of migration movements based on the ideas of Lee (1966). With a few relatively minor exceptions such as the forced relocation of people away from large-scale infrastructure projects (see box), all internal migration in Mexico in recent history has been voluntary. Migrants may have to

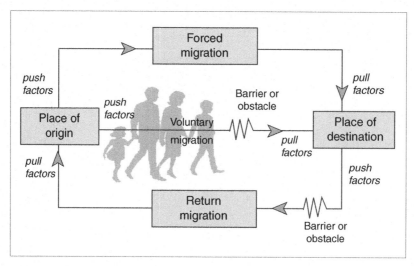

Figure 25.1 Model of migration movements[1]

overcome intervening obstacles. These are barriers, temporary or permanent, which tend to limit the flow of people in general, or of some selected subgroups of potential migrants. Political barriers affect international migration, but are irrelevant to Mexico's internal migration. However, barriers such as distance, expense, formal qualifications for specific jobs, language differences, incomplete knowledge, family ties and environmental hazards, such as floods, may all prevent or reduce the flow of migrants. We will explore some of these in more detail shortly.

Furthermore, migrants en route to a particular destination may be waylaid by the opportunities available in a place through which they have to pass. Some may choose to remain there rather than continue to their original intended destination. This concept is known as Stouffer's law of intervening opportunities.[2]

Benefits and costs

Migration also depends on the perceived benefits and costs of staying put versus moving to a different location. Benefits and costs may be economic, but also involve social, political, health, education and personal considerations.

Economic benefits and costs are often the driving force. Potential migrants must decide whether the benefits and costs of moving are more attractive than those of remaining where they are. Obviously it is not just a question of moving, it is a question of moving where? Each potential migration destination has its own set of benefits and costs.

Social benefits such as being close to one's family can also be very important. There may be social benefits from moving away from an oppressive family situation. There are also benefits from escaping political or religious repression. Social costs are incurred when moving from a familiar and comfortable community to a strange new place. On the other hand, the strange new place may offer benefits in the form of exciting new experiences and potential new friends. Comfort or pleasure benefits might also come into play, such as moving to an aesthetically attractive place with a great climate.

In some situations the costs of staying put may outweigh the costs of moving. When an employer transfers jobs to a new location, employees not prepared to move lose their incomes. Employees who choose to move must also decide whether it is better for their spouse and family to accompany them or to stay put.

The range of cultural, psychological, emotional, anxiety and uncertainty costs are often far greater than the monetary cost of transporting migrants and their belongings. How can potential migrants accurately assess all the benefits and costs when making a migration decision?

Information

Potential migrants never really know all the benefits and costs because they cannot predict what will happen in the future. Furthermore they never have full information on potential destinations. This was especially true of the migrants who move long distances

Forced migrations: the examples of Uxpanapa and Punta de Mita

Since most good dam sites are in remote highland areas, forced migrations due to new dams are relatively rare in Mexico. In the 1970s the building of the Cerro de Oro dam in northern Oaxaca, on a tributary of the River Papaloapan, flooded 360 km² (140 mi²) and meant the forced relocation of more than 5000 Chinantec Indians.[3] The resettlement plan was one of the most forward-looking of its time. Villagers received compensation for their existing homes, trees and crops, and were offered a choice of possible resettlement sites.

They chose an area of rainforest-covered ridges and valleys near the headwaters of the Rivers Coatzacoalcos and Uxpanapa in the Isthmus of Tehuantepec. With government assistance they built a dozen new villages named, somewhat unimaginatively, Poblado Uno, Poblado Dos, etc. Extensive agricultural support was provided for several seasons, but the plan failed to live up to expectations, in part because its architect, the distinguished Mexican geographer Jorge Tamayo, was killed in a plane crash in 1978.

Many of the area's young people have migrated (voluntarily) north. The remaining villagers grow *ixtle*, a fibrous cash crop produced from rainforest bromeliads that can be used for ropes and belts.

They are also trying to introduce ecotourism to preserve what is left of their tropical jungle hideout, complete with spider monkeys and jaguars.[4]

In recent years tourism developments have caused more forced relocations than dam construction. One example is the Punta de Mita peninsula, 50 km (30 mi) north of Puerto Vallarta, developed in the 1990s. The existing residents, mostly fishermen, were forced from their homes on the coast so that their *ejido* lands could be converted into a luxury tourist resort and Jack Nicklaus-designed golf course.[5]

The fishermen were moved from their breezy and somewhat ramshackle palapa huts, interspersed with palm trees, into ugly, concrete block houses a short distance inland, in the purpose-built small town of Emiliano Zapata, which adjoins a redeveloped coastal commercial/restaurant strip called Anclote. Attempts by the developers to build the fishermen a small boat-building workshop and breakwater to protect the beach caused sand to be eroded from one of the only two remaining beaches with public access. During the resort's construction an influx of workers from other parts of Mexico pushed prices up and led to social problems.

---

such as those who migrated from Europe or Asia to the Americas during the 16th to 20th centuries.

In many cases, information on potential migration destinations may be very sketchy. The more information a potential migrant has about a place, the more likely he is to move there. Very often, relevant information for a migration decision comes from friends and relatives who moved earlier and sent word back about their experience. In earlier centuries word came back by letter; now it mostly comes by phone or via the internet.

Virtually every migration flow gives rise to a flow of return migration. The idea of intervening obstacles will still apply. Some would-be return migrants find it very difficult or even impossible to return home. Those who succeed in returning have a great deal of information to share with those that are contemplating migration. This information may be positive or negative, but is never completely objective. Some re-

turn migrants, regretting their original decision to move, convey negative information; others exaggerate how wonderful their life was.

Risk–reward

The quality of information one receives about a place feeds into another important trade-off, which is risk versus reward. In most cases, the risks of migrating are far greater than the risks of staying put. But the potential rewards of migrating are also far greater. All migrants take a risk when they move from their original home to a new community or state or country. Obviously, the better and more accurate the information about the potential destination, the less is the risk.

A huge factor reducing risk is moving to a place where you have a family member, relation or close friend. For a typical Mexican migrant, having a family member at the destination who can show them the ropes, maybe even get them a job, greatly reduces the risk as well as increases the reward. In most cases Mexican migrants move to places where they have a relative or friend.

Migration channels

Migration channels form as a result of personal connections, feedback mechanisms and return migration. A migration channel develops when, over a period of years, many people from one area follow the path of others to a specific place. The early migrants send information back, which may encourage new migrants. They also form a support network for later migrants. Some of the migrants return to their place of origin, either temporarily or permanently, and bring back additional information.

There are numerous cases of migration channels. When indigenous workers from a small village in Oaxaca move to the capital, they settle in the same Mexico City neighborhood, often in the same dwelling as earlier migrants from their village. They often take the same jobs as earlier migrants. International migration provides numerous examples. Virtually all of the USA-bound migrants from the small town of Aguililla in Michoacán move to the relatively small community of Redwood City, south of San Francisco, California. Similarly, those from Napizaro near Lake Pátzcuaro, also in Michoacán, move to North Hollywood. Many migrants from Puebla end up in Brooklyn. Zapotecs from Oaxaca usually move to the San Fernando Valley.

Distance decay

The distance from the origin to the destination is also important. Potential migrants usually have more information about, and more contacts in, places nearby than those farther away. Longer migrations are more costly. Migration evidence from around the world and Mexico show very strong distance decay. For example, migrants to jobs in Cancún are far more likely to be from the nearby state of Yucatán than from the northern state of Sonora.

Temporary versus permanent migration

Some migrations are temporary, lasting a few months to a few years, while others are permanent. Some planned permanent moves do not work out, and become temporary when the migrant returns. Some migrations are intended to be temporary, such as a rural man moving to Mexico City for a year or two

to earn a nest-egg before returning to his rural community. However, such a move might end up being permanent if the migrant finds a great job, makes strong friendships in the city, asks his family to join him there or perhaps marries someone from the city. At the time of the initial move many migrants do not really know if the move is temporary or permanent.

Characteristics of migrants

Who is the typical migrant? What specific characteristics tend to distinguish migrants from non-migrants? Studies from all over the world indicate that migrants tend to be more ambitious, harder working, and have better education and job skills. Furthermore, migrants are more confident, more willing to take risks, and more adventurous. Migration rates are higher for young adults than for other ages. In some situations males are more likely to migrate, in others, females move more.

Think for a moment about your own community. In general, the ones who stayed were probably a bit less ambitious, less successful professionally, and more averse to risk. The ones who moved away were likely to be better educated, more confident and more willing to take risks to get ahead.

Mexican internal migration

Mexican internal migration is not completely separate from international migration. Actually the two are intertwined. Some Mexicans head for the USA and end up staying in Tijuana because they find a decent job there or have bad luck trying to cross the border. Others head for a maquiladora job in Ciudad Juárez but end up crossing into the USA when they learn about higher paying jobs across the border. In this section we focus on 20th century migrations that start and end in Mexico.

Migration has a long and interesting history in Mexico. Migration increased steadily throughout the 20th century. In 1900 only 6.2% of Mexicans lived outside their state of birth.[6] This percentage has edged up, particularly during the Mexican Revolution and following the second world war. It reached 12.8% by 1950 and 17.9% by 2000.

Overall, slightly more females than males migrated throughout the century. More females moved toward Mexico City, perhaps seeking domestic or service employment. On the other hand, males were more likely to head for the northern border states probably for jobs in manufacturing or agriculture.

The 2000 census indicates that each year about 0.85% of Mexicans move across state lines. An additional 0.56% moved from one municipality to another within the same state. Though these numbers sound small, when migration focuses on a limited number of destinations, the impact can be dramatic.

The geographic pattern of migration changed rather dramatically during the 20th century. Some areas that were once key migration destinations are now major sources of out-migration. The reverse is also true; states that used to be major senders are now important receivers of migrants. Of course some areas remained major net senders or receivers throughout the century. We should remember that for every migration flow there is a significant reverse flow. Therefore, states such as Zacatecas that have experienced large net outflows of migrants have also received numerous return migrants.

Early 20th century migration

Early in the 20th century migration focused mostly on Mexico City (see Appendix C). The pattern of migration was influenced significantly by the Mexican Revolution. By 1930 almost 48% of the capital's population resulted from net migration (the number of migrants arriving minus the number leaving). Migrants poured into Mexico City seeking better paying jobs and improved social services. A principle source of migrants was the surrounding State of Mexico. In 1930 net migration had reduced that state's population by over 18%. Migrants also came in large numbers from Puebla, Veracruz, Hidalgo, Querétaro, Guanajuato, Michoacán, Guerrero and Oaxaca.

Northern border states, with their expanding economies, were a secondary destination for migrants early in the century. In 1930 net migration accounted for over 64% of Baja California's population. Other northern states receiving a significant flow of migrants included Sonora, Chihuahua, Coahuila and especially Tamaulipas. Many migrants to the northern states came from the central states of Zacatecas, San Luis Potosí, Durango and Sinaloa. These states, like most states in Mexico, also contributed a flow of migrants into Mexico City.

A relatively small number of Mexicans migrated to Quintana Roo. Though few in number, they represented 30% of the territory's very small population in 1930.[7] It would not be until several decades later that a large flow of migrants would be attracted to

jobs associated with the enormous tourist development focused on Cancun.

Mid 20th century migration

During the middle of the 20th century, migration continued to focus on Mexico City. The rapid growth of the city was spurred by both high fertility rates and massive migration. Even by 1960 over 36% of the city's population resulted from net migration. About half of all interregional moves between 1965 and 1970 ended in the Core Region composed of the Federal District, State of Mexico and Morelos.[8] The main states contributing migrants to the core continued to be the neighboring states of Mexico, Guanajuato, Hidalgo, Querétaro and Puebla. Significant flows also came from Morelos, Tlaxcala, Veracruz, Oaxaca, Guerrero, Michoacán, as well as Jalisco, Aguascalientes, Zacatecas and San Luis Potosí. By mid century, Morelos was gaining migrants from Mexico City as well as other states. The State of Mexico was also beginning to become an important migration destination.

During the middle of the 20th century the northern states continued to be a significant migration destination. Migrants contributed to the very rapid growth of Baja California. Tamaulipas also grew rapidly as a result of migration. Interestingly, in 1960 more migrants had left Baja California Sur than had arrived. Other border states with significant net migration gains included Sonora, Chihuahua and Nuevo León. Following the principle of distance decay, many migrants to these states came from nearby states to their south. Baja California, Sonora and Chihuahua attracted migrants form Sinaloa and Durango. Migrants from Zacatecas, San Luis Potosí and Veracruz tended to move to Nuevo León and Tamaulipas. It is curious to note that Coahuila, which in 1930 had a large net migration gain, was a net migration loser by 1960. Net migration into Saltillo and other cities in Coahuila was not sufficient to offset the net out-migration from its rural areas. Many of those who left Coahuila moved to the Monterrey area in Nuevo León searching for urban employment.

Migration patterns at the millennium

The pattern of Mexican internal migration changed dramatically during the last quarter of the 20th century. To get an understanding of these changes and current migration patterns, it is useful to look

Figure 25.2 CONAPO's five major regions

at migration at different geographic scales. Data on migration among large national regions gives the most basic pattern. Looking at interstate migration provides more detail and reveals migration changes of individual states within large national regions. An analysis of migration among Mexico's 2443 municipalities gives a detailed picture of migration impacts on specific types of communities. All three scales are needed to get a full picture of Mexican migration in the years leading up to the millennium.

Migration among major national regions

For analytical purposes CONAPO divides Mexico into five major regions (Figure 25.2). The Border Region includes Baja California Sur and the six border states of Baja California, Sonora, Chihuahua, Coahuila, Nuevo León and Tamaulipas. The seven states in the West Region are Sinaloa, Durango, Zacatecas, Nayarit, Aguascalientes, Jalisco and Colima. The Center Region's eight states are Michoacán, Guanajuato, Querétaro, San Luis Potosí, Hidalgo, Tlaxcala, Puebla and Veracruz. The geographically small Core Region is the most interesting from a migration perspective. It includes the Federal District and the states of Mexico and Morelos. The seven states in South Region are Guerrero, Oaxaca, Chiapas, Tabasco, Campeche, Yucatán and Quintana Roo.

At the millennium the Core Region was still the dominant focus of migration. Half of all interstate migrations either started or ended in the Federal District or State of Mexico.[9] During the late 20th century the Core Region continued as the biggest magnet for migrants, but also became the largest source of out-migration. Between 1992 and 1997 the Core Region attracted 1.245 million migrants, far more than any other region. However, about 1.4 million migrants left the region seeking opportunities elsewhere. The number of migrants leaving had surged ahead of the number arriving. The Core Region became the biggest net migration loser. Much of the out-migration, particularly from the Federal District, resulted from the government's successful policy of shifting growth way from Mexico City.

Where did migrants from the Core Region go? Actually, over half (766,565) went to other states in the Core Region; mostly to the State of Mexico. Other migrants tended to go to the Center, South or Border regions.

What other regions attracted significant numbers of migrants? The Border and Center regions were the next biggest destination after the Core Region. Each attracted some 880,000 migrants. But about 944,000 migrants left the Center Region; therefore it experienced a net migration loss of about 65,000.

On the other hand, only about 537,000 left the Border Region giving it a net migration gain of almost 334,000. The Border Region, with its attractive job opportunities, was the only region with a net gain between 1992 and 1997. The other four regions all had net loses. Most migrants to the Border Region came from the Center and West regions. A significant number also came from the Core Region. Twice as many migrants moved to the Border Region from Center, West and Core regions than moved in the opposite direction.

Migration between states

The dynamics of migration within the Core Region changed very dramatically during the last quarter of the 20th century. The Federal District switched from being the predominant migration destination to being the largest source of out-migration in the country. About 4.46 million people or about 40% of those born in the Federal District were living in a different state by 2000 (Appendix C). Offsetting this were about 1.83 million living in the capital but born elsewhere. The difference or net migration loss was 2.63 million, or 30% of the Federal District's

population in 2000. This is clear evidence of the success of government policies to shift economic and population growth away from the Federal District (chapter 21).

Where did all those who left Mexico City go? While they went to all states in the country, the vast majority moved to the State of Mexico. It absorbed Mexico City's urban sprawl and captured much of the growth that was diverted from the Federal District by government policies. By 2000, the State of Mexico had over 5 million people born in other states. With only about 655,000 leaving, the state had a net migration gain of over 4.4 million, about a third of its total population. The State of Mexico also received relatively large flows of migrants from Puebla, Veracruz, Hidalgo, Oaxaca, Michoacán and Guerrero. Many of these migrants had worked in corn production, which suffered significantly from imports of cheap US corn enabled by NAFTA.

The migration dominance of the capital region continued for the 1995 to 2000 period. Almost 520,000 moved from the Federal District to the State of Mexico, while 183,000 migrated in the opposite direction. Together these two flows accounted for 17% of all interstate moves. This is impressive

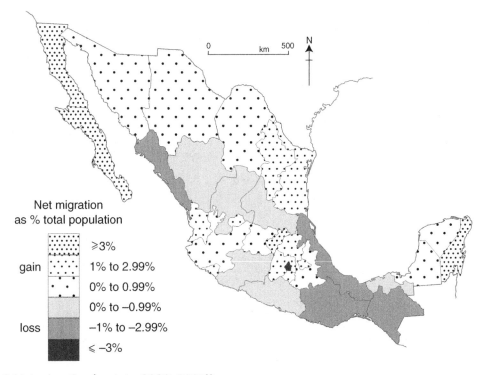

Figure 25.3 Net migration by state, 2000–2005[10]

given that there are a total of 992 possible interstate flows linking Mexico's 32 states to each other.

It is interesting to note that while the Core Region as a whole was a net loser of migrants, its most populous state, Mexico, became the largest net gainer. This observation demonstrates the value of looking at migration at different geographic scales.

Most of the northern states continued to attract many migrants (Figure 25.3). Most came seeking employment in activities stimulated by NAFTA such as the maquiladoras focused on serving the US market. Within this region, Baja California continued to grow as the most important migration magnet. By 2000, Baja California was home to about 1,026,000 Mexicans who were born in other states. On the other hand, only about 127,000 who were born in Baja California moved out of the state. The state's net migration gain of almost 900,000 represented just over 36% of its population. The main flow of migrants to Baja California came from Sinaloa, followed by the Federal District, Jalisco, Sonora and Michoacán.

Nuevo León also developed into a major magnet late in the century. Its net migration gain of 599,000 in 2000 represented about one sixth of its population. Most migrants came seeking work in Metropolitan Monterrey. They came mostly from Tamaulipas, San Luis Potosí and Coahuila. Chihuahua and Tamaulipas also had impressive net gains of 322,000 and 308,000, respectively. Durango and Coahuila were the main suppliers of migrants to Chihuahua. Those

moving to Tamaulipas came mostly from Veracruz, San Luis Potosí and Nuevo León. They streamed into Tamaulipas seeking employment, primarily in maquiladoras in the booming border cities of Nuevo Laredo, Reynosa and Matamoros.

The other major migration magnet was Quintana Roo with its booming tourist industry focused on Cancún. It attracted 451,000 migrants while losing only about 34,000. The net migration gain represented over half of the state's population in 2000. Main sources of migrants to Quintana Roo were the nearby states of Yucatán, Tabasco and Chiapas.

The interstate migration pattern at the turn of the century reveals a dynamic and complex situation in the capital area as well as a strong movement to northern states (Figure 25.3). Most of the western, central and southern states are experiencing significant net out-migration with a few notable exceptions. The exceptions are the states with more dynamic economies, such as Aguascalientes, Colima, Querétaro, Campeche and Quintana Roo.

Migration between municipalities

Municipal level migration data reveal movements between different types of communities within states. Given that there are 2443 municipalities, it is not practical to discuss migration flows into or out of individual municipalities. But we can look at movements between specific classes of municipalities to get an idea of migration dynamics within states.

Table 25.1 Migration in and out of municipalities, 1995–2000, by settlement size[11]

Municipality class population	Rural < 2499	Towns 2 500– 14 999	Small cities 15 000– 99 999	Mid-sized cities 100 000– 999 999	Large cities 1 000 000+
Total population, 2000	24 638 500	7 901 398	9 532 672	22 677 415	32 733 427
Migration in	783 854	413 145	487 328	1 614 004	1 338 130
Migration out	1 196 760	515 205	536 868	1 244 792	1 142 836
Intra-urban migration [a]	na	na	na	175 153	2 042 047
Net migration	−412 906	−102 060	−49 540	369 212	195 294
As % of 2000 population					
Migration in	3.2	5.2	5.1	7.1	4.1
Migration out	4.9	6.5	5.6	5.5	3.5
Net migration	−1.7	−1.3	−0.5	1.6	0.6

[a] Intra-urban moves = moves between municipalities within same urban area

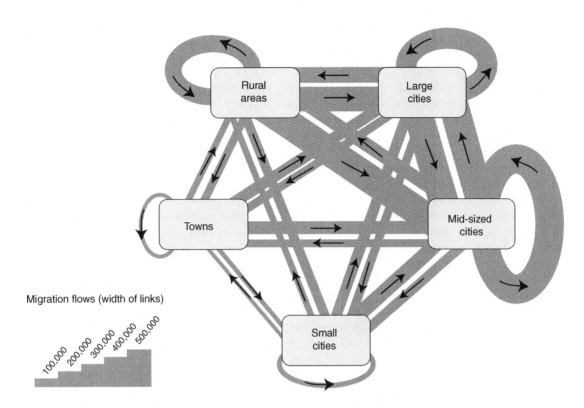

Figure 25.4 Migration between settlements of different sizes, 1995–2000[12]

Between 1995 and 2000, over 6.8 million Mexicans moved from one municipality to another (Table 25.1). Over 4.5 million of these moves were either to or from Mexico's nine largest cities with over one million inhabitants (Mexico City, Guadalajara, Monterrey, Puebla, Toluca, Tijuana, Ciudad Juárez, León and Torreón). Two million moves were intra-urban. Such moves between municipalities in the same urban area may not be considered true "migration" by some.

Over 1.5 million of the intra-urban moves were between municipalities within the Mexico City Metropolitan Area (ZMCM). Much of this was from the Federal District to suburban municipalities in the State of Mexico. Of the fifty largest flows between two municipalities, 42 were between municipalities in the same metropolitan area. Of these, 31 were in Metro Mexico City, seven in Metro Monterrey, three in Metro Guadalajara and one in Metro Cuernavaca.

Aside from intra-urban moves, the major focus of migration in Mexico has shifted from the largest cities to medium cities of less than one million. Medium cities, such as Mérida, San Luis Potosí, Queré-

taro and Hermosillo, attracted over 1.6 million new migrants compared to only about 1.3 million for the largest cities (Appendix C). The net migration gain of medium cities was almost 370,000, nearly twice that of the nine largest cities. The new focus of migration on medium cities rather than largest urban areas was stimulated by policies to shift growth away from Mexico City. This shift should help relieve the growing congestion in Mexico City and the other large cities.

The pattern of migration from small towns and rural areas to urban municipalities continued throughout the 20th century and into the 21st century. Between 1995 and 2000 over 1.7 million migrants left small towns and rural areas (Figure 25.4). Where did these migrants go? Over 60% went to cities of over 100,000, which is not surprising because these cities have more dynamic economies with more employment opportunities. What is a bit surprising is that a full 27% moved to other small towns and rural areas. Many of these moves were to new corporate agricultural developments in the north. Personal and family factors were also important.

Rural areas and small towns attracted almost 1.2 million migrants during the five year period. Over 60% came from cities of over 100,000, while almost 40% came from other towns and rural areas. Many of these moves were undoubtedly earlier migrants returning to their hometowns. The net migration loss of over half a million represented only about 1.6% of the population for the five year period. This is only about one eighth of the natural population increase in these areas. In summary, though small municipalities are experiencing relatively large rates of out-migration, they are also attracting many migrants. Their relatively low rates of net migration loss mean that Mexico should continue to have a substantial rural population for the next several decades.

Overview of 20th century patterns of internal migration

For most of the 20th century migrants flowed out of small towns and rural areas towards Mexico City. The economic dynamism and enormous job growth in the capital attracted millions of migrants from all over Mexico but mostly from the surrounding states in central and southern Mexico. These states experienced significant net migration loses throughout the century. The capital area not only attracted the greatest number of migrants by far, but it also became the main supplier of migrants. Throughout the century migration streams flowed in both directions as return migration was always very significant.

The main secondary magnet was the border region, particularly the coastal states of Baja California and Tamaulipas. Rapid economic development in the region pulled in migrants from all over, but predominately from states immediately to the south. Several of these non-border northern and western states, particularly Zacatecas, Durango and San Luis Potosí, were the biggest net migration losers throughout the century.

During the last quarter of the century the migration dynamic around the capital changed dramatically. Millions moved out of the Federal District while millions more moved into the neighboring State of Mexico. Taken together, the capital region shifted from the overwhelming magnet with net migration gains in the millions to the biggest net migration loser. The border region became the only area with net migration gains. At the state level, Mexico, Baja California, Nuevo León and Quintana Roo had the greatest net inflows of migrants. The largest flow of migrants was into and out of cities of over 100,000.

26

Migration to the USA

"Go north for opportunity" has become a Mexican rallying cry, just as "Go west for opportunity" was a US aphorism in the 19th century. Migrating to the USA has become deeply embedded in Mexican culture, especially in the rural areas of west central Mexico. In some areas over 80% of the young men make at least one trip to the USA, usually as an unauthorized worker.

This chapter traces the long history of Mexicans moving to the USA to take advantage of employment opportunities. It primarily focuses on the Mexican side of this equation. The next chapter looks into the other side of the equation by investigating the characteristics of the over 31 million Mexicans who live in the USA.

Historical migration flows

The migration of Mexican farm labor to the USA started in the late 19th century.[1] In the 1870s President Porfirio Díaz focused the Mexican economy on industrialization and neglected problems of rural poverty in Mexico. In this environment many rural Mexicans realized that they could benefit economically by migrating temporarily to the USA.

Larger scale migration started around 1900, when US-financed railroads penetrated the Mexican interior. About a third of the railroad labor came from three western states: Jalisco, Michoacán, and Guanajuato. Workers in these states quickly learned the advantages of working for US employers. Throughout the 20th century these three states remained the dominant source of USA-bound migrants.

During the Mexican Revolution migration increased as peasants fled violence in favor of stability

and better paying jobs north of the border. When the first world war restricted the flow of migrants from southern and eastern Europe, US industrialists actively recruited Mexican workers. The annual number of migrants grew from 10,000 in 1913 to 68,000 in 1920, and peaked at 106,000 in 1924. During the 1920s about 621,000 Mexicans entered the USA. Throughout this period there was a strong countercurrent of return migration; the net flow was far smaller than the gross migration figures cited above. Migration slowed and actually reversed during the Great Depression of the 1930s. From 1929 to 1938 the USA government deported 453,000 Mexicans, many of whom were US citizens.

Bracero program

In response to severe labor needs during the second world war, the governments of Mexico and the USA initiated the Bracero guest worker program in 1942. The program enabled Mexico to contribute to the war effort by sending temporary agricultural workers to the USA. Mexicans were granted renewable six-month visas to work on selected farms. Most migrants under the Bracero program came from the same three states, Michoacán, Jalisco and Guanajuato. They worked mostly in California and other states along the Mexican border.

As a result of the Bracero program, some farmers in the USA became very dependent on relatively cheap Mexican labor. The program was considered a great success by farmers. Unfortunately mistreatment of Bracero laborers was widespread. In protest, the Mexican Government threatened to stop the flow of migrants. During the war many Mexicans who were not recruited under the Bracero program entered the USA illegally looking for work. Tolerance for unauthorized migration developed on both sides of the border. With a large dependency in the USA on Mexican farm workers and a large supply in Mexico, there was virtually no way to put a halt to this migration stream.

Labor unions, churches and Latino groups in the USA opposed the Bracero program on the grounds that it held down farm wages and impeded the upward mobility of US Hispanics. They convinced the US Congress to halt the Bracero program in 1964. Between 1942 and 1964 an estimated 4.5 million Mexican Bracero workers entered the USA. At its height in the late 1950s more than 500,000 workers migrated each year. Most were temporary migrants who returned to Mexico within a year. The Bracero program set the stage for the continued high volume of Mexican labor migration to the USA.

Migration from La Joya, Jalisco[2]

La Joya is typical of many emigration villages in Jalisco. It has fewer than 1000 residents and a long tradition of migration to the USA. Agriculture is the major industry. Most farms grow corn and beans to feed themselves and their cattle. Dairy farming is a major local industry. Since NAFTA, these farmers can no longer earn a decent living growing corn. In fact about 20% of the former corn farmers have stopped growing corn altogether.

Only about half the adults have completed the nine year primary and middle school curriculum. The school in La Joya has about 50 students in grades 7–9 who range in age from 12 to 15. Very few of the 9th graders plan to continue their education even though there are several grade 10–12 high schools in the area. Reasons for not continuing education included the cost and time needed to travel to school, the cost of books and family pressure for them to start earning a wage. Almost all of the children have relatives in the USA. Virtually all the boys and many of the girls expected to work in the USA. When asked, none mentioned Guadalajara or other large Mexican cities as likely destinations, even though there were numerous jobs available in Guadalajara.

Post-Bracero migration

What happened to migration after the closure of the 22-year Bracero program in 1964? The US Congress attempt to reduce migration by closing the Bracero program did not work. Instead migration continued and even expanded. By 1970 there were almost 800,000 Mexican-born US residents compared to fewer than 600,000 in 1960. This figure increased to over two million by 1980.

Several factors combined to stimulate migration. The Bracero migrants became very familiar with work opportunities north of the border. They shared their experiences with their friends and relatives. Bracero families had become dependent on remittances sent back by migrant workers. Furthermore, rural poverty was a growing problem as the Mexican labor force grew faster than work opportunities. All these factors fostered increased migration to the USA. While some of this migration was legal, most was not. The number of Mexicans apprehended at the border increased, reaching about 1.7 million per year in the mid-1980s; however, this did little to slow the stream of migrants.

To combat rural poverty the Mexican government implemented corn subsidies that offered high prices for corn to help corn growers, and low priced corn tortillas for urban consumers. The corn program was expensive and did little to reduce poverty or stem the flow of migrants from rural areas. The corn policies were abandoned in the 1980s.

Migration to the USA had become an integral part of the socio-economic fabric of many rural areas in west central Mexico. These rural migrants tended to have low levels of education and few skills. Their first trip usually lasted four to eight months without their family. In many cases families and villages became trans-national. Working members of families divided their time between the USA and Mexico (see box on La Joya).

Continued migration growth in the 1980s

The 1980s was a critical decade for Mexico to USA migration. The Mexican peso was devalued in 1982 and again in 1986–87. For several years after 1982, there was virtually no formal sector job growth in Mexico. In Guadalajara half of the jobs in the shoe-making and sewing industries were lost in the late 1980s. With few opportunities for employment in Mexico many rural youth migrated to the USA. President Reagan's defense buildup created millions

Poblanos in New York City[3]

Over half a million *poblanos*, natives of the Mexican state of Puebla, live in the New York City area. In 1975 17-year-old Jaime Lucero left the small town of Piaxtla, Puebla, and waded across the Río Grande. He got a bus to New York and joined his older brother washing dishes in a restaurant. He became a legal resident under the 1986 ICRA amnesty program. Two years later he became a US citizen. Today Lucero is a millionaire who owns a women's apparel company in New Jersey and a factory in Puebla which employs 2500. "I came through the back door," Lucero says, "but I never intended to be a burden to this country."

Except for the millionaire part, Lucero's story is typical of many *poblanos*. Ricardo, 20, and Aldea, 19, came to New York by crossing the 49°C (120°F) Sonoran Desert in the summer of 2003. They work 70-hour weeks for less than the minimum wage of $5.15 an hour. She is planning a month long trip back to Puebla, which she will pay for by serving as a courier, or *paquetera*, a person who carries clothing, electronics and other gifts from immigrants to their families back in Puebla. Getting back and forth across the border without proper documents is a bit more difficult than it used to be but is not a significant problem. Most rely on trusted *polleros*, often called coyotes, who provide border crossing service for fees ranging from a few hundred dollars for just crossing the border to a few thousand dollars for door-to-door service.

Migration has had a profound impact on Piaxtla and other villages in Puebla. Most of the 5900 current residents of Piaxtla are either children or elderly (Figure 26.1). The mayor claims that "maybe three out of four of my constituents live in New York". The hundreds of millions of dollars sent back each year are having a dramatic effect on rural communities in Puebla. Forty years ago, virtually all the houses were made of palm-thatch adobe. Now they are mostly brick and concrete. Many are topped with satellite dishes. The towns also have new restaurants, taxis, video arcades, cyber cafes and newly paved streets, all made possible from remittances. Ironically the towns are sparsely populated and many of the new houses are empty because their owners are working in New York.

Most youth consider the prospect of migration. Few think about careers in Mexico or becoming artisans and continuing Puebla's long tradition of ceramics, woodworking and weaving. Youth show little interest in corn farming, the traditional mainstay of the local economy. In short, migrating to jobs in New York has become the norm.

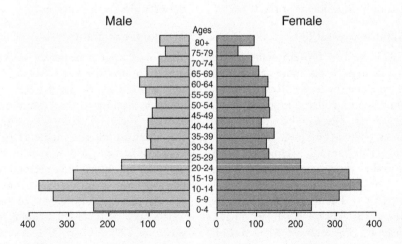

Figure 26.1 Population pyramid for Piaxtla, 2000[4]

of new jobs, especially in California. A labor shortage developed and Mexican migrants streamed in to fill job vacancies.

Two important policy changes during the 1980s encouraged migration. The Mexican Government changed its economic policy from import substitution to market-oriented export manufacturing. In 1986 Mexico joined the General Agreement on Tariffs and Trade (GATT). Agriculture no longer received favored treatment as export manufacturing gained center stage. Surplus Mexican agricultural workers migrated to the USA looking for work.

The government of the USA enacted the Immigration Reform and Control Act (IRCA) of 1986. The IRCA provided legal status to farm workers who had worked at least 90 days in the USA during 1985–86. This gave immediate amnesty to about 1.7 million undocumented migrants in the USA as well as opening legal migration to another million farm workers who had returned to Mexico. In short, ICRA provided legal immigration for about one-sixth of the adult men in rural Mexico. These were typically married men in their late 20s; ICRA specifically excluded their families from legal immigration to the USA. The belief of the policy makers was that these farm workers wanted their families to remain in Mexico while they commuted to seasonal jobs in the USA. The IRCA also incorporated sanctions for employers hiring illegal immigrants and stepped up border controls. But these were not successful. The now legal immigrants under ICRA began to bring their families to the USA. By 1990 there were about 4.5 million Mexican born residents of the USA.

Accelerated migration since 1990

Beginning in 1993 the USA government changed its border control strategy. It put more agents, more lights and more fences on the border. Resources were shifted from apprehending illegal migrants in the USA to deterring entry. The new border programs had several names: "Hold-the-Line", "Gatekeeper", "Safeguard", and "Río Grande". However, these efforts did little to slow the pace of migration.

The North American Free Trade Agreement (NAFTA) took effect on 1 January 1994. With free trade each country was expected to focus on their comparative advantage. For example, Mexico would produce more tomatoes and less corn, which can be grown more efficiently in the USA. Mexico was expected to export tomatoes and not tomato pickers.

However, some experts cautioned that NAFTA might only reduce migration in the mid- to long-term, not in the short term. Actually, migration increased after NAFTA partially as a result of Mexico's economic recession of 1995 which reduced formal sector jobs by about 10%. Those that had argued that NAFTA would quickly reduce migration were clearly wrong.

With continued migration, there was a noticeable increase in the number of both authorized and unauthorized migrants seeking public services. The most obvious was the large increase of migrant children in specific school districts in California. This resulted in a serious backlash against migrants as well as virtually all Mexican Americans. The backlash was aggravated by an economic recession in California in the early 1990s. Many Californians blamed Mexicans for their lost jobs. They claimed that their continued high taxes were being used to provide schooling and other public services for illegal aliens.

In 1994, California passed the infamous Proposition 187. This withheld public services such as education and health care from illegal immigrants. While sections of Proposition 187 were declared unconstitutional by US federal courts, other provisions were enacted into California State Law in 1996. The law restricted access of unauthorized aliens to welfare and other tax-supported benefits. The Mexican government reacted to what it perceived as growing anti-Mexican sentiment in the USA by allowing Mexicans to have dual citizenship. As a result, Mexicans who became naturalized US citizens could retain Mexican citizenship. This facilitated movement between the two countries.

Temporary migrants

Temporary migrants enter the USA for period of a few months up to three years. About 900,000 temporary migrants crossed the border every year in the 1990s; about half going to the USA and half returning to Mexico. Their characteristics are quite different from the Mexican-born residents of the USA discussed above. First, they are overwhelmingly male. Rarely do Mexican women leave their families and go to the USA with the intention of returning a few months or years later. In 1995 only 2.4% of temporary migrants were female. This more than doubled by 2002 but still was only 5.8%.[6] Over 90% of temporary migrants are between the age 12 and 45.

The characteristics of temporary migrants are changing rather significantly. The traditional pat-

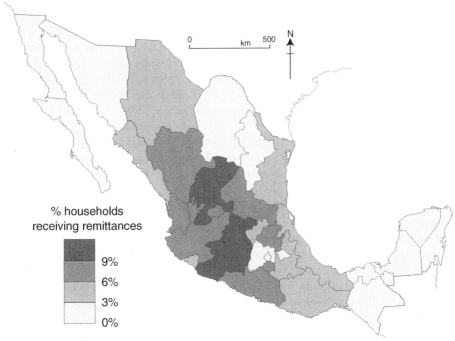

Figure 26.2 Remittances to Mexico, 2005[5]

tern was one of poorly educated temporary migrants from rural western Mexico heading north to work in agriculture. This is being augmented by better educated new migrants from the rest of Mexico going to work in nonagricultural jobs. In 1995 only 29% were first time migrants and 48% had legal migration documentation. By 2003 72% were first time migrants and only 25% had legal documentation. The average time spent in the USA was 5.5 months in 1995, about the length of the harvest season. By 2002 the duration had increased to 12.2 months as many nonagricultural workers extended their stay to earn more money.

The proportion completing middle school increased from 34% in 1995 to 48% in 2002. In 1995 about 44% were working in agriculture, undoubtedly those with less education; by 2002 only 20% were working in agriculture. Clearly, a wider range of Mexicans were becoming temporary migrants and less attention was being given to legal documentation. Many temporary migrants eventually become permanent migrants and move their families to the USA.

Remittances

How much money do migrants send back to Mexico? Remittances sent to Mexico from migrant workers

have grown very rapidly: from $3.7 billion in 1995 to $6.6 billion in 2000, $16.6 billion in 2004 and over $25 billion in 2008. In terms of foreign exchange earnings, remittances are behind automobile and oil exports, but well ahead of tourism. Mexico, along with India, is the world leader in remittances from migrant workers.

As migrants move their families and settle permanently in the USA, the amount of remittances they send back to Mexico declines. Thus, states with many new and single migrants such as Chiapas, Tlaxcala, and Tabasco receive more in remittances per migrant than states that sent migrants decades earlier.

A growing number of Mexican families depend on remittances (Figure 26.2). Between 1992 and 2005 the number of households receiving remittances grew from about 660,000 to over 1.5 million, about 6% of Mexican households. Remittances are particularly important to many poor families in rural areas. About 14% of rural households receive remittances amounting to an average of about $2200 a year.[7] Remittances are the main source of income for most of these families. About 78% of remittances are used for basic necessities, 7% for education and 8% for savings. About 60% of the households receiving remittances have earned incomes of less than $200 a month.

Almost 4% of urban households receive remittances, which average about $2800 a year per household. Migrants from urban areas tend to have higher skill levels and thus earn more in the USA and remit more. Urban households are slightly less dependent on remittances for basic necessities; thus they are more likely to invest the remittances in education, housing or enterprises.

Are remittances contributing to economic development? In many areas remittances are funding employment creating investments. For example, remittances have been used in Jalisco to create several sewing factories as well as improved cattle breeds that increase production of milk and meat. Many investments are made with the help of hometown associations. These are Mexicans in the USA who form groups to invest in economic and civic improvements for their hometowns. One such group was responsible for investing $10 million to build several sewing factories in Guanajuato which now employ 600 people. Another group, involving 336 families, invested $1.3 million in Atacheo de Regalado, Michoacán, to improve production of turkeys, vegetables and flowers. The community exported 220 tons of tomatoes to the USA in 2003. Other investments improved town plazas, sports fields and municipal centers.

The geographic source of migrants

From what areas of Mexico do most migrants come? Since 1870 three states—Michoacán, Jalisco, and Guanajuato—have been the dominant source of migrants to the USA. The number of Mexican-born US residents from the three states increased from 1.9 million in 1990 to 3.4 million in 2005 (Appendix D). Before 1970 they accounted for about half of all migrants but this dropped to about a third by 2005.

Six other western states also have historically been important sources of migrants: Aguascalientes, Colima, Durango, Nayarit, Sinaloa and Zacatecas, as well as two border states—Baja California and Chihuahua (Figure 26.3). In the last thirty years the source of migrants has spread from western Mexico to virtually all parts of the country. This corresponds to the trend of migrants going to all states in the USA.

A few states are very dependent on migration and remittances. Michoacán, a relatively poor state, receives more dollars in remittances than any other state. More than 10% of households receive remittances, which in 2005 amounted to over $2.6 billion, over one-eight of the state's total income.

When these remittances are spent on housing or consumer items they generate additional economic activity and jobs. Including these multiplier effects,

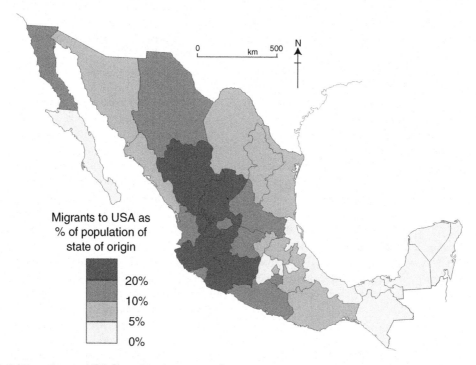

Migrants to USA as
% of population of
state of origin

20%

10%

5%

0%

Figure 26.3 Migration to USA from Mexican states[8]

remittances account for about a third of Michoacán's economy.

About 9% of households in Guanajuato receive remittances which account for slightly over 6% of total income. Jalisco has a fairly large economy so the remittances received by about 8% of the households account for only about 3% of the state's total income. Zacatecas-born Mexicans in the USA represented 36% of the state's 2005 population, far more than any other state. About 12% of Zacatecas households receive remittances which account for almost 8% of the state's total income.

Perhaps surprisingly, the six northern border states are no longer an important source of migrants. The border states are now relatively prosperous and modern by Mexican standards; therefore their citizens have less incentive to migrate. While border states accounted for 26% of the Mexican-born US residents in 1990, this number was down to 20% by 2005. The increase for Baja California was only 19% over the period compared to the national increase of 96%. In recent years relatively few Mexicans born in Baja California migrated to the USA. In 2004, border states accounted for just 9% of net migration and only 7% of remittances which accounted for only 0.7% of total income. Migration is not one of the ways in which border states benefit from being next to the USA.

Mexicans in the USA are increasingly coming from states outside western and northern Mexico. Several states have experienced enormous growth since 1990. Tlaxcala, Hidalgo and Veracruz had more than six-fold increases between 1990 and 2005; Chiapas was not far behind. Near fourfold increases

were experienced by Puebla, Oaxaca and Guerrero, while the number from the states of Mexico, Morelos and Tabasco more than tripled. These ten central and southern states represented 12% of Mexican-born US residents in 1990; but by 2005 this had doubled to 24%. They accounted for almost 35% of net migration and received 40% of all remittances in 2005. The remittances helped considerably since many of these states are among Mexico's poorest. Migration to the USA and dependence on remittances are becoming a way of life for more and more Mexicans in the central and southern parts of the country.

Relatively few migrants come from southeast Mexico (Tabasco, Campeche, Yucatán and Quintana Roo) but the number is increasing. By 2005 about 100,000 were living in the USA. This is a significant number but far smaller than that for other regions of Mexico. Remittances are relatively unimportant representing less than 1% of state income.

Migration Trends

What has happened to migration flows during the past couple of decades? Net migration generally increased during the 1990s reaching 530,000 by 2000 (Figure 26.4). Then it dropped rather precipitously to around 369,000 by 2003, the largest three year decline since the 1930's. Migration rapidly recovered reaching about 550,000 by 2006 but fell to only 208,000 by 2008.

What caused the dramatic fluctuations? While there are numerous reasons for year to year changes, existing theory and available data strongly suggest that employment is the predominant cause. Migration flows and US employment data are very closely associated. The three years with the highest migration flows (1998–2000) in Figure 26.4 are the years with the lowest unemployment rates in the USA. Migration increased significantly in 2004 when US employment picked up and unemployment rates declined. For 1991 to 2004, the correlation coefficient between net migration and US unemployment is –0.90. The current worldwide economic downturn and high unemployment rates in the USA are greatly reducing the incentives for Mexicans to migrate. Net migration dropped by over 50% in 2008 to about 208,000. It is expected to drop even more in 2009–10 and could even become negative. Despite the recession in the USA, the number of Mexican-born migrants choosing to return home (about 400,000 a year) has not increased significantly since 2005.[10]

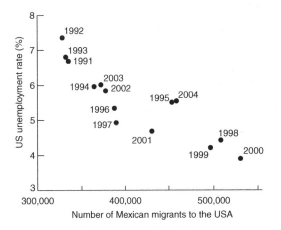

Figure 26.4 Migration and U.S. unemployment[9]

Two relatively large 2005 surveys in Mexico suggested that Mexican migration might continue for years.[11] Over 43% of 2400 surveyed Mexican adults indicated that they would go and live in the USA if they had the means and opportunity. More than one-fifth said they were inclined to live and work in the USA without legal authorization. The percentages were higher for males, young adults and those with relatives already in the USA. The interest in going to the USA crossed all socioeconomic groups; 35% of college graduates said they would go (if they had the means and opportunity). Since attitudes such as these do not change rapidly, these data suggest that the migration flow may continue for years as long as there are employment opportunities in the USA. This seems especially true considering that less than 10% of the over one million Mexicans caught entering the USA each year said they would give up trying.[12] The other 90% indicated that they would make additional attempts to cross the border. These data suggest migration flows to the USA might grow significantly after the US economy recovers from the current economic downturn.

Counterflow: Migration to Mexico

Echoing the flow of Mexicans seeking a brighter economic future in the USA, is a flow of illegal migrants from Guatemala and other Central American countries across Mexico's southern border to jobs in Chiapas (see box). But these migrants are very few in comparison with the total number of foreigners resident in Mexico, recorded as 493,000 in the year 2000.[13]

Unfortunately, the statistics on non-Mexicans residing in Mexico are nowhere near as comprehensive as those on Mexicans living in the USA. For instance, we have virtually no data for second or third generation foreigners and very little information on which to base an analysis of how the households of non-Mexicans compare with those of Mexicans in terms of incomes, education and demographic characteristics. Nevertheless, we can make some general observations, based on the 2000 census.

Seven states—Baja California, Chihuahua, Federal District, Jalisco, Tamaulipas, Michoacán and the State of Mexico—are home to more than 60% of all the non-Mexicans in the country. More than two-thirds of foreign residents were born in the USA

Central Americans coming north for opportunities in Mexico?

Is it possible that Chiapas, Mexico's most marginalized state, attracts illegal immigrants seeking work? Actually conditions in Chiapas are significantly better than they are in rural areas across the border in Guatemala and other Central American countries. Furthermore there are jobs in Chiapas that Mexicans prefer to avoid and thus are done by immigrants. For example, of the 300 scavengers at the Tapachula municipal dump in southern Chiapas, only about 15 are Mexican.[14] Most of the other 285 are from San Marcos across the border in Guatemala.

They live in tents on the horrible smelling dump site and suffer numerous health problems linked to trash burning and garbage handling. They come to the dump because the $2.75 to $4.00 a day they earn there is significantly more than they could make in San Marcos. Though very poor by Mexican standards, Chiapas is better off than many areas of Central America. Guatemalans moving to Chiapas to take low level jobs in many ways mirrors the migration of Mexicans to the USA.

---

and about 10% in Europe. About 54% of all residents born in Europe or South America live in the greater Mexico City region, either in the Federal District or in Mexico State. About 40% of all Central Americans in Mexico reside in Chiapas; they account for 93% of all that state's foreign residents. Of the migrants in the states along the northern border, more than 90% were born in the USA.

Whereas the majority of immigrants from Central America and the northern part of South America are female; the majority of Europeans choosing to reside in Mexico are male. According to the census, more than half of all US-born residents are under the age of ten; virtually all children born to Mexican immigrants in the USA. This contrasts markedly with immigrants from Spain where more than a third are over the age of 65. The majority of Central and South Americans and Europeans in Mexico are of working age.

27

Mexicans in the USA

After finishing his final gardening tasks on a Friday afternoon, Diego Gómez hurries to his Los Angeles home to help his spouse and two daughters pack for their trip home to Jalisco. It is their eleventh trip home in the 26 years he has worked in the USA.

"I want my girls to remember where they come from", says Diego, "I want them to remember our Mexican traditions". Like most Mexicans in the USA, the Gómez family maintains its Mexican identity and loyalty.

Like Diego, millions of Mexicans have a long history of working and living in the USA. Migration is one of the most important linkages between North America's two most populous countries. The Mexican diaspora in the USA (see box) is an integral part of both Mexican and US society. Each year roughly 250 million legal border crossings are made, about half by Mexicans. A much smaller number, perhaps

a few hundred thousand, cross the border illegally despite US efforts to tighten border controls. The Mexican communities on either side of the border are very closely linked.

As of 2008 over 31 million Mexicans lived in the USA (Figure 27.1). This is more than one fifth of all Mexicans anywhere and a larger number than in any single Mexican state. Almost 19 million Mexican-Americans were born in the USA of Mexican parentage; these have always outnumbered migrants (Figure 27.1).

Roughly 10% of everyone born in Mexico now lives in the USA. This figure was only 5% as recently as 1990 and only 1.4% in 1970.

Migrating Mexicans are as likely to move to the USA as within Mexico. Clearly, in recent decades, an increasing number of Mexicans have chosen to live in the USA.

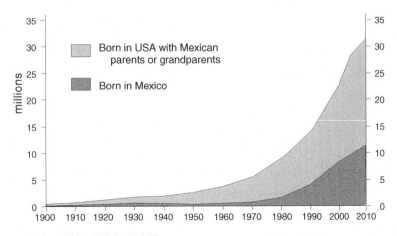

Figure 27.1 Mexicans in the USA, 1900–2008[1]

Table 27.1
Characteristics of Mexican migrants, compared to all USA-born residents, 2008[2]

	USA-born [a]	Mexican migrants[b]
Males	49%	57%
Median age (yrs)	35.7	35.4
USA citizens	100%	15%
Entered USA before 1990	na	35%
Entered USA before 2000	na	68%
Aged 0 to 18 years	27%	9%
Aged 18 to 64 years	60%	85%
Average household size	2.4	3.8
Married	60%	70%
Home owners	70%	44%
Over age 25 graduating high school	90%	39%
Over age 25 graduating college	30%	5%
Enrolled in school (K-12)	23%	9%
Annual earnings (median)	$31,000	$20,000
Full time year round workers	$40,000	$23,000
Annual household income (median)	$50,500	$33,300
Household income per person (median)	$21,042	$8,763
Poverty rate	12%	25%
Unemployment rate	5.3%	8.1%
Occupations: number employed (millions)	122.6	7.6
Management & professional	37.5%	7.5%
Sales & office support	26.1%	10.9%
Health care	6.7%	1.7%
Construction	5.5%	18.8%
Production & manufacturing	6.1%	13.9%
Cleaning & maintenance	3.5%	13.5%
Farming, fishing, forestry	0.6%	5.9%

[a] includes those born abroad of USA citizens.

[b] born in Mexico living in the USA

The Los Angeles Metro Area is said to be the second largest Mexican urban area in the world. One-tenth of all Mexican-Americans can trace their heritage to ancestors who lived in Mexico before part of its territory was annexed by the USA in the middle of the 19th century (see chapter 12). Others may have arrived in the USA only last week. Still, all 31 million consider themselves either Mexicans or Mexican-Americans.

About 12.7 million were born in Mexico. Many in this group have lived in the USA for many years; 35% entered the USA before 1990 and 68% entered before 2000 (Table 27.1). Despite living in the USA for a long time 55% are considered "undocumented", about 30% have legal documentation and 15% are now US citizens. About half of those who are now citizens entered the country illegally. The process to become legal can take a long time. Through various amnesty programs and other arrangements, almost 90% of those who entered illegally become legal US residents after being in the country for 25 years.

Mexican households in the USA

How do Mexican households in the USA compare to other US households? Whereas data are readily available comparing Mexico-born US residents (Mexican migrants) with all USA-born residents, data on the specific characteristics of Mexicans born in the USA are relatively scarce. What data are available suggest that the characteristics of Mexicans born in the USA are somewhere between Mexican migrants and all USA-born residents.

Compared to all USA-born residents, Mexican migrants are more apt to be male, between the ages of 18 and 49, less educated, poorer, married and renters (Table 27.1). In 2008 57% of Mexican migrants were male compared to 49% for USA-born residents. Many Mexican men migrate to the USA to support their families in Mexico. More Mexicans are married (70% versus 60%) because there are far more Mexicans between the ages of 18 and 49 (72% versus 42%). In many cases Mexican parents are counted as migrants but their children have been born in the USA and therefore are not counted as migrants. Consequently there are far fewer migrants in the 0 to 18 age group (9% to 27%) and far fewer migrants enrolled in school (9% versus 23%). These children, as well as extended families, explain why the average household size of migrant families is significantly larger.

Mexican migrants over age 25 have far lower levels of education. In 2008, only 38% had graduated from high school and 5% had college degrees, compared to 90% and 30% for USA-born residents. These data suggest that migrants have lower levels of education than Mexicans who do not migrate. The education differential largely explains the differences in median household income: $33,300 versus $50,500. On a per person basis, this gap is even larger: $8,763 compared to $21,042.[3] On the other hand some migrant households are doing very well; 22% had annual incomes over $62,000 and 6.6% over $100,000.

The enormous income gap explains the observed differences in poverty rate (25% versus 12%) as well as home ownership (44% compared to 70%). That 44% of migrant households own their own home is impressive, given their relatively low incomes. This observation and survey data indicate that many migrants intend to stay in the USA for many years. In a large 2004–2005 survey of 4,836 migrants in the USA, 59% indicated they expected to remain in the USA either "for the rest of my life" or "as long as I can."[4] Only 27% expected to stay for five years or less. By a ratio of over four-to-one, they said they would

---

Mexican diaspora

The term diaspora is used for a group of people (sharing a common ethnic identity) who migrate internationally and become an identifiable cultural group in another country. Their relocation is usually permanent. The cultural traits of traditions, dress and consumer habits that distinguish a particular diaspora eventually develop differently (diverge) from those of the population remaining in the country of origin.

The degree on this divergence depends on the distance and amount of interaction between cultural communities in the new and original countries. Language and religion tend to persist longer than most other cultural vestiges in a diaspora. The Mexican international diaspora is predominately in the USA. There are about 95,000 Mexicans in Canada, a sizeable group in Spain, and several thousand scattered among the other countries of the world, mostly in Europe and Latin America.

---

participate in any legal program that allowed them to cross the border legally if they eventually returned to Mexico. But since no such program exists most migrants intend to stay as long as they can and thus are considered permanent migrants.

How do migrant occupations compare with those of USA-born residents? Given the large income gap it is not surprising that few migrants are employed in higher income occupations. Migrants lag very significantly with respect to employment as managers or professionals, 7.5% versus 37.5% (Table 27.1). The data suggest that very few Mexicans with professional degrees migrate to the USA and it is very difficult for migrants to move up into managerial positions.

Migrants are also very under-represented in lower level white collar jobs in sales and office support, 11% to 26%. One major reason for this is their lack of English language capability; more than half of all migrants admit that they do not speak English well. English capability is related to the number of years lived in the USA and education level.

With low levels of education and English, migrants are over-represented in lower paid occupations like construction, factory work, cleaning and maintenance, and agriculture (Table 27.1). Several decades ago most Mexican migrants found work in agriculture. However, with increased mechanization employment in agriculture has declined. In 2008 about 6% of working migrants were employed in agriculture compared to only 0.6% of USA-born residents.

Many types of farm work are dominated by Mexican migrants. For example, the harvest of fruits and vegetables in California, the USA's leading agricultural state, is almost entirely dependent upon Mexican migrant workers. Increasingly California farm workers are Mexican women because the men have gravitated toward manufacturing and construction jobs which pay more than twice as much. Other migrants have gravitated toward service jobs.

Millions of migrants find work in relatively low level service jobs such as landscaping and gardening, restaurant work, car washing, and cleaning homes, hotel and motel rooms and office buildings. They represent the majority, sometimes the vast majority, of workers in these occupations in many parts of the USA.

Many services in California, Texas and other border states would be virtually nonexistent without migrant labor. The importance of these workers was dramatically illustrated in the 2004 film *A Day Without a Mexican*.

As USA-born residents gained more education and moved into white collar jobs, migrants started finding employment in blue collar jobs that paid far better than farm work or services. Some USA factories are becoming very heavily dependent on Mexican migrant workers. The animal slaughter and packing industry is particularly dependent. For example, the Tyson's Food chicken processing plant in Shelbyville, Tennessee now employs over 400 Mexicans, almost half of the total labor force, compared to fewer than 40 in 1993. Without the Mexican workers the plant would not be able to run two shifts. Tens of thousands of Mexicans are employed in meat packing plants throughout the USA from North Carolina all the way west to California.

Migrants are often hired to do dangerous jobs. The on-the-job death rate for Mexican migrant workers is now about 80% higher than that for USA-born workers. It was only about 30% higher in the mid-1990s. It is far higher now because many more migrants are now taking relatively dangerous construction and industrial jobs. On average more than one Mexican migrant a day dies on the job. The number of work related deaths is roughly equal to the number of deaths among illegal migrants crossing the border.

The situation is worst in the southeast, where the death rate for Mexicans is four times that for USA-born workers. A partial reason for this is that migrants to the southeast tend to be younger and have less English capability.

The lowest rates are in California and Texas, two states with good support systems for migrants. Migrant workers rarely receive safety training and are often not given safety equipment as required by the US government Occupational Safety & Health Administration (OSHA). Investigators claim that 90% of the deaths could have been avoided if employers complied with OSHA standards.

Most are killed while working in construction. Each year one of every 3100 Mexican construction workers is killed. This is nine times the rate for USA-born workers. For example, two teenage brothers were killed when the trench they were digging for a new suburban high school in South Carolina collapsed on them. They should have been attending a high school, not building one.

Where are the Mexican households in the USA?

During the past two decades Mexicans have moved to all corners of the USA. By 2008 the two most populous US states—California and Texas—were almost one third Mexican (Table 27.2). Interestingly, among the most popular names for new born males in each of these states, are José, Angel and Juan. Mexican families prefer to give their sons traditional Mexican names while they more often give their daughters Anglo names such as Jessica, Emily or Madison.

The number of people of Mexican heritage in the USA exploded from 13.5 million in 1990 to about 31 million in 2008. Over 60% live in California and Texas. Most of this rapid increase came from births in the USA as opposed to migration. Since 1990 the Mexican population of these two states increased by an impressive 80%; however, the increase for the other 48 states was an incredible 270% from 3.5 million to about 13 million. There was an almost tenfold increase in North Carolina and Georgia, which had relatively few Mexicans in 1990. The Mexican population of most other states has tripled since 1990. The heaviest concentration of Mexican-Americans is still in the southwest and west; there is also a sizeable number in and around Chicago (Figure 27.2).

Table 27.2 Location of Mexicans in the USA, 1990-2008

State	1990 ('000s)	2008 ('000s)	% increase since 1990	% of state population, 2008
California	6 119	10 970	79	29.9
Texas	3 891	7 100	82	30.6
Arizona	616	1 685	174	26.7
Illinois	624	1 500	140	11.7
Colorado	282	687	144	14.2
Florida	161	600	273	3.4
Nevada	85	502	491	19.5
Washington	156	489	213	7.2
Georgia	49	470	859	5.1
New Mexico	329	454	38	22.9
N. Carolina	33	413	1 152	4.6
New York	93	409	340	2.1
Total USA	13 500	31 000	130	7.3

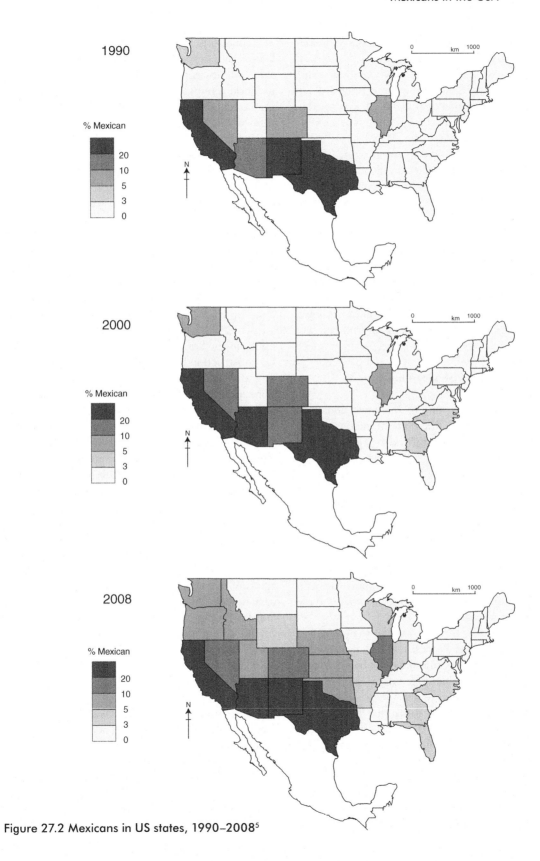

Figure 27.2 Mexicans in US states, 1990–2008[5]

The rapid employment growth in the southeast attracted a massive flow of migrants. The migrants in the southeast tended to be newly arrived young males without high school education, English fluency or legal immigration documents.[6] Most worked in either manufacturing or construction. The number of migrant workers in Alabama, Mississippi, Tennessee and Kentucky increased by an amazing 3808% between 1990 and 2000 and continued to increase until the 2008–10 economic slow down.

In general, migrants from specific areas of Mexico do not disperse widely in the USA. Rather they follow historical migration channels to specific areas of the USA. As described in chapter 25, migrants from Aguililla, Michoacán, head for Redwood City, south of San Francisco, while those from Napizaro, near Lake Pátzcuaro, move to North Hollywood. Similarly, migrants from Puebla end up in Brooklyn and Zapotecs from Oaxaca head for the San Fernando Valley.

How the USA views Mexican migration

Mexican migration is among the most controversial topics in the USA. There are numerous people who feel that migrants from Mexico take jobs away from US citizens, keep wage rates low, pay little or no taxes and crowd schools and other public services. These people are particularly incensed about "illegal" (undocumented) migrants and tend to view most Mexicans as "illegals."

This sentiment is particularly strong among lower income groups that feel the most threatened. Some feel that all Mexicans in the USA should be forced to learn English. They also believe that many Mexican males drink too much, are a public nuisance and are prone to commit crimes.

It was beliefs like these that led to the passage of California's infamous Proposition 187 in 1994. In general, the data do not support these beliefs except perhaps for the impact on wage rates.[7]

On the other hand, many people, including economists and employers, think that Mexican migrants are crucial to the US economy. They point out that many migrants take difficult, often dangerous, low-paying jobs that US citizens will not take. They claim that without migrant labor key crops could not be harvested, food processing plants could not meet demand, and services like housecleaning, gardening and car washing would become far more expensive.

Economists note that most migrants pay more in US taxes than they use in public services.[8] Survey research indicates that less than 4% of illegal migrants use food stamps and less than 10% have children in public schools. Two-thirds of migrants have federal taxes withheld from their paychecks. Since many do not work a full year and do not file tax returns, they generally do not obtain the tax refunds and earned income credits that they deserve.

The controversy is particularly heated when the US economy slows or goes into recession and unemployment rates creep up. When US unemployment rates were relatively high, as in 1991–93, 2002–3 and 2008, migration was relatively low. Conversely, in 1998–2000, when unemployment was low, migration levels were high.

When severe labor shortages occur such as for the clean-up effort after Hurricane Katrina hit New Orleans in 2005, thousands of Mexican workers show up to do the hot, nasty, dangerous work. When the US construction boom ended in 2007 about 150,000 migrants lost their construction jobs. During recessions such as the 2008–10 economic slowdown many migrants lose their jobs and some of these return to Mexico. In calendar year 2008 the unemployment rate for Mexican migrants increased from 3% to about 8% and the number of migrants entering the USA dropped by over 100,000 to just over 200,000. Even higher unemployment and lower migration are expected for 2009–10.

In general, Mexicans have a very positive attitude toward migration. It is not surprising that 80% of Mexicans in the USA say that migrants strengthen the USA because of their hard work.[9] The percentage is 89% for migrants born in Mexico and somewhat lower, 65%, for Mexicans born in the USA. Similarly, migrants born in Mexico have a more favorable attitude toward illegal migration than USA-born Mexicans.

US policy issues

The numerous changes in the way the US government has viewed migrants have been aptly described by some commentators as the flower petal policy: "I need you, I need you not, I need you…"

Obviously, US policy toward Mexican migration is controversial. President Bush supported a new temporary worker program that would have enabled Mexican workers to legally cross the border and work in the USA for a number of years. Some Democratic Party leaders supported a program that would lead to amnesty and legal status for many undocumented migrants. It appears that many powerful private enterprise groups are happy with the status quo which provides them with an enormous supply of cheap labor with virtually no government control over hiring practices.[10]

A number of populist groups and media personalities are loudly opposed to the massive influx of "illegal" migrant workers. Some anti-migrant vigilante groups have even been formed. In this situation it is not surprising that US government policy is essentially gridlocked. The Obama Administration has placed the immigration issue on a back burner while focusing on pressing economic and health care problems.

Most US citizens support tighter border restrictions to keep out illegal migrant workers and potential terrorists. From 1993 to 2005 the budget for border enforcement increased from $480 million (inflation adjusted) to $1.4 billion.[11] The Border Patrol increased from 3400 to 9700 agents. The increased resources are having an impact; over a million potential illegal migrants are being arrested each year. While apprehensions have increased dramatically since 1993, illegal border crossings have increased as fast or faster. Furthermore, over 90% of those apprehended indicated that they would try again to cross the border.

With the border more difficult to cross, more and more Mexicans are hiring professional smugglers ("coyotes") to get them into the USA often across the desert. Such crossings, especially in summer, result in about 400 deaths a year in normal times. During the 2008–10 economic downturn fewer Mexicans are trying to cross the border illegally; consequently fewer are dying in the process.

Many experts say that fortifying the border has not worked because it ignores the enormous draw of jobs in the USA. They also point out that instead of keeping illegal migrants out of the USA it is keeping them in. Surveys indicate that migrants previously used to travel back and forth from their jobs in USA to their families in Mexico.

With the stepped up border controls and growing cost of coyotes these migrants are opting to stay in the USA and bring their families to stay with them. Thus, the tougher border controls appear to have backfired resulting in increased migration of women and children. Many do not accept these facts and continue to demand ever stronger border controls.

Mexican government policy

Mexican leaders have changed their view of migration in recent decades. Migrants used to be regarded as somewhat disloyal citizens for leaving the country. But now they are seen almost as heroes who suffer separation from their families to work in the USA and send back billions of dollars that are crucial to the Mexican economy.

The government of Mexico views protecting the human rights of Mexican migrants in the USA as one of its primary responsibilities. This is particularly important because numerous groups in the USA have tried to restrict migrant access to human rights and public services. The Mexican government now has 54 offices and 41 consulates in the USA. There is one in Honolulu to serve the estimated 15,000 Mexicans in Hawaii, and one in Anchorage for the 20,000 Mexicans in Alaska. On frequent occasions the Mexican government has taken very strong positions with the US government concerning the treatment of Mexicans migrants in the USA.

The Mexican government has encouraged the development of hometown associations that maintain links and remittance flows between migrants in the USA and their areas of origin. Both federal and state governments have initiated several fund matching and other programs to channel remittances into productive, employment-generating activities. In general, these programs appear to be achieving their objective.

The future of the Mexican American community and migration

The Mexican-American community will continue to grow from its current 31 million in the decades ahead, mostly from births in the USA. Fertility levels in this community are declining but are higher than those of the USA as a whole. With increased numbers the community will become a growing force in the economy, politics and culture of the USA.

As with other immigrant groups, the language and cultural divide between Mexican Americans and other US residents will probably diminish in future decades. However, the linkages between Mexican-Americans and Mexicans in Mexico are expected to remain strong. The big question is what will happen to migration in the decades ahead.

Will the stream of migrants increase, level off, or decline? Some analysts think that migration has already peaked and will decrease in the future. Others feel that it may have slowed with the economic downturn in the USA but will accelerate again when the US economy recovers.

Migration theorists are divided on whether economically motivated migration is self-limiting or never-ending. This latter view contends that migration forms a vicious circle that drains supplying areas of energetic young workers and turns them into dependent nurseries and nursing homes. From this perspective, employment opportunities in the USA will continue to be far more attractive than those in Mexico. Thus the incentive for continued migration will continue unabated for decades. Furthermore, migrating to the USA has become such an integral part of the Mexican culture that it is expected to continue for generations except for periodic lulls when US unemployment rates are high.

Economic theory supports the view that migration is self-limiting. The idea is that eventually the incentive for migration diminishes as an oversupply of labor develops in the receiving area and the remittances invested in the donor area create well-paying jobs there. Another point is that rural migrants learn technical skills and become far more productive workers when they return. In addition, demographic changes may curtail the supply of labor in the sending area. This is happening in Mexico with its declining fertility rates.

There are many examples of massive economically motivated migration streams that have petered out. These include the migration of Europeans to North America in the 19th and early 20th centuries; the migration from Puerto Rico to the USA mainland; the rural to urban migration in Canada and the USA in the 19th and 20th centuries; and finally the flow of migrants into Mexico City from 1940 to 1970.

So the question remains, "Will migration increase in the years ahead, level off, or decline?" The weight of the evidence, largely influenced by Mexico's declining fertility, suggests that migration should diminish significantly in future decades. However, a series of scenarios analyzed by the Mexico's National Population Council (CONAPO) suggest that despite fertility declines and rapid economic growth in Mexico large flows of migrants to the USA should continue until 2030.[12]

It seems we will just have to wait and see. In any case, the diaspora of over 31 million Mexicans in the USA will clearly be a very important component of Mexican and USA society for many, many decades to come.

28

Quality of life in Mexico compared to other countries

In chapter 14 we discussed Mexican income levels, but quality of life involves several other things besides income. It also includes education, health, freedom, and security as well as having access to a broad range of opportunities. Being happy is an important, if not the most important, component of quality of life. In this chapter we will attempt to describe Mexico's quality of life and compare it to that of other countries. The chapter draws upon data measuring access to education and information, health, crime, political rights and income. We also will discuss the United Nations human development index and efforts to measure levels of happiness.

Education

Education is intrinsic to quality of life. It enables people to acquire knowledge, to better care for children, to live a healthier life, to make better decisions, to work more efficiently, to earn a higher income and to take advantage of a wider range of opportunities.

What is the status of education in Mexico? Education levels have increased in recent years but still have a way to go. Mexicans on average receive 7.2 years of schooling (Figure 28.1), up from 6.5 in 1990. The adult literacy rate is 92% compared to 67% in 1970. Almost everyone in Mexico can read and write. The 8% that are illiterate are mostly the elderly who didn't get sufficient schooling during their childhood in the 1940s and 1950s.

Almost all Mexican children now receive some primary schooling. About 90% complete the six-year primary school curriculum. About 60% attend three-year junior high school (*secundaria*, equivalent to US

junior high) which is compulsory for everyone under age 16. An encouraging 21% continue their education in either a trade and business school or in a senior high school (*preparatoria*) prior to attending university.

The amount of education received by Mexicans compares favorably with other major countries and regions of the world (Figure 28.1). Mexico is above average for Latin America and for the world. It is behind Argentina but way ahead of both Guatemala, its southern neighbor, and Brazil. Mexico is also ahead of China, the Middle East and many Asian countries.

The quality of education is difficult to measure. In some respects, the quality of public primary and sec-

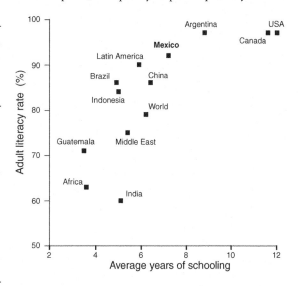

Figure 28.1 Literacy rates and years of schooling[2]

ondary education in Mexico is not adequate.[1] Quality is particularly poor in rural areas. But even in large urban areas the quality of public education may be an issue. For this reason about 12% of children attend private schools. In 2005 the number attending private schools was 4.1 million, an increase of 24% since 1999.

Access to education in Mexico contributes to the quality of life but would contribute much more if education levels were higher and the quality of education was better. This is particularly true for Mexicans living in rural areas.

UN Millennium Development Goals

More than 190 countries have signed up to the development goals, agreed in 2000. Mexico is well on its way to meet most of the eight goals (Table 28.1). Each goal has numerous specific targets. Specific targets that Mexico has not yet reached include an increase in the proportion of GDP that corresponds to the poorest 20% of the population (part of goal 1); an increase in the number of women in government (goal 3); a further decrease in maternal mortality (goal 5); an increase in forested area (goal 7) and an improved employment rate for young people aged 15–24 (goal 8).

Table 28.1 UN Millennium Development Goals[3]

	2015 goal	Met	On track	Falling behind
1	Eradicate extreme poverty and hunger		✓	
2	Achieve universal primary education	✓		
3	Promote gender equality and empower women		✓	
4	Reduce child mortality	✓		
5	Improve maternal health			✗
6	Combat HIV/AIDS, malaria and other diseases		✓	
7	Ensure environmental sustainability		✓	
8	Develop global partnership for development			✗

Access to information

How is access to information related to quality of life? It is similar to education in that it enables people to make better decisions, to work more efficiently, to earn more money and to take advantage of a wider range of opportunities.

Access to information has expanded rapidly in Mexico in the past few decades as literacy has increased and more homes have televisions and telephones. Cellular phones, and particularly the use of the internet, have revolutionized access to information.

Most Mexicans get their news from television. With about four people per TV set, Mexico has better access to TV than many areas of the world (Table 28.2). The 3% of Mexicans living in remote areas without electricity and access to TV signals are at a real disadvantage. Usually they must rely on radios.

Telephones are very important for intercommunication. In 2007 there were three times as many cellular phones as land-based telephone lines in Mexico. This is somewhat unusual for countries at Mexico's level of development and probably reflects both the difficulties associated with providing landlines to remote mountainous areas, and the policies of Mexico's largest telephone company (Telmex) which enjoyed a monopoly position for decades.

In 2007 there were 811 landlines and cell phones for every 1000 Mexicans. Of course one person may have several lines; a main home telephone, a cellular phone and a dedicated line at their office. Still, most Mexicans have access to either a private or public telephone. On the other hand, the majority still does not have a telephone in their home and thus are at a disadvantage because they cannot be rapidly contacted. In terms of telephone access Mexico lags behind Argentina, is about even with Brazil and China, and is ahead of India and most countries of the world (Table 28.2).

Radios are an important source of information for Mexicans who lack ready access to television, newspapers or the internet. With three radios for every ten Mexicans, virtually everyone has access. Radio access in Mexico is about the same as in China, but considerably lower than Argentina, Russia, or the world as a whole.

Newspapers as sources of information are still quite important but have declined relative to television and the internet. Still, many Mexicans read newspapers. There are about 17 Mexicans for every newspaper in circulation. Given that some newspapers are read by more than one person, the actual readership is higher.

The internet has led to a virtual explosion in information access. Currently only about 20% of Mexicans use the internet but this is increasing very rapidly. Internet cafes are opening throughout the country. With user fees below a dollar an hour, the majority of Mexicans are gaining access to information that was virtually unimaginable just two decades ago. Farmers are using the internet to get instant information on crop prices and weather conditions. Most Mexicans rely on word of mouth, television, radio and newspapers for their information, which contributes to their quality of life. The internet will contribute much more as usage grows.

Long and healthy life

Obviously, being healthy is a crucial aspect of quality of life. It might be the most important aspect. Life expectancy at birth is the most common measure of a long and healthy life. Though it is a measure of quantity of life, it is arguably the best single indicator for quality of life.

How long do Mexicans live? The 20th century brought dramatic increases in longevity. From under 30 years at the beginning of the century it rose to 38 by 1930. From there it went up to 50 by 1950 and reached 62 by 1970. By 2000 it was 72, almost double the 1930 value. Women live longer than men. Life expectancy for Mexican women is about 78; that for men is roughly 73 years. In the future Mexican longevity is expected to increase at about 2.5 years per decade. This is not as rapid as in the past but still significant.

It is not easy to find an accurate and reliable indicator of health. The most common indicator is infant mortality, the percentage of children who die before their first birthday. This simple indicator does actually provide a reasonably good measure of the general quality of health in a society.

Table 28.2 Access to information[4]

Country or region	TV sets /1000	Land phones /1000	Cell phones /1000	Radios /1000	News-papers /1000	Web users /1000	KOF index 2009 rank
USA	950	533	835	2080	226	725	38
Canada	728	555	617	1050	232	730	8
Mexico	**276**	**186**	**625**	**325**	**59**	**208**	**65**
Argentina	327	240	1022	683	97	259	63
Brazil	358	205	631	251	62	352	79
Guatemala	158	105	760	79	69	102	86
Peru	199	96	553	273	na	274	69
Latin America	303	178	663	na	na	na	na
Egypt	243	149	398	290	50	140	78
Ghana	52	16	324	134	15	38	110
Kenya	48	7	302	218	15	80	129
South Africa	195	96	871	323	55	82	54
China	380	275	412	336	108	160	91
India	98	34	200	120	135	69	122
Indonesia	152	77	353	156	31	56	100
Pakistan	82	29	384	104	79	107	116
Russia	350	310	1146	416	10	211	61
World	265	191	501	421	na	208	na

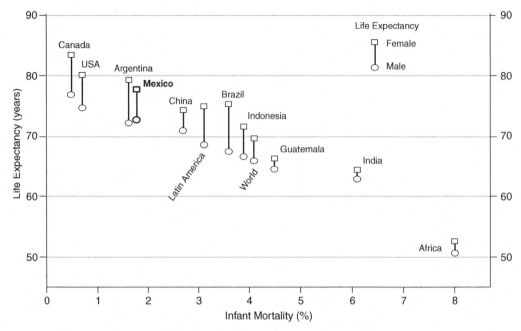

Figure 28.2 Infant mortality and life expectancy for a range of countries and regions[5]

Mexico has made impressive progress; its infant mortality rate dropped from 7.5% in 1970 to 1.7% by 2005. More improvements are expected in the years ahead.

Mexicans clearly are living longer and healthier lives than they did in past decades. How does Mexico compare to other major countries? Though Mexico trails Canada, the USA and Argentina (Figure 28.2), it is slightly ahead of Brazil, China and the weighted average for Latin America. Mexico is significantly ahead of Indonesia, the world average and its southern neighbor Guatemala.

Malnutrition and the nutrition transition

Malnutrition is commonly associated with people not getting enough to eat, potentially resulting in vitamin-deficiency diseases and an increased risk of starvation but the concept also includes, at the other end of the spectrum, over-nutrition and issues related to obesity. How prevalent is malnutrition in Mexico?

A National Nutrition Survey in 1999 of 23,000 households found that the type and incidence of malnutrition in Mexico had changed dramatically in a single generation. Rates of under-nutrition (insufficient intake of calories and/or vitamins for good health) have declined. This helped Mexico meet one of the key targets—a 50% reduction in the propor-

tion of children suffering from hunger (under-nutrition) between 1990 and 2015—of the UN Millennium Development Goals (see box), with several years to spare. Severe undernourishment (as defined by the World Health Organization) among children fell from 6% in 1988 to 2% in 1999.[6] The proportion of children under 5 years of age identified as underweight has been reduced from 14% in 1988 to 5% in 2006.[7]

However, the National Nutrition Survey simultaneously revealed startling increases in the numbers classified as either overweight or obese. These two categories of over-nutrition are measured by calculating the body mass index, a measure of weight adjusted for height. The percentage of women considered obese rose 160% between 1988 and 1999. In 1999 59% of women and 55% of men were either overweight or obese; by 2008 the figures were 64% and 60% respectively. Only the USA has higher rates of obesity.

Even more alarmingly, the rate of childhood obesity in Mexico is also increasing rapidly. A 2002 study found that 30% of elementary school children in Mexico City and 45% of adolescents were either overweight or obese.

The increase in over-nutrition has led to rapid rises in diet-related chronic diseases such as diabetes and cardiovascular disease. The overall effects of diseases on a country's population can be assessed by working out the disability-adjusted life years (DALY), the years of expected life lost through disease or premature death. In Mexico, the DALY lost to diseases normally thought to be more typical of the developed world such as diabetes, heart attacks and strokes is estimated to be three times greater than the DALY stemming from childhood and maternal under-nutrition.[8]

Mexico has passed rapidly through a "nutrition transition". The traditional Mexican diet was based on corn and beans, supplemented by fruits and vegetables with relatively little meat and dairy products. Over a 15-year period the average Mexican ate 29% less fruits and vegetables and 6% more carbohydrates while consuming 37% more soft drinks. In fact Mexicans enjoy the dubious distinction of being the world's second greatest consumers of soft drinks (after USA), downing 150 liters a year on average. White bread is replacing tortillas, fast food is replacing home cooking.

This nutrition transition, together with a more sedentary lifestyle, fueled a "disease transition", characterized by a shift from high mortality due to infectious diseases to high mortality from non-communicable chronic diseases. Mexico has the highest rate of diabetes in the world, more than 11%.[9] The total number with diabetes has risen seven fold since 1990. Diabetes is now the leading cause of death and costs the country more than $300 million annually, one-third of the public health care budget.

Mexico's role in the Green Revolution

The Green Revolution, which began in Mexico in the 1940s, refers to the application of science and technology to increase crop yields and agricultural productivity. In the Green Revolution, special high yield varieties (HYVs) of several cereals were developed. To grow most effectively they needed carefully calibrated applications of fertilizers, pesticides and water. The Green Revolution allowed countries to expand their cereal production to more than keep pace with the growing demands of their rapidly rising populations.

The initial stimulus for the Green Revolution was Mexico's desire to become self-sufficient in wheat. Rockefeller Foundation funding helped establish the Mexican Agricultural Program in 1943, an institution which later became CIMMYT, the International Wheat and Maize Improvement Center based in Texcoco near Mexico City.

Dr. Norman Borlaug directed a plant breeding program to develop new hybrid varieties of wheat and maize. These had higher yields and more resistance to common diseases. Successful strains were then crossed with dwarf or semi-dwarf varieties to reduce the height of the plants, preventing them from collapsing under the strain of the heavier ears of grain.

By 1963 95% of Mexico's wheat fields were growing the new seeds. Yields were much higher. The 1964 harvest was six times larger than in 1944. Whereas Mexico had imported half its wheat in 1943, by 1964 it was exporting 500,000 tons a year. (Since that time the combined effects of a growing population and farmers changing to other crops have returned Mexico to its previous status of being a net importer of wheat).

The success of the program was repeated elsewhere in the developing world. India's wheat production increased more than 400% between 1965 and 1986 turning India into the world's third largest producer. Pakistan became self-sufficient in wheat within three years of adopting the high yielding hybrids. A similar breeding program in the Philippines produced IR8 Miracle Rice which was quickly adopted with spectacular increases in yield throughout Asia.

The Green Revolution also boosted agriculture in developed nations. Corn yields in the USA, for example, quadrupled in 60 years.

In recognition of his pioneering work, in 1970 Borlaug was awarded the Nobel Peace Prize, becoming the first non-politician to do so.

In recent years CIMMYT has developed strains of wheat that are resistant to the deadly Ug99 strain of stem rust fungus, first identified in Uganda in 1999, which threatens world wheat supplies. Existing wheat hybrids had resistance to several other forms of wheat rust but not Ug99 which quickly spread to wheat fields in Iran and looked set to enter southern Asia. A new CIMMYT-developed wheat variety, immune to Ug99, has been planted in Bangladesh, Nepal, Pakistan and other countries in an effort to halt its spread.[10]

Crime

Crime, particularly violent crime, is detrimental to the quality of life. Crime has always been a problem but has received greater attention in recent years as crime rates have increased. Reported crimes in Mexico increased by about 70% between 1991 and 1998.[11]

The accuracy of crime rate data is always suspect. Police records only include crimes reported to the police. Large surveys which ask people if they have been victimized by crime always indicate that the true crime rate is far higher. The main reason given by Mexicans for not reporting crimes is that reporting the crime doesn't do any good. Survey data indicate that 77% of crimes in Mexico City and 74% of those in Monterrey are never reported.[12] The rates are a bit lower for other cities: 45% for Guadalajara and 38% for Tijuana. This clearly suggests that many urban Mexicans lack confidence in their law enforcement agencies.

How do crime rates in Mexico compare with other major countries? Given the problems of crime data and lack of cross-national uniformity, international comparisons must be taken with several grains of salt. That being said, there are some data that enable international comparisons.

At the most general level, the overall crime rate, Mexico does quite well. For every 1000 Mexicans there were 14 crimes reported in 2005 (Table 28.3). This is less than the rate in Japan and about 1/6th that of the UK, USA or Canada. However, overall crime is not a good measure of crime related to quality of life. Many so-called victimless crimes such as the use of illicit drugs do not have much impact on the quality of life of the general populous.

Violent and property crimes have a clear impact on the quality of life. The murder rate (about one murder per year for every 4000 people in 2006) has increased sharply in recent years. Mexico's murder rate is a third lower than that of Colombia or South Africa, but is 13 times higher than that of the UK or Canada.

Robberies (the taking of something of value from a person by force) are a frequent crime in Mexico. They affect about one in every 500 people each year, or about one in every 100 families. The robbery rate in Mexico is very high by world standards, only surpassed by South Africa and a handful of other countries. It is over twice the rate of Canada and about 50% higher than that in the USA.

Burglaries (the unlawful entering of a property with the intention of committing a crime, usually theft) are also a serious problem, directly affecting

Table 28.3 Security: freedom from crime[13]

Country or region	Total crimes /1000	Murders /1000	Robberies /1000	Burglaries /1000	Car thefts /1000	Prisoners /1000
UK	86	0.02	1.58	13.91	5.6	124
USA	82	0.06	1.41	7.23	4.0	738
South Africa	80	0.39	4.60	9.22	2.3	335
Canada	77	0.02	0.83	9.11	5.0	107
South Korea	32	0.02	0.10	0.06	na	97
Russia	20	0.17	0.91	na	0.2	611
Japan	19	<0.01	na	2.33	2.4	62
Mexico	**14**	**0.25**	**2.05**	**1.40**	**1.5**	**196**
Colombia	5	0.38	0.58	0.32	0.8	134
Turkey	4	na	0.02	0.20	na	91
India	2	0.03	0.03	0.10	na	30
Indonesia	na	0.01	0.26	na	0.1	45

about one of every 150 families each year. The threat of burglary is a major reason why most homes in Mexico are protected by iron bars. On the positive side, Mexico's burglary rate is a tenth that of the UK and about a fifth that of the USA. It is even lower than the rate in Japan but is much higher than the reported rates for Columbia, Turkey and India. Of course, we must remember that many burglaries in Mexico go unreported.

Mexico is also plagued with a serious car theft problem. While its rate per 1000 of the population is far less than that of Canada or the USA, there are far fewer cars in Mexico. Each year about one of every 90 cars in Mexico is stolen, compared to roughly one in 110 for Canada and about one in 200 for the USA.

Crime itself obviously affects the quality of life of its victims. But only about one or two percent of Mexicans are crime victims each year. On the other hand, the threat of crime affects everyone's quality of life. The threat is particularly great to those who live in cities and have material possessions such as cars, expensive jewelry, costly household electronics or money. The quality of life of Mexico's wealthy class is also diminished by the threat of kidnapping.

Freedom

Most people would agree that freedom is very important to quality of life. But what do we mean by freedom? We are talking about such things as free speech, freedom from oppression, freedom to assemble and organize, freedom of religion and the freedom to elect government officials. These concepts are not easy to measure. Luckily, an organization called Freedom House systematically scores all world countries on two dimensions of freedom, namely, political rights and civil liberties.[15]

Political rights involve numerous questions. Are elections free and fair? Are there competitive parties or other political groupings? Is there a political opposition and does it play an important role? Can voters freely choose from among candidates? Are candidates chosen independently of the state? Do those who are elected actually rule? It also looks at political corruption, political violence, political discrimination against minorities and foreign or military influence on politics.

Civil liberties include freedom of speech, assembly, association, education and religion. Is there a

Table 28.4 Freedom House indicators, 2005[14]

Country	Political rights	Civil liberties	Freedom rating
Canada	1	1	Free
USA	1	1	Free
South Africa	1	2	Free
South Korea	1	2	Free
Mexico	**2**	**2**	**Free**
Ghana	2	2	Free
Brazil	2	3	Free
India	2	3	Free
Peru	2	3	Free
Argentina	2	3	Free
Turkey	3	3	Partly Free
Kenya	3	3	Partly Free
Indonesia	3	4	Partly Free
Guatemala	4	4	Partly Free
Nigeria	4	4	Partly Free
Russia	6	5	Not Free
Pakistan	6	5	Not Free
Egypt	6	5	Not Free
China	7	6	Not Free

just and equitable legal system and rule of law? Is there severe censorship? Is there a reasonable right to privacy? Are minority religions and ethnic groups free of oppression?

The Freedom House scores go from one (the most free) to seven (the least free). In 1999, Mexico rated three on political rights and four on civil liberties for an overall freedom rating of "partly free". Freedom in Mexico has improved significantly in recent years. By 2005 it had earned a two in both categories and was classified as "free" (Table 28.4).

How does Mexico compare to other major countries of the world? Actually Mexico scores quite well but not as well as Canada, the USA, and most European countries. On the other hand, it scores as well or better than all South American, and almost all African and Asian countries. It also scores far better than Russia and China. While there is some room for improvement, the freedoms enjoyed by Mexicans add to their overall quality of life.

Income: freedom from want and hunger

Everyone would agree that freedom from want and poverty is an important component of quality of life. In an earlier chapter we saw that the Mexican economy is quite robust but the benefits are distributed very unevenly. Poverty is a major problem. Lack of sufficient income adversely affects the quality of life of millions of Mexicans.

It is important to distinguish between absolute poverty and relative poverty. Absolute poverty is lacking the means to acquire a basic standard of living—food, shelter, health care, etc. Relative poverty is how impoverished the poor are compared to mainstream society. It also looks at how poor people feel when compared to others. For example, the lower 20% in the USA feel poor but they have an annual per person income of almost $11,000 a year, about $44,000 for a family of four. On the other hand, a Pakistani family of four with $40,000 a year feels wealthy because they are in the upper 20% of Pakistani society. Many Mexicans feel poor when they see the relatively affluent lifestyle of middle class Mexican families on television.

Given its overall robust economy, it is unfortunate that Mexico has such a serious poverty problem.

The level of absolute poverty in Mexico is among the worst of major world countries. The poorest 20% of the population get only about $1848 per person or only about one-sixth of the national average. This is only slightly better than India or Indonesia, countries that are not as rich as Mexico.

Relative poverty in Mexico is a particularly acute problem because the lower 20% in Mexico get less than 4% of national income (Figure 28.3). They are extremely poor compared to the upper classes in Mexico and the extreme wealth of its northern neighbor. Among major countries, only Brazil and South Africa are worse. In terms of relative poverty Indonesia and India are far better than Mexico, while China, Russia and the USA are significantly better.

The quality of life of lower income Mexicans is severely limited by poverty. Ameliorating the extent and consequences of poverty is a major challenge.

Human Development Index

In this chapter we have looked at quality of life in terms of access to education and information, living a long and healthy life, crime, political and civil rights as well as income. Is there any way to combine these various measures to get an overall indicator of

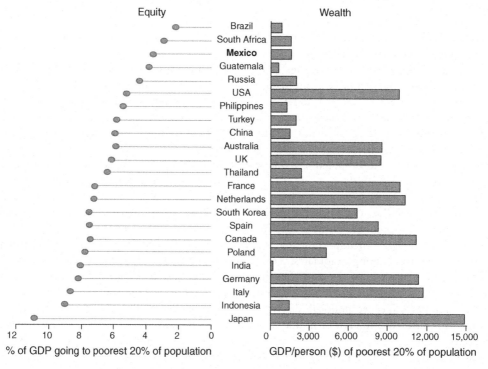

Figure 28.3 Equity and wealth for the poorest 20% of population in a range of countries[16]

quality of life or overall level of human development? Such an indicator would be useful in monitoring improvements and comparing countries.

The United Nations (UN) has been working on this issue for several decades. In their view,

> The basic purpose of development is to enlarge people's choices…. In principle, these choices can be infinite and can change over time. People often value achievements that do not show up at all, or not immediately, in income or growth tables: greater access to knowledge, better nutrition and health services, more secure livelihoods, security against crime and physical violence, satisfying leisure hours, political and cultural freedoms and sense of participation in community activities. The objective of development is to create an enabling environment for people to enjoy long, healthy and creative lives.[17]

The UN has developed a composite human development index (HDI) which is often used to compare the quality of life in different countries. Their approach is based on three basic dimensions of human development: a long and healthy life; education and knowledge; and a decent standard of living. While the UN's HDI does not include political freedom, civil liberties or freedom from crime, it is the most widely recognized and used indicator of quality of life.

How does Mexico stack up on the HDI scale? Figure 28.4 indicates that Mexico had an HDI score in 2005 of 0.829. This puts Mexico behind Argentina, but ahead of Russia, Brazil and China.

Mexico has made impressive progress since 1975. Its HDI score moved up 0.145 points indicating that human development and the quality of life have improved significantly during the past three decades. Mexico's improvement has begun to narrow the gap with Canada, the USA and Argentina, though some other countries, including Brazil and Guatemala, have made even more progress. The largest increases, over 0.200 points, were experienced by Egypt, Indonesia, China, South Korea and India. On the other hand, the HIV/AIDS pandemic has resulted in almost static HDIs for numerous African countries such as South Africa and Kenya. Turmoil in Russia following the breakup of the Soviet Union caused its HDI to decline significantly after 1991.

It is interesting to note that Argentina achieved a HDI level of 0.800 about 20 years before Mexico. Mexico reached a HDI level of about 0.750 about 20 years before Peru, China and Turkey. If Mexico maintains its current rate of HDI improvement, it will reach the 1975 HDI levels of Canada and the USA in about 2015.

Comparing Mexico to its NAFTA partners

In general, the quality of life in Mexico trails its northern neighbors Canada and the USA. It might be useful to try to determine how far behind Mexico is. In terms of HDI scores, it appears that Mexico is perhaps forty to fifty years behind.

Mexico's current education and literacy levels are about equal to those of Canada and the USA in the 1950s. On the other hand, Mexico's widespread television, telephone and internet access puts it only about a decade behind its northern neighbors in terms of access to information. Mexico's current health indicators are similar to those of Canada and the USA in the 1970s.

Purchasing power in Mexico is similar to that of its northern neighbors about forty or fifty years ago. However, Mexicans today can buy many products that were not available forty years ago such as modern

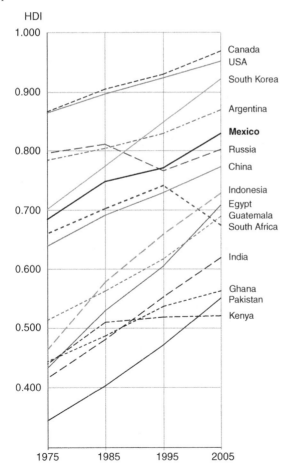

Figure 28.4 Human Development Index[18]

medicines, internet access, personal computers, hand calculators, digital devices, low-cost color televisions, etc. Thus, it is difficult to compare Mexico's current purchasing power with historical levels of its northern neighbors.

In general it appears that the quality of life today in Mexico is about similar to that of its northern neighbors during the 1960s. The quality of life in Canada and the USA was considered to be quite good during the 1960s. In fact, some feel it was better then than it is now!

Happiness

All of the indicators described above overlook one very important dimension in quality of life. That dimension is happiness. To many people, feeling happy and satisfied with one's life is more important than education, health or income. On the other hand, education, health and income often contribute to happiness and satisfaction.

Measuring level of happiness is more subjective and challenging than measuring other aspects of quality of life. Since the 1990s researchers have been collecting survey data and working on methods to compare levels of happiness among nations.[19] This involved integrating data from hundreds of diverse surveys undertaken by scores of researchers using a variety of methodologies. Researchers compiled and synthesized data on 90 countries. Their results indicate a mild positive relationship between happiness and other quality of life indicators, with numerous exceptions. Table 28.5 presents happiness scores for some major countries. The scores in the table are not precise and differences between countries of less than 0.3 should not be considered significant.

Mexico's happiness score of 7.5, places it the upper 20% of the 90 countries analyzed. The data indicate

Table 28.5 Happiness scores[20]

Country	Score	Country	Score
Switzerland	8.1	France	6.5
Canada	7.6	Nigeria	6.4
Mexico	**7.5**	South Korea	6.3
Colombia	7.5	India	6.2
USA	7.4	Japan	6.2
Germany	7.3	Bangladesh	6.0
UK	7.2	Peru	6.0
Brazil	7.0	Turkey	5.9
Argentina	6.8	South Africa	5.4
China	6.7	Russia	4.4
Indonesia	6.6	Ukraine	3.6
Guatemala	6.6	Tanzania	3.2

that Mexicans in general are a happy people, about as happy as people from Canada, the USA and Colombia. In general, Mexicans are happier than people from such countries as the UK, Brazil, Argentina, China, France, India, Japan and Russia.

The information presented in this chapter indicates that most Mexicans enjoy a good quality of life and are relatively happy. Unfortunately, more detailed specific data are not available on Mexico's lower income groups. As a result we cannot be certain of the extent to which they share the general happiness and quality of life enjoyed by most Mexicans. The next chapter looks at variations in quality of life for different areas of Mexico.

29

Variations in quality of life within Mexico

The previous chapter shows us that Mexico enjoys a relatively high quality of life compared to most of the rest of the world. This chapter addresses a number of related questions. Which parts of Mexico have the highest quality of life? Which have the lowest? How do urban areas compare with rural areas? Are all rural areas similar in terms of education, health and quality of life?

Chapter 14 revealed that per person income levels in some states are four to five times that in others. But income is only a small part of quality of life. As we discussed in chapter 28, quality of life is usually measured by such things as education, access to information, health, crime, political freedom, income and housing. Overall happiness is also important. Quality of life is also influenced by interpersonal relations, climate, culture and environmental factors such as beautiful scenery and absence of pollution.

Finding relevant data on all quality of life variables is not easy. Obtaining such data on areas within a country can be extremely difficult. Fortunately, Mexico's National Population Council (CONAPO) has developed two comprehensive measures which incorporate education, health, housing, income and access to urban services. This chapter depends heavily on the most recent data from two CONAPO measures: marginalization (2005) and human development index (HDI, 2000). We also look at some information on crime. Unfortunately, data are not available on the general levels of satisfaction or happiness for different areas within Mexico. In addition we have not attempted to measure the impact of culture and environmental factors such as climate on the quality of life.

Crime

Crime rates in Mexico are very low in some areas, but extremely high in others. Which places have the highest crime rates? Getting an accurate answer to this question is not easy. As noted in the previous chapter, crime data are notoriously inaccurate.

In general, crime rates are related to community size. Rates are lowest in rural areas and small towns. Urban areas have higher rates and large metropolitan areas have the highest rates. Within metropolitan areas, crime rates differ significantly from one neighborhood to another and even from one street to another. The data that are available for different states indicate that crime rates are highest in Baja California, Baja California Sur, Sonora, Chihuahua, Morelos, Yucatán and Quintana Roo.[1]

Domestic violence is a particularly serious problem which greatly affects the quality of life for Mexican families. In 2003 a surprising 47% of women over age 15 and 29% of children reported being abused during the previous year, either physically, emotionally or sexually.[2] Available information indicates that rates are highest in the Federal District, Baja California, Chihuahua, Campeche and Sonora. Rates are lowest in Nuevo León, Tamaulipas and Yucatán.

Variations among states

The CONAPO data used for marginalization and human development index (HDI) make it relatively easy to compare states in terms of quality of life. Marginalization is similar to poverty and roughly the opposite of HDI or quality of life. The CONAPO

The geography of minimum wages

In terms of minimum wages, Mexico is divided into three zones. In 2009 the minimum wage in Zone A (Mexico City, Baja California, Baja California Sur, Acapulco, all major northern border cities and parts of Veracruz) was 54.80 pesos (about $4.18) for an 8-hour work day. It was 53.26 pesos in Zone B (Monterrey, Guadalajara, parts of Sonora, Tampico, Altamira and some other medium-sized cities) and 51.95 pesos in Zone C (the remainder of the country).

The minimum wage is used as the basis not only for labor agreements but also for contracts such as rental agreements. To obviate the need for periodic inflationary adjustments, it is also used in the calculation of maximum penalties for many criminal offences and even for traffic violations! Government policy in recent years has tended to reduce the disparities between the minimum wages in each of the three zones, in order to promote the economic development of poorer areas (Zone C).

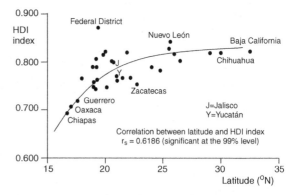

Figure 29.1 Correlation between latitude and HDI

marginalization indicator for communities is composed of the nine percentages: illiteracy and not finishing primary school for those over age 15, as well as those living without sewers, electricity, piped water, in crowded housing, with dirt floors, in localities of less than 5000 population and making less than twice the minimum wage.

The CONAPO human development index (HDI) parallels the UNPD indicator and uses four variables: life expectancy at birth, literacy over age 15, percentage of 6 to 24 year olds attending school and adjusted per person income in US dollars. Reliable life expectancy at birth data are not available at the municipal level, so CONAPO substituted infant mortality data.

What parts of Mexico have the lowest quality of life? We saw in chapter 24 that marginalization is related to lack of access. Rural areas, particularly isolated rural areas, are the most marginalized. This implies that the most rural states would be the most marginalized. Is this true?

It turns out that the three most marginalized states, which also have the lowest HDIs, are among the most rural: Guerrero, Chiapas and Oaxaca. In

these contiguous states, about one in five persons over age 15 is illiterate and less than three in five have completed primary school. Over 6% lack electricity; one in four does not have piped water; and one in three lives on dirt floors. Over 70% of workers earn less than about $8/day or $2,500/year (twice the minimum wage, see box).

Aside from being rural, what other factors are common among highly marginalized, low HDI states? In general, HDI scores are lowest for the southern states and highest for the northern states along the USA border. There is a close connection (rs = 0.6186, significant at the 99% level) between the HDI of each state and its latitude (Figure 29.1). The main exceptions to this general rule are the Federal District which is not in the north but has the highest HDI and Zacatecas, a non-southern state with a relatively low HDI score.

The Federal District has the highest HDI in Mexico but how does it compare with places elsewhere in the world? Its HDI score in 2000 of 0.871 placed it just behind South Korea and Portugal and ahead of where the USA and Canada were in 1975.

Chiapas, Oaxaca and Guerrero have the lowest HDI scores. They trail the Federal District by about 0.165 HDI points or roughly 35 years. However, we should note that in terms of HDI Mexico's three poorest states are even with El Salvador, slightly behind China but ahead of Indonesia and Egypt.

In looking at the differences among states, it is useful to focus on the specific factors that go into HDI and marginalization. The variation in life expectancy is relatively small. The lowest, 72.4 years for Chiapas, is only 2.9 years below the national average, which is 2.9 years less than the Federal District. The current life expectancy in Chiapas is equal to what it

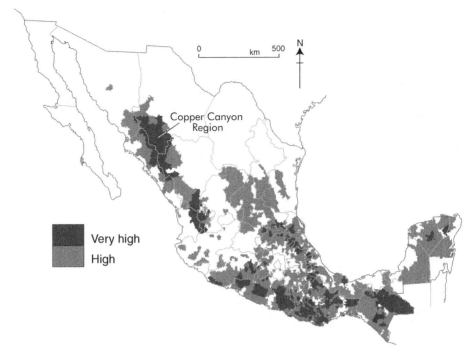

Figure 29.2 Municipalities with high levels of marginalization, 2005[3]

was in the Federal District in 1981. The gap in infant mortality rates is also not that great, 31.9 (per 1000) in Chiapas versus 19.8 for the capital. Mexico has been relatively successful in delivering the benefits of modern health care to all its citizens.

Differences in adult literacy are significant. The Federal District literacy rate of 97.4% in 2005 was 19% higher than that in Chiapas. The gap was even larger for the over 45 age group: 56.6% for Chiapas versus 93.0% for the capital. In Chiapas about 43% of those over age 15 did not complete primary school compared to less than 10% in the capital. In the years ahead, as current students mature and enrollments continue to increase in lagging areas, the gap will close and Mexico's overall education levels will increase significantly. This will contribute a great deal to improvements in health, income, and overall quality of life.

Housing is significantly better in the north and the capital, where roughly 99% have electricity compared to about 94% in Guerrero, Oaxaca and Chiapas. Overall, 97.5% have electricity which is impressive given that so many Mexicans live in very remote locations. Only about 4% in northern states live on dirt floors or lack piped water compared to over a quarter in the south.

The greatest inequality among states is with economic indicators. While there are low income workers in all areas of the country, there are more in the south where over 65% earn less than twice the minimum wage compared to about 25% in the north. The largest gap is in income per person. The value for the Federal District is over twice the national average and over five times that of Chiapas or Oaxaca. It is the enormous differences in income per person that account for most of the variation in the HDI values among states.

Variations among cities and municipalities

The discussion above reveals large quality of life inequalities among states. Do cities and municipalities exhibit similar inequalities? Actually, the inequalities within states are significantly greater than those between states.

For analytical purposes, CONAPO divides Mexican municipalities into four levels based on their HDI score. Of Mexico's 2442 municipalities in 2000, 31 of the poorest had HDI scores under 0.500 and were classified as "low." Fortunately, only about 0.35% of the population live in these 31 very remote, mostly indigenous municipalities, 15 of which are in Oaxaca, seven in Guerrero, seven in Chiapas and two in Veracruz. They are mainly involved in semi-subsistence farming and have HDI scores similar to Pakistan, Bangladesh, Nigeria, and Haiti.

At the next level up are 625 municipalities in the "medium low" group with HDI scores between 0.500 and 0.649. About 6% of the population lives in these rather remote municipalities. They are mostly in the poorer southern states though some are located in mountainous areas farther north. Traditional agriculture is the main activity. This group has human development levels similar to India, Egypt, Ghana, Morocco and Guatemala.

Further up is the "medium high" group with HDI scores between 0.650 and 0.800. The 1584 municipalities in this group cover most small urban and rural areas of the country. The 46% of Mexicans in this group live in municipalities with HDI scores

similar to China, Russia, Indonesia, Saudi Arabia, Brazil and Venezuela.

At the top of the list are the "high" municipalities with HDI scores above 0.800. Almost half (47%) of all Mexicans live in these 202 municipalities which include virtually all the large urban areas as well as many smaller cities and even some rural communities. These 202 municipalities represent modern Mexico and have human development characteristics similar to Poland, Kuwait, Argentina, Chile and Costa Rica.

The HDI scores by themselves do not tell the whole story. Table 29.1 provides selected quality of life indicators for four states: Chihuahua in the north, the State of Mexico in the center and Guerrero and Chiapas, both in the south. Three types of municipalities are shown for each state: a major city,

Table 29.1 Municipality variations in quality of life[4]

Place (municipality)	2005 population	2000 Census data			2005 Marginalization data (% of people)			
		HDI	Infant deaths /1000	Adjusted income/ person (US$)	Not literate age 15+	Did not finish primary school	Live with no piped water	<200% minimum wage
National	103 263 388	0.790	25	7 495	8	23	10	45
Chihuahua	3 241 444	0.820	23	10 324	4	19	6	27
Chihuahua City	758 791	0.863	19	13 741	2	10	2	15
Casas Grandes	8 413	0.764	26	4 695	4	32	10	44
Batopilas	13 298	0.513	60	1 451	43	67	71	56
Federal District	8 720 916	0.873	20	17 696	3	10	2	33
Benito Juárez	355 017	0.930	18	35 594	1	4	0	18
México State	14 007 495	0.790	22	5 672	5	16	6	41
Toluca	747 512	0.849	20	14 046	5	13	7	32
Otumba	29 873	0.735	25	2 936	7	23	5	56
Sultepec	24 986	0.611	37	1 215	26	48	44	55
Guerrero	3 115 202	0.718	30	4 112	20	36	31	65
Acapulco	717 766	0.806	21	8 280	9	21	18	60
San Marcos	44 959	0.646	31	1 407	25	45	60	79
Metlatónoc	17 398	0.363	67	417	61	76	29	87
Chiapas	4 293 459	0.690	32	3 302	21	43	26	78
Tuxtla Gutiérrez	503 320	0.819	19	8 116	7	18	17	51
Solosuchiapa	7 900	0.638	37	1 921	24	50	27	90
Sitalá	10 246	0.451	54	1 029	56	76	59	88

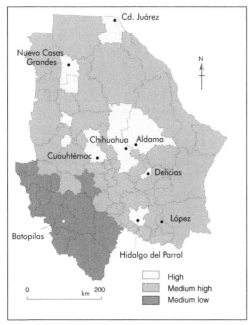

Figure 29.3 HDI in Chihuahua[5]

a median or typical rural area and one of the poorest rural areas. For comparison, data are also given for the Federal District and its most affluent area Benito Juárez, a community of about 350,000 just south of the city center.

In each of the four states the major city is much better off than the typical rural area which in turn has a far better quality of life than the poorest rural area. Compared to a major city in the same state, rural areas have significantly higher rates of illiteracy, lack of electricity and wages below twice the minimum wage. In the poorest municipalities these rates are multiple times that of the major city. Inequality is greatest for income per person. Compared to major cities, rural incomes usually are less than a third. Incomes in the poorest rural areas are extremely low; for example, the income in Sultepec is less than a tenth that in Toluca. Clearly, there are extreme inequalities within states.

The levels of inequalities within states tend to be greater in the poorer southern states which have large areas of extreme rural poverty (Figure 29.2). However, great inequalities are found in some northern states such as Chihuahua and Durango which have severe poverty in remote mountain areas.

Chihuahua is a prosperous state. The quality of life in its eponymous capital city is among the best in the country: average income is almost twice the na-

tional average and the city has very low levels of illiteracy, homes without electricity and persons earning less than twice the minimum wage. Its HDI of 0.863 is similar to that of the Czech Republic. Chihuahua's other cities such as Hidalgo del Parral and Ciudad Juárez also score well

In contrast, the remote southwestern Chihuahua municipalities in the Western Sierra Madre, in the area known as the Copper Canyon, are some of the most marginalized in Mexico. These municipalities with lower HDIs are prominent in Figure 29.3 and closely linked to patterns of indigenous culture (chapter 10) and cultural regions (chapter 13). The community of Batopilas in this area is among the most marginalized municipalities in all Mexico. Over 65% of homes have no electricity; its rate of illiteracy is 25 times that of Chihuahua City and its income is about a tenth. Its HDI in 2000 was the same as that of Kenya. Fortunately, Batopilas is not typical of most Chihuahua rural communities. Casas Grandes, for example, enjoys a far better quality of life.

Extreme inequalities are also apparent in the State of Mexico (Figure 29.4). The high HDI municipalities are immediately north of the Federal District, in Amecameca (in the east) and around the state capital Toluca (in the center of the map). The low HDI areas are the remote rural areas in the west and southwest. Incomes in Toluca are five times those in typical rural areas and ten times those in Sultepec in the southwestern part of the state.

Guerrero exhibits a similar pattern (Figure 29.5). At the top are Acapulco and the state capital Chil-

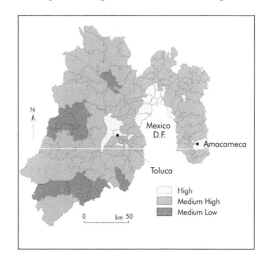

Figure 29.4 HDI in the State of Mexico[6]

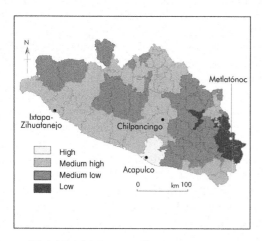

Figure 29.5 HDI in Guerrero[7]

pancingo which is only 0.011 points from the "high" category. Most of the municipalities in the "medium high" category are along the coast and the main highway north from Acapulco through Chilpancingo to Mexico City. Acapulco which has a relatively low quality of life for a major city still has an average income six times that in typical rural areas of Guerrero and 20 times that in Metlatónoc. This municipality in eastern Guerrero is one of the poorest in Mexico; it has 60% illiteracy, 42% of homes are without electricity and its income per person in 2000 was only $417. (The dubious distinction of having the lowest HDI in Mexico falls on the adjacent municipality of Coicoyán de la Flores in the state of Oaxaca). The HDI scores of Metlatónoc and surrounding communities in Guerrero and Oaxaca are similar to those of Ethiopia, Afghanistan and Burundi, three of the poorest countries on the planet.

World renowned program to fight poverty

Oportunidades (Opportunities) is a government social assistance program to help families overcome poverty. Begun in 2002, it is an extension of *Progresa*, a program which started in 1997. *Oportunidades* provides conditional cash transfers every two months to families which meet specific geographic and economic criteria of poverty. The transfers only continue if family members meet a series of goals including children's regular attendance at school and family visits to the nearest clinic for regular nutrition and health advice. Additional economic incentives are offered for the completion of each grade of school with special emphasis on ensuring that girls complete high school. The payment recipients are usually mothers, who make most child and family health decisions.

In 2008, *Oportunidades* managed a budget of $3.6 billion. This budget is managed very efficiently with only 4% going towards administrative expenses and on-going research. It helps 5 million families, about one-quarter of all families in Mexico. These families tend to live in the most marginal communities. *Oportunidades* operates in 93,000 different localities throughout the country, 86% of which are in rural areas. In Chiapas the program helps 61% of all families. The corresponding figures for two other poor states—Oaxaca and Guerrero—are 53% and 52% respectively.[8]

How successful has the program been?

In eleven years what has been achieved? Enrollment in junior high schools has risen 30% for 14-year-olds. The graduation rate from high schools is 23% higher for those supported by *Oportunidades* than for those not in the program. In rural areas, teens with five and half years in the program complete a full year more of high school than non-beneficiaries. Turning to the health aspects, maternal deaths and infant mortality nationwide have decreased 11% and 2% respectively since the program was introduced. In urban areas children in the program under three years old have increased their average height by 1.42 cm with respect to non-beneficiaries. In rural areas, children under 5 have 20% fewer sick days than previously.

Oportunidades is one of the most-studied social programs on the planet.[9] It has been very positively received by international agencies and is a model for similar conditioned payment programs in some 30 other countries. A pilot program called Opportunity NYC is being evaluated in New York City.

Smaller states tend to exhibit less variation between the top and bottom municipalities. In Colima, for example, the per person income of the wealthiest municipality is only about twice that of the poorest. On the opposite coast, Tabasco is also a relatively small state with less variation than most. All its municipalities have HDI scores classified as "medium high", except the state capital Villahermosa which is in the "high" group.

The north to south gradient also applies to specific types of communities. Aside from the exceptions noted above, the poorest municipalities in the northern states are significantly better off than those in southern states. For example, there are virtually no highly marginalized municipalities in Baja California, Baja California Sur, Sonora, Coahuila or Nuevo León (Figure 29.2). Typical rural areas in the north have quality of life characteristics slightly below national averages whereas those in the middle are significantly lower and those in the far south are even lower. Compare Casa Grandes, Otumba, San Marcos and Solosuchiapa in Table 26.1. The north to south gradient is also apparent for small and mid-sized urban areas.

Major cities of over 500,000, all of which enjoy a relatively high quality of life, do not fit the north–south gradient as tightly. Some cities in relatively northern latitudes do not score as well as those farther south. Per person incomes are a particularly important distinguishing factor; the northern cities of Tijuana ($9,815 in 2000), Hermosillo ($10,404), Reynosa ($9,174), Culiacán ($6,970) and Durango ($9,137) are significantly lower than the more southern cities of Cancún ($15,656), Querétaro ($17,479), Mexico City ($17,696) and Toluca ($14,046). Appendix F gives quality of life indicators for many major cities and other municipalities of particular interest to foreigners living in or traveling to Mexico.

The most extreme inequalities are between the nation's poorest rural areas and its wealthiest urban municipalities like Benito Juárez and San Pedro Garza García, just south of Monterrey, which had a per person income of $32,877 in 2000. Benito Juárez's HDI score of 0.931 in 2000 puts it just ahead of where Canada and the USA were in 1995. Its per person income was higher than that of Canada or the USA but its health and education levels were a bit lower. Based on the HDI measure, the quality of life in Benito Juárez is a bit better than that of France, Germany and the UK, whereas life in the poorest municipalities is more like that in countries such as Ethiopia.

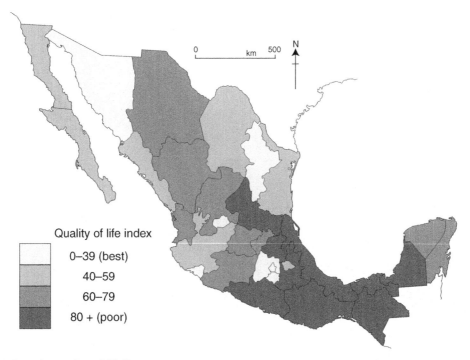

Quality of life index

0–39 (best)

40–59

60–79

80 + (poor)

Figure 29.6 Female quality of life[10]

Of course, even very wealthy areas have low income residents; for example, 18% of those in Benito Juárez earn less than twice the minimum wage.

As discussed in chapter 22, there can be enormous inequalities within some urban municipalities.[11] For example, within Benito Juárez and the neighboring municipalities of Miguel Hidalgo and Cuauhtémoc, 234,000 people are considered "rich" and 245,000 are considered "poor". The remaining 750,000 are somewhere in the middle. The range is even greater in the municipality of Huixquilucan, which is adjacent to Miguel Hidalgo but in the State of Mexico. Of its 46 *colonias* (neighborhoods), 22 are gated communities classified as "rich" and 22 are classified as "poor". The remaining two *colonias* are classified as "very poor". There are very poor *colonias* right next to rich *colonias* with per person incomes more than 15 times larger.

Female quality of life and gender inequalities

In addition to the regional differences in quality of life which have already been discussed at a variety of scales, there are also significant gender differences across Mexico. In this section we will examine the quality of life for females and the evidence for gender inequality.

Females comprise 51.3% of the Mexican population (there are 94.8 men for every 100 women). However, with isolated exceptions, Mexico has been a male-dominated society for a long time and the spirit of *machismo* is still very strong in many parts of the country. Mexico has never had a female head of state and has had very few female cabinet members. The precise roles of women in Mexican society vary greatly from one region to another. The indigenous Zapotec community of Juchitán in Oaxaca is at one extreme. It functions as a matriarchal society where women play a much more important role than men in trading and decision-making.[12] There are also vast differences across the country in terms of economic well-being. María Asunción Aramburuzabala is a billionaire who has proved that Mexican women can be incredibly successful in business yet thousands of women face a daily struggle against starvation and violence in the home.

The composite index used for Figure 29.6 is based on combining the state rankings for four variables: female years of schooling; fertility rate; female life expectancy at birth and the percentage of females on voters' lists. The pattern of female quality of life is very similar to that for overall economic standards. Females in southern Mexico have a comparatively

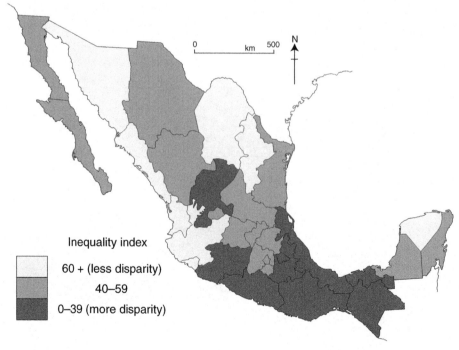

Inequality index

60 + (less disparity)

40–59

0–39 (more disparity)

Figure 29.7 Gender inequality[13]

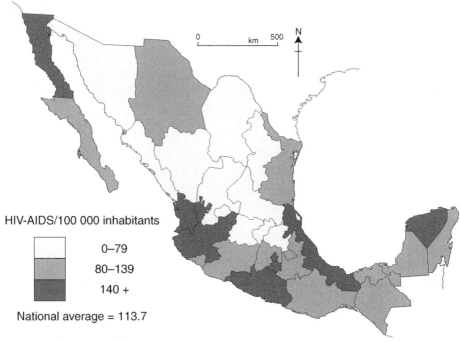

HIV-AIDS/100 000 inhabitants

▢	0–79
▨	80–139
▩	140 +

National average = 113.7

Figure 29.8 HIV-AIDS in Mexico[14]

lower quality of life. In central Mexico there are stark differences; the Federal District and nearby states of Mexico, Tlaxcala and Morelos offer a much higher quality of life than the neighboring states of Hidalgo, Puebla and Guerrero. Such differences have undoubtedly contributed greatly to the migration patterns discussed in chapter 25.

Overall, the situation is improving. More females are now enrolling in university courses though the difference in rate between females and males is still pronounced. More women are seeking paid employment and more are entering politics. About 20% of the senators in the 2006–2009 legislature are female, so their influence in national politics is increasing. On the other hand, at the local level, only 3.5% of 2006 municipal presidents were female.[15]

The percentage of the workforce that is female doubled from 17% in 1979 to about 40% in 2005. In that year the active female workforce comprised 16.2 million women whereas the male workforce numbered 26.0 million. Fully 71.5% of working females have jobs in the tertiary sector, 22.0% in the secondary sector and only 6.2% in the primary sector compared with 47.6%, 27.9% and 24% respectively for male workers.[16] However, it is important to remember that women perform far more unpaid but socially vital work in the home than men do.

The composite gender inequality index used for Figure 29.7 is based on the state rankings for three variables: difference in literacy rates between male and females, differences in rates of economic participation and the percentage of municipal leaders who are female.

There are significant differences in the spatial patterns of these variables taken individually but by combining them into a single composite ranking a more general picture emerges. The overall pattern of disparity is quite similar to the pattern for female quality of life but there are some anomalies. Southern states are those where both the quality of life for females and the gender disparities are greatest. However, while females living in the three states comprising the Yucatán peninsula have a comparatively low quality of life, the gender disparities in those states are relatively low. On the other hand, while the quality of life in and around Mexico City is quite high for females, the level of disparities in central Mexico remains considerable.

Gender inequality is not an intangible aspect of life. Figures show that there are significant differences in the median wages of male and female employees in every subsection of the workforce with the exception of skilled technicians where females' median wages are fractionally higher. For instance, the median wage for female teachers is 91.2% that for men; for professionals, 82.7%; and for industrial supervisors 66.9%. When levels of education are taken into account, female wage discrimination is even more pronounced in most occupations. With equal educational levels, female skilled technicians make 97.3% of what males make, teachers 97.6%, professionals 76.6%, and industrial supervisors only 68.4%.[17]

In Mexico, female headed households constitute about 20.6% of all households rising in the Federal District to 25.8%.[18] The most frequent reasons for females to head households remain the desertion or death of the male partner but an increasing number are the result of women exercising their right to choose their family structure. Such households do not necessarily suffer from a greater degree of poverty than other households but may increase the pressures on children to play an active economic role,

implying more likelihood of child labor. Given that most women are employed in the service sector and that service industries are heavily concentrated in the larger urban centers, it may also promote continued migration to the big cities.

Not all gender inequality is in favor of men. On average, women live longer. The life expectancy at birth for females in Mexico is 77.9 years compared with 73.0 years for males. In addition the incidence of HIV-AIDS is more than five times higher for men than for women.

Figure 29.8 shows how the incidence of HIV-AIDS in Mexico varies greatly from one state to another. In 2007 the three states with the highest accumulated incidence of HIV-AIDS were the Federal District with 240.9 cases per 100,000 inhabitants, followed by Baja California (178.4) and Morelos (167.3). The lowest reported figures were in Zacatecas (46.7), Guanajuato (55.7) and Hidalgo (56.6).

30

Environmental trends and issues

Our environment is far from being static. The Earth's interrelated ecosystems, food chains, hydrological cycles, climatic regimes and landforms are in a process of continual dynamic readjustment. Through most of human history, people have had to adapt to the vagaries of the natural world and to natural environmental change. Aided by technology, human populations have had significant impacts on the environment for millennia. In some cases these impacts even contributed to the collapse of their formerly powerful civilization. We discuss Mexico's natural environment in chapters two through seven and reflect on tourism-related aspects of it in chapter 19. This chapter focuses on the overall impacts that people have had on Mexico's environment and how Mexico's experience compares to other countries.

A long history of environmental impacts

Mexico's indigenous farmers had developed numerous ways to ensure successful harvests. They mitigated erosion by building earth banks and check dams in gullies. They practiced polyculture, recognizing that it minimized the risks inherent in monoculture. They terraced steep slopes and channeled water to where it was most needed. Their expertise in water management enabled them to develop highly productive systems of farming in wetlands[1] such as the *chinampas* or so-called 'floating gardens' in central Mexico. Similar systems were also in use in the coastal marshes along the Gulf coast. These water management principles were successfully resurrected in the 1990s as a development strategy for small farms in the swampy wetlands of the Chontalpa region of Tabasco.[2]

For most of the last century, it was fashionable to claim that pre-Columbian groups lived in harmony with their environment practicing simple, but energy-efficient and ecologically-effective, forms of agriculture and resource use. According to this thesis it was only after Europeans arrived (with draught animals, metal plows and their own crops and livestock) that this delicate ecological balance was disturbed. This view is now recognized as a gross oversimplification. The collapse of Classic Maya civilization may have been due in part to environmental mismanagement.[3] In the Valley of Mexico, the Aztecs seemed to their 16th century conquerors to be very well adapted to their local environment but modern research has shown that surrounding hillsides had already been deforested causing severe erosion.[4]

The environmental impacts of pre-Columbian civilizations were relatively minor compared to the massive changes wrought during the first century of colonialism.[5] The Spanish brought thousands of Old World species, the worst being diseases like smallpox which wiped out up to 90% of the indigenous population. In their efforts to preserve the lifestyle and diet of their mother country, the colonists brought pigs, cattle, sheep, goats, chickens, wheat, barley, grapes, olives, cabbage, lettuce, etc. (see chapter 5). They also introduced, albeit inadvertently, new species of rodents, weeds, insects and numerous plant and animal diseases. Many of these new species spread like wildfire, drastically changing the environment.

Pigs were introduced as a source of protein. Many escaped, multiplied rapidly by feeding from indigenous cornfields, and spread across North America as wild boar. Cattle brought by the Spanish also multiplied, and soon numbered in the millions, overgrazing pasturelands compacting the soil and causing erosion. Uncontrolled herds devastated cornfields; their manure contaminated local water sources. Sheep and goats caused even more damage since they crop grasses closer and feed on steeper hillsides. They caused severe erosion. In the late 1500s over a million sheep helped destroy the irrigated, terraced fields and tree-covered hillsides of the Mezquital Valley in the state of Hidalgo (see map, Figure 23.1). Their impact was aided by drought and by the indigenous Otomí population ceasing to maintain their terraces.[6]

Colonial authorities practiced environmental management as early as the 16th century when they restricted livestock grazing to areas that were a minimum of 1000 paces from any village. In the succeeding century, demands for timber (construction, mine supports, charcoal for smelting silver) resulted in the deforestation of entire hillsides and more erosion ensued. By 1620 Mexico's environment had been drastically and irreversibly changed.

Current human impacts on land

Deforestation and soil degradation (see chapter 5) remain on-going concerns. The government has passed numerous laws to protect forests in the last 150 years; however until recently enforcement has been lax. Accurately comparing rates of deforestation is very difficult, but available data suggest that the rate for Mexico is roughly equal to that of Argentina, better than that of Brazil or Guatemala, but not as good as that in Colombia or Peru.[7]

Soil degradation in Mexico's arid regions is leading to desertification in some areas. Degraded soils support less vegetation and erode easily. About 12% of Mexico has suffered significantly from soil erosion. Fortunately, numerous government programs have been initiated to try to halt erosion and revive soil fertility in degraded areas.

Disposal of solid wastes has become a serious problem. In general the more affluent a society, the more solid waste it generates. Technologically advanced civilizations tend to produce many wastes that are not biodegradable, further complicating the disposal problem. With each succeeding decade Mexico faces greater and more complex challenges in managing its solid waste.

In terms of weight, the vast majority of solid waste is produced by the agricultural sector. Fortunately most of this waste in readily biodegradable

and is produced in areas of relatively low population density. However, agricultural wastes in the form of fertilizers and pesticides which are carried into steams and rivers have significant impacts on water quality. Animal wastes from concentrated feed lot operations are another major concern particularly because they are often located relatively close to densely populated areas.

Municipal solid waste includes waste from most commercial establishments and many small industrial operations. Mexico's urban waste exceeds 36 million tons a year, three times the equivalent figure for Canada (see chapter 23). Many municipalities in Mexico have initiated recycling programs, primarily focused on aluminum, glass, certain plastics and paper. However, in 2008 only 3.3% of Mexico's total urban waste was recycled. Waste from larger towns and cities, about half of the total, is deposited in properly operated sanitary landfills. Waste from smaller communities often ends up in dumps, two thirds of which are uncontrolled.

The management (treatment or recycling) of hazardous wastes has improved greatly in recent years particularly in the states of Nuevo León, Tamaulipas, Mexico, Tabasco and the Federal District. About half of all hazardous waste originates either in the state of Chihuahua (31% of the total) or in Mexico City (17%).[8]

In chapter 5 we examined the megadiversity of Mexico's ecosystems which include more than 10% of all the world's living species. Mexico's biodiversity is under pressure from several quarters. Plant and animal trafficking is the country's third largest criminal activity after illegal drugs and arms smuggling. Favored items include cacti, live birds (some species sell for upwards of $100,000), spider monkeys, sea turtles, snakes and jaguars. Mexico is one of 175 nations that have signed the Convention on International Trade in Endangered Species (CITES) but this has had no discernible effect on the trafficking of flora and fauna.

Mexico's megadiversity presents both opportunities, for activities such as ecotourism, as well as challenges such as preventing biopiracy. In its simplest form, biopiracy occurs whenever a bioprospector takes biological material from a place and then acquires a patent or intellectual property rights on it, or one of its constituents, elsewhere. The best documented example of biopiracy in Mexico occurred in 1999 when a US patent was granted to Colora-

Table 30.1 Selected UNESCO World Heritage Sites[9]

Heritage site	State	Description
Sierra de San Francisco	Baja California	Ancient rock paintings.
Campeche	Campeche	Historic fortified (walled) city.
Palenque	Chiapas	Pre-Hispanic city and national park.
Paquimé, Casas Grandes	Chihuahua	Archeological zone.
Guanajuato and adjacent mines	Guanajuato	Colonial architecture and silver mining landscapes.
Amatitlán, Arenal and Tequila	Jalisco	Agave landscapes and old tequila making facilities.
Campus of the National University (UNAM)	Mexico D.F.	Architectural merit.
Casa Museo Luis Barragán	Mexico D.F.	The 20th century home of the famous architect.
Mexico City historic center and Xochimilco	Mexico D.F.	Colonial architecture and canals/*chinampa* remnants.
Teotihuacan	Mexico State	Pyramids of the Sun and Moon.
Morelia historic center	Michoacán	Colonial architecture.
Oaxaca City center and Monte Alban	Oaxaca	Colonial architecture and pre-Hispanic city.
Sierra Gorda	Querétaro	Franciscan missions.
El Tajín	Veracruz	Pre-Hispanic city.
Chichen Itza and Uxmal	Yucatán	Pre-Hispanic settlements.
Zacatecas historic center	Zacatecas	Colonial architecture.

do-based company Pod-ners for the exclusive right to market Enola beans bred from Mexican yellow beans bought only five years previously.[10] Mexico's bean export business collapsed overnight as shippers were accused of patent infringement. Yellow bean production in Sinaloa fell by 62% in three years. Mexican growers subsequently proved that the yellow beans they had been breeding for decades are genetically identical to Enola beans but the damage had been done. Subsequently, the patent was challenged by the International Center for Tropical Agriculture. In 2008 the US patent office finally reversed its decision and rejected any patent claims on yellow beans. While this case of biopiracy was thwarted, acts of biopiracy, by their very nature, are usually clandestine and there are certain to be other instances in the future.

Mexican farmers share concerns about the on-going loss of genetic diversity, especially in native crops. For example, if all corn farmers planted imported hybrid corn seeds, native diversity would quickly be lost. In Tlaxcala, where about 90% of the corn is grown on non-irrigated land and where two-thirds of farmers grow corn only for their own use, local varieties have been selectively bred by farmers not only for their yields but also because of their color, taste, resistance to pests and ability to withstand strong winds or short-term droughts. Such characteristics are not necessarily important to commercial seed producers.[11]

Events in other countries often have unexpected consequences in Mexico. For example, the price of Mexico's corn imports from the USA has increased sharply as a result of the high subsidies offered in that country for corn-based biofuel and bio-additives. The rising import price of corn led to an increase in the price of tortillas which adversely affected the poorest sectors of Mexican society.

Despite land-related issues like deforestation, erosion, soil degradation, solid waste disposal and biopiracy, Mexico has made impressive progress in protecting its ecosystems, preventing further habitat loss and managing its wildlife. Much of its land area is now formally protected (see box and Table 5.1) as is about 20% of its 209,000 km^2 (81,000 mi^2) of territorial waters.

Protected areas: Biosphere Reserves and World Heritage Sites

In total, more than 11.5% of Mexico's land area is now protected. This percentage has risen steadily for more than a century. Sites considered significant for their natural beauty are protected in a variety of ways ranging from nature sanctuaries of local importance to protected areas and national parks.

In addition, many sites have been granted international recognition either as Biosphere Reserves or World Heritage Sites by UNESCO (United Nations Educational, Scientific and Cultural Organization).

Mexico has 34 Biosphere Reserves (Table 5.1) protecting areas of ecological significance, a number only exceeded by the USA (47), Russia (38) and Spain (37). The guiding principle of Biosphere Reserves is that the local people are not displaced but actively involved in all aspects of management, research and monitoring. Biosphere reserves have a research-intensive core, surrounded by a buffer zone where sustainable development is fostered before gradually transitioning into the surrounding region.

World Heritage Sites are cultural or natural sites of "outstanding universal value". Mexico has 29 sites on the UNESCO list of 890 World Heritage locations in 145 countries (Table 30.1), considerably more than any other country in the Americas. By comparison, the USA has 20, Brazil 17 and Canada 15. Worldwide, only five countries have more World Heritage Sites than Mexico: Italy (44), Spain (41), China (38), Germany (33) and France (33).

Human impacts on water

Water quantity and quality are major environmental concerns. As we saw in chapter 6, Mexico's water is very inequitably distributed with an abundance in the south but shortages in the north and in the Valley of Mexico. More than a third of all water consumed

Pemex: the government cash cow that environmentalists love to hate

Petroleos Mexicanos (Pemex), the giant, state-owned petroleum company, is a symbol of national pride with revenues of over $100 billion in 2008. However, it is cash poor because most of its revenue goes to the government, covering 40% of the national budget. Pemex is $40 billion in debt and its maintenance budget is insufficient to keep its old infrastructure operating safely. About a third of Pemex's 50,000 km of pipeline is over 30 years old and susceptible to failure.[12]

Environmentalists love to hate Pemex because it has inflicted enormous environmental damage. The June 1979 blowout at the Ixtoc-I drilling rig in the Bay of Campeche resulted in the world's largest ever unintentional oil spill: over 450,000 tons, more than ten times the size of the 1989 Exxon Valdez disaster.

In November 1984 a series of explosions at a Pemex storage facility in San Juan Ixhuatepec in northern Mexico City started major fires killing about 500 people.[13]

A massive gasoline leak into Guadalajara's sewers in 1992 resulted in a series of explosions that resulted in over 200 deaths. In recent years numerous smaller, but still fatal, explosions and pipeline failures flooding rivers with oil have brought new attention to Pemex's environmental damage and failing infrastructure.

It has long been recognized that environmental damage is particularly severe near the conglomeration of Pemex facilities in southern Veracruz near the mouth of the Coatzacoalcos River. The river suffers from chronic heavy petroleum pollution, receiving massive doses periodically when pipelines break. Possibly the only beneficial outcome of the decades of widespread damage caused by Pemex in its principal areas of operation in Veracruz, Tabasco and Campeche was that it prompted the publication in 1983 of *Cómo destruir el paraíso* (*How to destroy Paradise*)[14], a book which gave an immense boost to Mexico's then fledgling environmental movement.

Federal environmental agencies have had only limited success in forcing Pemex to take corrective actions. Pemex recognizes the problems and applies each year for more maintenance funds from the government. The government, however, sets a higher priority on funding exploration since Mexico's oil reserves are running out. Pemex is fundamental to the Mexican economy but needs investment in maintenance and must become more accountable for its environmental impacts.

comes from aquifers and 60% of this amount comes from over-exploited aquifers (Figure 6.7). Obviously, overexploitation of aquifers is a serious problem particularly in Mexico City, analyzed in more detail in chapter 23. The recently-enacted National Water Law recognizes that the current situation is not sustainable and strengthens the regulations governing water usage. Protecting aquifers will be difficult and costly, but is absolutely essential.

As detailed in chapter 7, the quality of Mexico's surface fresh water is rather poor by world standards. Among the most polluted rivers are the Lerma which drains major agricultural and industrial areas in Guanajuato and Jalisco, the Tula-Moctezuma-Panuco system which receives the waste from the Valley of Mexico and the Coatzacoalcos, in Veracruz, which is heavily polluted from petroleum industry discharges (see Pemex box).

Air pollution from human activities

Air quality, like water quality, reflects the effects of natural contaminants such as dust, pollen and the products of volcanic emissions, as well as pollutants derived from human activities. Because natural contamination is difficult to control and is usually not concentrated in highly populated areas, the primary focus for mitigation efforts is man-made urban air pollution which is affected by both emissions and environmental factors like prevailing winds and mountain ranges.

Transportation, predominantly motor vehicles, is responsible for 76% of urban air contaminants by weight, primarily carbon monoxide but also hydrocarbons and microparticulates. About 13% of air pollution results from natural sources, mainly dust, nitrogen oxides (NOx) and volatile organic compounds. Services (power plants and methane producing sanitary landfills) contribute over 5%. About 4% comes from other industries which produce a full range of contaminants including lead, nitrogen oxides (NOx) and sulfur oxides (SOx) which contribute to acid rain.

Air quality in Mexico City has improved dramatically (see chapter 23). However, air quality in most other large cities in the country has not improved in the past decade. Air pollution data for seven major cities— Mexico City, Guadalajara, Monterrey, Toluca, Ciudad Juárez, Tijuana, and Mexicali—reveal the extent of the problem.[15] Levels of carbon monoxide (CO), a lethal gas produced by incomplete combustion of carbon-based fuels such as gasoline, coal and wood, now rarely exceed daily norms; carbon monoxide is therefore no longer a serious health problem in Mexico's large cities. On the other hand, ozone concentrations in the lower atmosphere continue to be a serious problem especially in cities at higher elevations such as Mexico City. Excessive ozone causes respiratory problems and lung damage as well as harming forests and crops. Microparticulates (PM10) are the third most important pollutant. These tiny suspended particles can lodge deep in the lungs and cause serious cardiopulmonary problems. They result from the burning of fossil fuels (vehicles, power plants and other industries) as well as from volcanic eruptions, dust storms and forest fires. The highest levels of PM10 are in cities located in the arid and semi-arid northern areas of Mexico, such as Mexicali, Monterrey and Ciudad Juárez.

Carbon dioxide emissions and global climate change

Carbon dioxide (CO_2), the most important greenhouse gas, is formed from the combustion of carbon-based fuels. Living trees help remove some of this carbon dioxide from the atmosphere, but deforestation reduces the amounts transferred. In 2002 Mexico emitted an estimated 400 million tons of CO_2 and the equivalent of an additional 150 million tons of CO_2 in other greenhouse gases, predominantly methane. The main Mexican sources of greenhouse gases are transportation and industry, responsible for about a third each. Agriculture is also a major contributor with livestock alone being responsible for 18% of all greenhouse gas emissions.

By 2005 Mexico was emitting about 1.7% of the global emissions total (up from 0.7% in 1971) compared to 21.4% for the USA, 18.8% for China, 5.7% for Russia, 4.5% for Japan and 4.2% for India.[16] Mexico's per person emissions in 2002 (1.4 metric tons/person) were slightly below those of China and the global average.

The Mexican government is giving high priority to greenhouse gas emissions and has taken a leadership position among newly industrialized economies.[18] It was the first of these countries to adopt international standards to track and report greenhouse gas emissions from its industries as a first step towards establishing a voluntary national greenhouse gas reduction program. Reporting of greenhouse gas emissions will follow the Greenhouse Gas Protocol,

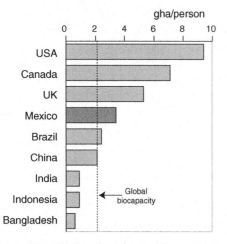

Figure 30.1 National ecological footprints[17]

jointly developed by the World Resources Institute and the World Business Council for Sustainable Development.[19] With less than 2% of emissions, Mexico's ability to directly influence global emissions is limited; however, it is setting a positive example for other developing countries. Any global agreement to reduce worldwide greenhouse gas emissions will have economic implications running into trillions of dollars and consequently will not be easy to achieve. Chapter 4 discusses some aspects of climate change and chapter 31 considers the possible future consequences of on-going global warming.

Ecological footprint

In the 1990s, Mathis Wackernagel, who formerly directed the Center for Sustainability Studies in Mexico, and William Rees developed the concept of the ecological footprint.[20] It is defined as the area of land (and water) required by a population, given prevailing technology, to produce the resources it consumes and to absorb any wastes created. The ecological footprint takes into account the population's needs for arable land, pasture land, forests, oceans and infrastructure (land used for transportation, housing and factories). It also incorporates energy costs, including the land required for absorbing carbon dioxide emissions. Calculations do not usually include the loss of land through soil degradation or the pollution of air and water.

Ecological footprints are measured in 'global hectares' (gha). A global hectare encompasses the average annual productivity of all biologically productive land and ocean areas in the world. In 2005

the world's population required the resources of 2.7 gha/person.[21] Unfortunately, the world's biocapacity— the amount of resources its ecosystems can supply each year—was only equivalent to 2.1 gha per person and is declining each year as population increases. The deficit between biocapacity and our ecological footprint causes damaging environmental changes to forests, fisheries, rivers, coral reefs, soil, water and air, and plays a major role in global climate change. The figures mean that our current usage of the world's resources is inherently unsustainable. Since we are unable to significantly alter biocapacity (though future technological changes may enable us to make better use of what ecosystems provide), we clearly need to reduce our ecological footprint.

Figure 30.1 shows the ecological footprint of several countries. China's footprint matches global biocapacity while the footprints of India, Indonesia and Bangladesh are fully sustainable. On the other hand, the USA's footprint of 9.4 gha is surpassed only by the United Arab Emirates. Australia and Canada both have footprints over 7 gha. In simple terms, their populations require more than three times their fair share of the world's biocapacity. How is this possible? Part of the reason is because countries with such large footprints rely on other (poorer) countries to provide them with raw materials. In other words, the richer countries owe an 'ecological debt' to poorer countries. This realization has serious implications for world development. Poorer countries trying to catch up (in economic terms) to their richer neighbors may well incur equally large ecological debts with potentially disastrous environmental consequences for

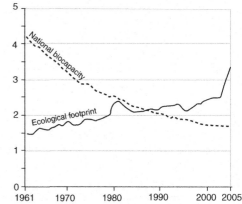

Figure 30.2 Mexico's biocapacity and ecological footprint, 1961–2005[22]

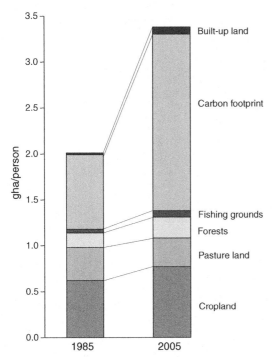

Figure 30.3 Composition of Mexico's ecological footprint, 1985–2005[23]

2005. Until 1990, Mexico's ecological footprint was within its available biocapacity; by 2005 it was double the biocapacity.

Ecological footprints provide a sound theoretical measure of overall resource consumption and offer a compelling argument for an urgent need to reduce consumption in the interests of future generations.

Urban areas generally have higher ecological footprints than rural areas: 2.75 ha/person and 2.28 gha/person respectively in the case of Jalisco.[24] Footprints also depend on lifestyles. For example, the average footprint of national tourists visiting Puerto Vallarta equates to 4.36 gha/yr while for international tourists it is 11.29 gha/yr.[25] Mexico's ecological footprint from tourism was discussed further in chapter 19.

In Mexico's case, more than 50% of the footprint represents the area needed to absorb carbon dioxide (Figure 30.3). With increasing energy consumption in recent years, the contribution of CO_2 absorption to the footprint has risen rapidly.

Environmental sustainability

Environmental sustainability is a highly politicized term which almost all nations now eagerly claim as one of their goals. How true are these claims? The Environmental Sustainability Index[27](ESI) combines five major components (76 separate measurements in all) to assess how close countries are to environmental sustainability. The ESI includes the ecological footprint but also looks at levels of pollution, susceptibility to environmental disruptions, the effectiveness of environmental policies and each country's contribution to global stewardship.

all. The improvement of living standards in poorer countries can probably only be achieved if richer countries consume less resources.

Figure 30.2 shows how Mexico's ecological footprint has changed since 1961. Mexico's available biocapacity has declined from 4.1 gha/person in 1961 to 1.7 gha in 2005 as population has increased. Meanwhile, Mexico's ecological footprint has grown from 1.4 gha/person in 1961 to 3.4 ha/person in

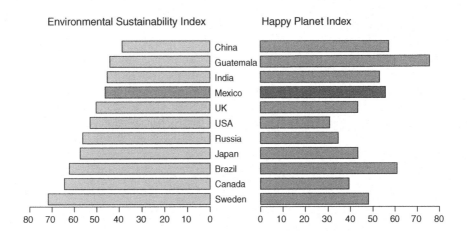

Figure 30.4 Environmental Sustainability Index and Happy Planet Index for selected nations, 2005[26]

The countries with the highest ESI scores (Figure 30.4) are predominantly resource-rich nations with low population densities, such as Finland, Norway and Sweden. Some small wealthy states such as Switzerland also make the top ten. In general, densely populated countries such as India and Bangladesh do not score as well.

Mexico's low ranking in the pilot 2000 ESI table led to Mexico's Environment Secretariat (SEMARNAT) exploring ways to ensure that international organizations such as the World Bank and World Resources Institute had faster access to updated data from Mexico. Government policy was modified to embrace the use of quantitative environmental data relating to sustainability.

In terms of global stewardship, Mexico and the USA are closer to the target for environmental sustainability than Canada (Figure 30.5). For reducing environmental stresses, Mexico and Canada are ahead of the USA. However, for the other three components, Mexico lags well behind both its North American partners.

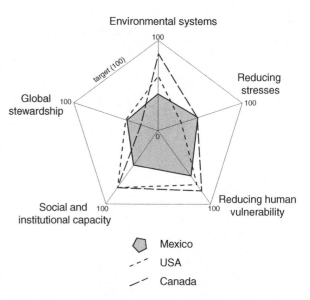

Figure 30.5 Comparison of ESI components for Mexico, USA and Canada[29]

The Happy Planet Index

We close this chapter with a look at the Happy Planet Index (HPI)[28] which combines life expectancy, life satisfaction and the ecological footprint. It shows how successfully people are achieving the good life without having to consume a disproportionate share of the Earth's resources.

The unbridled global pursuit of economic growth over the past fifty years has left more than a billion people in dire poverty. Far from bringing economic stability, it has encouraged the rampant abuse of resources while increasing the very real risks of unpredictable global climate change.

The HPI attempts to quantify an alternative vision of progress where people strive for happy and healthy lives alongside ecological efficiency in how they use resources. A high HPI score is only possible if a country is close to meeting the targets for all three components.

HPI scores (Figure 30.4) paint a very different picture to that suggested by either the ecological footprint or the ESI discussed earlier. While happy and healthy lives often go hand in hand, many countries with high values for those components (such as the USA and Canada) have disappointingly high footprints, and end up with low HPI scores. The lowest HPI scores of all are found in sub-Saharan Africa where several countries do badly on all three components.

At the other end of the scale, nine of the top ten HPI scores are for countries in Latin America and the Caribbean where relatively high life expectancy and high personal lifestyle satisfaction is combined with modest footprints. Mexico ranks 23rd of the 143 countries studied, behind Argentina and Guatemala but well ahead of the UK, Canada and the USA.

In summary, countries often considered to be 'developed' are some of the worst-performing in terms of sustainable well-being. And, unfortunately, given that the HPI scores for the world's three largest countries (China, India, and the USA) all declined between 1990 and 2005, it does not seem that the situation is improving. Business as usual appears to be literally costing us the Earth.

31
What does the future hold?

What are the prospects for Mexico in the 21st century? Will Mexico make as much progress as it did in the 20th century? In 1900 Mexico was a predominately rural dictatorship of less than 14 million. Life expectancy was only 30 years and 30% of infants died before their first birthday. Agriculture was mostly subsistence farming using centuries-old technologies. Railroads, mules and horses were the principal means of transportation; there were virtually no automobiles, trucks or paved highways. The fastest communication between cities was by telegraph but this was only available to urban businesses, officials and elites. Other forms of communication were very slow. There were some newspapers but most of the population was illiterate.

During the 20th century Mexico evolved into a relatively modern, urban, industrialized democracy of almost 100 million people. By 2000 it was a major world country in terms of area, population and economic production. Life expectancy had risen almost 150% to 75 years. Infant mortality was slashed by 93%. Mexico had fully embraced the digital age of the internet, e-mail, cell phones, satellite communications and advanced medical technology not to mention jet aircraft and almost universal access to cars, buses and telephones as well as household refrigerators, washing machines and TVs.

Nobody in 1900 could have predicted the direction and degree of 20th century progress. The advances were truly mind-boggling. Technological change and its benefit to society are expected to be even faster during the 21st century. It is impossible to predict or even imagine all these changes. What can safely be said is that the technology of the year 2100 is beyond our current comprehension. If the past century is any guide the standard of living in Mexico in the year 2100 should be far, far better than it is today.

Natural, environmental and climatic changes

The 20th century brought numerous disasters resulting from natural hazards; this century will probably bring as many or more. Since 1900 Mexico has experienced five very big earthquakes (at or above 8.0 on the Richter scale) and another 36 big 'quakes (over 7.0) as well as several volcanic eruptions (see chapter 3). The frequency and intensity of earthquakes and volcanic eruptions will probably be similar to the last hundred years but casualties and damages should be reduced due to more earthquake-proof construction, better preparedness and improvements in prediction and risk assessment.

Unlike geological hazards, both the number and strength of hurricanes and floods (see chapters 4 and 7) are expected to increase significantly as a result of global warming. In the 25 years from 1960 to 1985, only one category five hurricane (Beulah in 1967) struck Mexico; in the 25 years since, four have done so—Gilberto in 1988, Mitch, the most devastating, in 1998, Wilma in 2005 and Dean in 2007. The data clearly indicate that Mexico is currently being hit by more and larger hurricanes, a trend expected to worsen during the rest of the 21st century. Smaller storms also are expected to be more prevalent.

Current global warming models indicate that Mexico's precipitation in all seasons will decline causing droughts and adversely affecting ecosystems, agriculture and forests.[1] Droughts will be particularly devastating for Mexico's arid north contributing to crop failures and forest fires. Current levels of irrigation especially in northern Mexico where farmers are already overexploiting underground aquifers may not be possible. Farmers will have to introduce new crops requiring less water and water saving technologies such as drip irrigation. The northern limits for water intensive crops such as sugar cane may have to be moved south to wetter areas. Mexico's severe water issues (see chapters 6 and 7) including those of Mexico City will be seriously exacerbated.

Global warming could melt Mexico's remaining mountain snowpacks. In addition, associated sea level rise will have a significant impact on Mexico's low-lying areas such as Tabasco (see box, chapter 7). Global warming is expected to have massive impacts on Mexico's ecosystems leading to the accelerated extinction of many plant and animal species.

Social change

What social changes are expected? Mexico is addressing its population growth issues. By 2020 its fertility rate will drop below the replacement level of 2.1 children per woman. Depending on rates of migration to the USA, Mexico's population is expected to peak about mid-century at between 130 and 150 million. Some fast-growing places like Quintana Roo, Baja California Sur, border areas and cities between 100,000 and 500,000 will probably experience continued growth. Many areas may lose population, including the Federal District, rural municipalities and the states of Zacatecas, Durango, Michoacán and Oaxaca. A major social, economic and health challenge for the 21st century will be coping with a rapidly aging population.

Mexican dietary habits may have to change if global warming significantly increases the prices of basic agricultural commodities like corn, beans, wheat, rice, chicken, beef and dairy products. This could act as a catalyst for a shift away from meat and dairy products and towards basic grains, vegetables and fruits. Such a shift might result in a healthier, less obese, population. On the other hand, higher incomes could stimulate higher consumption of beef and dairy products.

Can the culture of existing indigenous groups survive? If 20th century trends continue, the number of Mexicans speaking indigenous languages will decline and several languages will be lost forever. As a growing number of indigenous Mexicans obtain high levels of formal education and join the mestizo mainstream, they will become modernized, improve their living standards and, after a generation or two, will gradually lose their indigenous language and culture. By the end of this century there will be far fewer indigenous Mexicans.

Great civil rights progress was made in the 20th century. Mexican women have gained increasing rights and access to opportunities but still face some forms of discrimination. Progress in gender equality will continue this century. Minority groups such as dark skinned ethnic groups and the physically and mentally-challenged are also likely to experience diminishing discrimination in future decades. Improved civil rights for all Mexicans will not come easily and will required tenacious effort but long term trends suggest that progress will definitely be made.

It is difficult to forecast changes in religion and values. Protestantism and secularism will continue to grow but Catholicism is likely to remain the dominant religion throughout the 21st century. Traditional social and family values will continue to evolve.

Forecasting political change is equally problematic. Mexico started the 20th century as a dictatorship, experienced a successful revolution, and was then dominated by a single party for 72 years before emerging as a relatively stable, multi-party democracy. Whether or not events in the 21st century are equally volatile, Mexicans seem firmly committed to democratic principles. Populism, as demonstrated by the Obrador presidential campaign in 2006, could disrupt the current status quo.

Drug wars, powerful drug cartels and associated corruption are also potential threats to political and social progress. A major economic downturn could increase the already enormous gap between rich and poor, and might stimulate political disruption. Political tensions might also erupt between the wealthier, generally more conservative north and the poorer, more liberal, south. Fortunately, most people in the country view themselves first and foremost as Mexicans rather than as members of a particular regional cultural, ethnic or linguistic group.

Economic trends

What types of economic changes can we expect? During the 20th century, Mexico shifted from an agricultural economy to one dominated by services and manufacturing. This trend will continue. Traditional pre-modern farming is still widely practiced but will decline significantly in the decades ahead. The days of small, semi-subsistence family farms are numbered. The family farms that survive will tend to be large-scale modern operations. With the expected continued growth of modern, high yield agribusiness, Mexico's agricultural production should continue to increase even as the number employed in agriculture declines. However, as discussed above, climate change will have profound impacts on Mexican agriculture.

Mexico started the 20th century with a growing industrial base, with numerous foreign-owned enterprises attracted by the Porfirio Díaz regime. Manufacturing has grown rapidly in recent decades stimulated by cheap labor and easy access, via NAFTA, to the enormous US market. However, Mexico has already lost some manufacturing enterprises to even lower cost countries such as China and India.

Export-oriented industries may continue to thrive in future decades but this depends on Mexico's ability to compete in the world market which in turn is linked to labor costs, productivity and economic policies. Industries producing for the Mexican market should continue to grow as domestic demand increases. However, overall expansion of manufacturing will probably not be as rapid as it was immediately following the passage of NAFTA.

Services, already 70% of the economy, will continue to grow. A gradual shift is expected from low productivity, poorly paid services such as manual labor towards higher productivity, white collar jobs in administration, information technology and health care. The speed of this shift and the associated income benefits will largely depend on technological change and on Mexico's ability to better educate and train high level workers. Mexico needs a well-qualified high tech work force in order to compete in the decades ahead.

The proximity of Mexico to the USA has had an enormous, generally positive, impact on the Mexican economy and this should continue. The USA has been the dominant market for Mexico's exports of manufactured goods, oil, selected agricultural products and, perhaps most importantly, labor. Migration absorbed excess Mexican labor and remittances improved the quality of life and investment in many rural areas. Migration will be a very significant eco-

nomic factor for at least the next few decades. As discussed in chapter 26, it is impossible to say whether migration will increase or decrease in the future. Close ties to the USA can be a double-edged sword. Mexico suffers significantly when the US economy goes into recession. If for any reason the USA loses its dominant position in the global economy, Mexico's economy will be adversely affected.

The Mexican government currently relies on oil revenues for about 40% of its budget. With a continued decline in oil production, the government must look to other revenue sources. This will require more efficient collection of existing value-added and income taxes, as well as the possible imposition of new taxes.

The enormous economic progress and improvements in the standard of living achieved during the 20th century should continue well into this century. While all classes are likely to experience significant improvements, will the current very wide gap between the rich and the poor (see chapters 14 and 29) narrow or widen? During the last 20 years, the gap between rich and poor declined in only five of the 30 OECD (Organisation for Economic Co-operation and Development) countries.[2] Mexico is one of these five countries but still has the widest gap by far of any OECD member country. Strong government policies are needed to address income inequity.

As a result of global warming and declining oil reserves, the world and Mexico will have to move beyond the age of fossil fuels sometime in the 21st century. Given the abundance of fossil fuels, especially coal, this probably will be implemented relatively gradually. Improved energy efficiency and successful CO_2 sequestration could slow this process. The shift away from fossil fuels should not hurt Mexico more than most other countries.

The use of renewable energy is expected to increase significantly in future decades particularly for the production of electricity. Rapid improvements in solar, wind, biomass, tidal and geothermal technologies will continue. Mexico should benefit from these developments because it is a world leader in terms of its solar, wind and geothermal resource potential. There will also be renewed interest in exploiting sources of hydro-power.

The use of nuclear energy which currently provides about one sixth of the world's electricity is also likely to increase dramatically as a reliable, emission-free source of electricity. Mexico's 20 years experience operating its Laguna Verde nuclear power plant should facilitate the operation of any new nuclear plants that might be built. By the close of the 21st century, hydrogen and/or fusion power could be widely available, essentially replacing the need for energy derived from fossil fuels.

Transportation and communication

While there undoubtedly will be incredible transportation and communication advances in the 21st century, it is very difficult to say how these will affect life in Mexico. It is probably safe to say that, within Mexico, road vehicles will become more fuel-efficient and faster, while new forms of air travel may replace buses as the dominant means of travel for trips longer than about 200 km. Developments in cheap, short haul air technology could revolutionize the lives of the millions of Mexicans who currently live in remote areas.

Worldwide audio and visual communications are already virtually instantaneous. In future decades, access to new communications technologies should become available to almost all members of Mexican society. This should enable even those living in remote areas to merge with the mainstream, with both positive and negative consequences. In general, 21st century technological changes in transportation and communications are likely to have a bigger impact on the lives of people in the more remote and relatively underdeveloped parts of Mexico than on residents of urban areas.

Conclusion

Mexico faces a number of challenges in the 21st century including water management, maintaining a stable democracy, dismantling drug cartels, providing education for an increasingly technological world, reducing the gap between rich and poor, coping with climate change and successfully negotiating the coming energy revolution. Fortunately Mexico appears to be well positioned to meet the challenges ahead.

Notes

Chapter 1
1 GDP/PPP = GDP purchasing power parity, used throughout this book for international GDP comparisons.
2 Lanegran, D.A. and Natoli, S. 1984.

Chapter 2
1 INEGI 2006; UNAM 1990.
2 SSN undated; Yarza, E. 1992; UNAM 1990.
3 INEGI 2006.
4 Rose, W.I. and Durant, A.J. 2008.

Chapter 3
1 UNAM 1990.
2 SPP 1981; INEGI 1984.
3 Burton, T. 2003a.
4 Burton, T. 2008a.

Chapter 4
1 UNAM 1990.
2 UNAM 1990.
3 CONAGUA/CNA 2008a.
4 CONAGUA/CNA 2008a.
5 UNAM 1990; CENAPRED 2008; SMN 2008.
6 Eakin, H. 2006.
7 Hewitson, B. and Crane, R. 1992.
8 García, E 1973.
9 SPP 1981.
10 Data from CONAGUA database.
11 Jauregui, E. 2003.
12 Jazcilevich, A, et al 2000.
13 Jauregui, E. 2004.
14 Endfield, G.H. 2008.
15 Liverman, D. 1991.
16 Tejeda M., A and Rodríguez 2007.

Chapter 5
1 CONABIO 2008.
2 FAO/AGL 2007.
3 INEGI undated.
4 SEMARNAT 2009.
5 Toledo, V.M. et al 1995.
6 LMER March 2003.

7 SEMARNAT 2009.
8 SEMARNAT 2009.
9 LMER March 2003.
10 Whyte, A.V.T. 1977.
11 SEMARNAT 2006.
12 SEMARNAT 2006.

Chapter 6
1 Aguayo Q., S. (ed) 2000: 40.
2 CONAGUA 2006.
3 Sources: Average precipitation, Water consumed per person, and Agricultural land total: FAO 2009; Available water per person: CIESIN 2009; Water Quality Index: UNESCO-WWAP 2003; Water footprint per person: Hoekstra and Chapagain 2008.
4 Aguayo Q., S. (ed) 2000.
5 FAO 2009.
6 FAO 2009.
7 Aguayo Q., S. (ed) 2007.
8 CONAGUA 2006.
9 Cohen et al. 2001; IBWC 2009.
10 Source for data: CONAGUA/CNA 2008b.
11 Burton, T. 2004.
12 CONAGUA/CNA 2006.
13 Source for data: SEMARNAT 2008.

Chapter 7
1 Nationmaster.com 2008.
2 Hoekstra. and Chapagain 2008.
3 Esty, D.C. et al 2008.
4 CONAGUA /CNA 2008b.
5 CONAGUA /CNA. 2008b.
6 O'Rourke and Associates 2009.
7 Ooska News Weekly 2008.
8 Endfield, G.H. 2008.
9 Conde, C. and Gay, C. 1999.
10 CONAGUA/CNA 2006.

Chapter 8
1 Simon, J. 1997: 17.
2 Diamond, J. 1998: 210, 77.

3 MacLachan and Rodriquez 1980: 197; Diamond, J. 1998: 210, 77; Aguayo (ed) 2000: 60; INEGI 1985; INEGI 2004b; Nationmaster.com; CIA 2003.
4 idem
5 UNPIN 2009.
6 Raw data: Gobierno de los Estados Unidos Mexicanos 2009b.
7 UNPIN 2009.
8 Area includes the Federal District, the states of Mexico, Morelos, Puebla, Tlaxcala, Hidalgo, Querétaro, Guanajuato and 40% of area, and 80% of the population, of Veracruz and Jalisco.
9 The area between Boston and Washington DC which includes the states of Massachusetts, Rhode Island, Connecticut, southern New York, New Jersey, eastern Pennsylvania, Maryland and northern Virginia.
10 Raw data: INEGI 1985; INEGI 2007a, INEGI 2007b.

Chapter 9
1 nationmaster.com.
2 UNPIN 2009; nationmaster.com.
3 The formal definition is the average number of children that would be born alive to a woman (or group of women) during her lifetime if she were to pass through her childbearing years conforming to the age-specific fertility rates of a given year.
4 Raw data: INEGI 2006.
5 See, for example, Haggett, P. 1975.
6 Raw data: INEGI 1985; INEGI 2004b; nationmaster.com.
7 Raw data: INEGI 1985; INEGI 2004b; CONAPO 2006.

Chapter 10
1 INEGI 2001; INEGI 2005.
2 OAS 1998.

3 Indigenous municipalities have far smaller populations and are relatively more numerous. e.g. Oaxaca, with only 3.5% of Mexico's population, has 23% of Mexico's municipalities and 18% of its indigenous language speakers.
4 Vinson III, B. and Vaughn, B.2004.
5 Bakewell, P.J. 2002.
6 Fernández H., P. et al. 2006.
7 INEGI 2005.
8 Based on Hernández C., R.A. 2001.

Chapter 11
1 INEGI 2001.
2 Data: Lagarda L., I. undated.
3 Clark, J. 2005.
4 Dow, J.W. 2003.
5 Hernández C., R.A. 2001, chapter 3.

Chapter 12
1 PAN won five of six northern border states, seven central states from Jalisco through Mexico City, and Morelos.
2 PAN did well in Baja California, Nuevo León, Aguascalientes, Guanajuato, Querétaro and the Federal District.
3 Cárdenas received less than 10% of the vote in ten states, mostly in western and northern Mexico. The PRD won 19% of Congressional votes, winning 68 of 500 seats in the Chamber, about half of the 125 seats they had in 1997. The PRD took 17 of the 128 seats in the Senate, won Congressional elections in Baja California Sur and Michoacán, and did well in southern states.
4 PRI placed 435 deputies in state legislatures, PAN 355 and PRD 229.
5 PAN won the presidential vote in 16 states compared to 20 in 2000.
6 The PAN block comprises Baja California, Sonora, Chihuahua, Coahuila, Nuevo León, Tamaulipas, Sinaloa, Durango, San Luis Potosí, Jalisco, Guanajuato and Querétaro. Puebla and Yucatán also voted PAN in both elections.
7 Selee, A. 2009.
8 Coahuila, Chihuahua, Jalisco, Morelos, Nuevo León, Puebla, Sonora, Tamaulipas and Yucatán.
9 Guerrero, States of Mexico, Nayarit, Oaxaca and Tabasco.

10 Aguayo Q., S. 2007; SEGOB 2009.

Chapter 13
1 Based on Map 17 in Manrique C., L (coordinator) 1988.
2 Terry, T.P. 1947.
3 Manzanilla, L. 1996; Burton 2003b.
4 West, R.C. and Augelli, J.P. 1966.

Chapter 14
1 Volpe P. 2000.
2 CIA 2009.
3 LMER, December 2002, April 2004.
4 Nationmaster.com.
5 Raw data: INEGI 1985; INEGI 2004b; CIA 2009.
6 Kuznets, S. 1955.
7 Nationmaster.com.
8 Raw data: INEGI 2008a.
9 Raw data: INEGI 2008a.
10 Molina, D.J. and Peach, J. 2005; Angeles-Castro, G. 2007.

Chapter 15
1 Aguayo Q., S. 2003: 151, 161-163, 185.
2 Gobierno de los EUM 2009a, 2009b.
3 Gobierno de los EUM 2009b.
4 Gobierno de los EUM 2009b.
5 LMER, January 2005.
6 DGE 1975.
7 LMER, April 2004.
8 Castillo, A. and Toledo, V.M. 2000.
9 LMER, March 2002.
10 LMER, March 2001.
11 Gobierno de los EUM 2009b.
12 Seawatch 2009.
13 McHugh, M. 2009.
14 Gobierno de los EUM 2009b.
15 Gobierno de los EUM 2009b gives the following percentages of total value of metallurgical production in 2007: copper 34%. gold 23%, zinc 22%, silver 17%, lead 2%, others 2%.
16 Gobierno de los EUM 2009b.
17 Gobierno de los EUM 2009b.
18 EIA 2009.
19 EIA 2009.
20 Petroleum Intelligence Weekly.
21 LMER for February 2001, November 2002, April 2003, July 2003, August 2004; Gobierno de los EUM 2008b.

Chapter 16
1 O'Rourke and Associates 2009.

2 INEGI 2008a.
3 Katel, P. 1997.
4 Kennelly, R.A. 1954, 1955.
5 Expansión 2009.
6 Weber, A. 1909.
7 Smith, D. M. 1971.
8 Townroe, P. 1971.
9 Gobierno de los EUM 2009b.
10 Gobierno de los EUM 2009b.
11 LMER February 2002.
12 INEGI 2008b.
13 Data: Gobierno de los EUM 2009b.

Chapter 17
1 Data: Terry, T.P. 1909, 1947; Norman, J. 1966; Dodge, D. 1969; Siemens, A. H. 1990; SCT undated; SCT road trip calculator; Moats, L. B. and Moats, A-L. 1935; Conkling, A.R. 1886.
2 Janelle, D. 1968.
3 Terry, T.P. 1947.
4 Wellington, A.M. 1886. The terms positive and negative deviation in this context were first used by Peter Haggett 1965.
5 The railroad information in this chapter is based on Werner, M.S. (ed) 1997.
6 Werner, M.S. (ed) 1997: 1451.
7 Data: SCT Road trip calculator for representative journeys by car; approximate travel time (hours) from Mexico City.
8 Kyle, C. 1997.
9 Aguayo Q., S. (ed) 2007.
10 SCT statistics for 2008.
11 Formula used for Spearman's rank: rs = $1 - [6 \times d^2] / [n (n^2 - 1)]$.
12 SCT 2008.
13 INEGI 2008a.
14 Mexicana.com: prices listed on-line on 9 April 2009 for flights on 22 April 2009 to all domestic destinations served by Mexicana.

Chapter 18
1 Harvey, D. 1989.
2 Much of the history in this chapter is based on various entries in Werner, M.S. (ed) 1997.
3 Byerlee and Hesse de Polanco 1986.
4 Redrawn after Byerlee, D. and Hesse de Polanco, E. 1986.
5 Zeder, M.A. et al. 2006.

6 Dow and Sandstrom (eds) 2001.
7 Dow and Sandstrom (eds) 2001.
8 Brown, L.A. and Lentnek, B. 1973.
9 ITU 2003.
10 CIA 2009.
11 de Moura C., C. et al 1999.
12 de Lizaur, B. 1997.
13 After Borroto R.J. and Martinez-Piedra R. 2000.
14 PAHO 1997.
15 Graham, S. 1998: 165.

Chapter 19
1 CESTUR 2005.
2 UNWTO 2008.
3 SECTUR: Datatur system.
4 UNWTO 2008.
5 FONATUR 2009; Gobierno de los EUM 2009b; SPP 1982.
6 SECTUR 2006.
7 Gobierno de los EUM 2009b.
8 UNWTO 2008.
9 SECTUR: Datatur system.
10 SCT 2008.
11 SECTUR Datatur system.
12 SECTUR: Datatur system.
13 AMMT 2009.
14 SECTUR: Datatur system.
15 INEGI 2008.
16 FONATUR 2009.
17 Cone 1995; van den Berghe 1995.
18 SEGOB-CENAPRED 2006b.
19 SEGOB-CENAPRED 2006b.
20 Butler, R.W. 1980.
21 SEGOB-CENAPRED 2006b.
22 SEGOB-CENAPRED 2006b.
23 Gössling, S., et al. 2002.
24 McCool, S. F. 1994.
25 Gössling, S., et al. 2002.
26 Martínez M., L.A. 2008.
27 CESTUR 2007.
28 CESTUR 2002.
29 Burton, T. 2008.
30 Lamont, R. 1988.
31 Truly, D. 2006.
32 Doxey G.V. 1975.
33 Boehm S., B. 2001; Stokes, E.M. 1981.
34 Truly, D. 2006.
35 Burton, T. 1994.
36 CESTUR 2002.

37 UNWTO 2001.
38 UNWTO 2007.
39 Gosline, A. 2005.

Chapter 20
1 LMER, December 2003, December 2004.
2 Gobierno de los EUM 2009b.
3 INEGI 2004a.
4 Banco de Mexico 2005.
5 OECD 2005.
6 Deutsche Bank Research 2006.
7 Juvenil Obrera, P. 2003.
8 nationmaster.com; CIA 2009.
9 Park, K. 2001: 221.
10 LMER, April 2004.
11 nationmaster.com.
12 nationmaster.com.
13 LMER, February 2004.
14 BBVA 2009.
15 Haggett, P. 2001.
16 KOF 2009.
17 Stratfor 2008.
18 A.T. Kearney 2006.

Chapter 21
1 Much of the material for this chapter is based on Kemper, R.V. and Royce, A.P. 1979, 1983.
2 INEGI 1985; 2000a, 2002; 2008b; Gobierno de los EUM 2009b.
3 Rhoda, R. 1983.
4 INEGI 1985, 2004b.
5 ZMCM = Zona Metropolitana de la Ciudad de México.
6 World Bank 2002: 1.
7 White, M. et al 2003.
8 Partida B, V. 2003; Gobierno de los Estados Unidos Mexicanos 2009b.
9 Ariza, M. and Ramírez, J.M. 2005.
10 Partida B, V. 2003.

Chapter 22
1 Based on Janoschka, M. 2002.
2 Park, R.E. et al 1925.
3 Morrison, A. undated.
4 Hoyt, H. 1939.
5 Connolly, P. 2003.
6 Source: adapted from Connolly, P. 2003.
7 Adapted from Burton, T. 1982.
8 Burton. T. 1982.
9 Based on Connolly, P. 2003.

10 Harris, C.D. and Ullman, E.L. 1945.
11 Redrawn based on map by José Luis Escalante published in *Público*, Feb. 7, 1999.

Chapter 23
1 Parnreiter, C. 2003.
2 Dickerson, M. 2005.
3 Urban system boundary based on Garza, G. 2003.
4 Garza, G. 2003.
5 Garza, G. 2003.
6 SEMARNAT 2006.
7 OECD 2008.
8 SEMARNAT 2009.
9 SEMARNAT 2006.
10 Simon, J. 1997; Connolly, P. 1999.
11 Molina, L.T. et al. 2009.
12 SEMARNAT 2009.
13 Molina, L.T. et al. 2009.
14 AFP Breitbart 2009.
15 Gobierno de los Estados Unidos Mexicanos 2008b.
16 Blackman, A. et al 2004.
17 Muller, A. 2007.
18 Muller, A. 2007.

Chapter 24
1 CONAPO 2000b.
2 CONAPO 2000b.
3 CONAPO 2000a. Our "very marginalized" combines the population weighted average of locality level data for two CONAPO categories: "very highly marginalized" and "highly marginalized."
4 This comparison is not completely valid because municipalities are larger than localities.
5 CONAPO 2000a. We use "modern" for CONAPO's "very low marginalization", with the following representative characteristics (mimimum figures in each case): 3% illiteracy, 15% not completing primary school, 2% of houses lack piped water, 4% lack indoor toilets, 4% have dirt floors, 35% are overcrowded, 1% lack electricity, 40% make less than twice the minimum wage.
6 INEGI 2006.
7 For a dated, yet useful, in-depth anthropological study of Oaxaca's markets, see Beals, R.L. 1975.

8 Unpublished student interviews in Pachuca, Hidalgo, 11 November 1983.

Chapter 25

1 Based on ideas in Lee, E.S. 1966.
2 Stouffer, S.A. 1940.
3 Aguilera Reyes, S. 2004.
4 Ginsberg, S. 2000.
5 Vallarta Opina 2009.
6 INEGI 2000b.
7 INEGI 1999.
8 CONAPO 1999.
9 INEGI 2000b.
10 INEGI 2006b, 2009.
11 CONAPO 2001.
12 CONAPO 2001.

Chapter 26

1 Durand, J. et al 2000.
2 Linquist, D. 2000.
3 Kandell, J. 2005.
4 Data from INEGI 2001.
5 Aguayo Q., S. (ed) 2007.
6 CONAPO 2004.
7 CESOP 2004.
8 CONAPO various; Tépach 2008.
9 Passel, J.S. and Suro, R. 2005.
10 Passel, J.S. and Cohn, D. 2009.
11 Roberto Suro, 2005b.
12 González, D. and Carroll, S. 2005.
13 Data in this section: CONAPO 2008.
14 The Miami Herald 2005.

Chapter 27

1 Fix, M. et al 2001; Pew Hispanic Center 2009b.
2 Pew Hispanic Center 2009b.
3 Median household income divided by average household size.
4 Suro, R. 2005a.
5 US Census Bureau 2009a, 2009b, 2009c; Pew Hispanic Center, 2009a.
6 Kochhar, R. et al. 2005.
7 A rather dated analysis—Cato Institute 1995—concluded, "Immigrants have practically no negative effect in the labor market on any person except other immigrants. The effect on wages is modest by any appraisal, and the effect on unemployment apparently is zero."

8 Massey, D.S. 2006.
9 Suro, R. 2005b.
10 The number of businesses fined for immigration violations declined from 909 in 1995 to only 124 in 2003.
11 González, D. and Carroll, S. 2005.
12 Simon, D. 2002.

Chapter 28

1 Aguayo Q., S. 2000: 95.
2 nationmaster.com; UNDP 2007.
3 UN Millennium Development 2009.
4 Data : Land phones, Cell phones, Web users (2007 data) : ITU 2008 ; TV sets, Radios, Newspapers (latest available years): World Resources Institute 2007; Newspapers (2006): WAN 2008.
5 nationmaster.com.
6 LMER, August 2000.
7 Gabinete de Desarrollo Humano y Social/Comisión. Intersecretarial de Desarrollo Social. 2006.
8 Jacoby, E. R. 2004.
9 Malkin, E. 2005.
10 MacKenzie, D. 2009.
11 Aguayo Q., S. 2000: 168.
12 Aguayo Q., S. 2000: 169.
13 nationmaster.com ; UNDP 2007.
14 Freedom House, undated.
15 Freedom House.
16 nationmaster.com.
17 Quote from Mahbub ul Haq: http:// hdr.undp.org/en/humandev.
18 UNDP 2007.
19 Veenhoven R. 2009.
20 Veenhoven R. 2009.

Chapter 29

1 Aguayo Q., S. (ed) 2007.
2 INEGI 2004d.
3 CONAPO 2005.
4 CONAPO 2000c; 2005.
5 CONAPO 2000c.
6 CONAPO 2000c.
7 CONAPO 2000c.
8 http://www.oportunidades.gob.mx/.
9 Rosenberg, T. 2008.
10 Data: Years of Schooling: INEGI 2000a; Fertility Rate (2002): CON-

APO 2006; Life Expectancy (2001): CONAPO 2006; Females on voters' lists (2002): IFE 2009.
11 Parnreiter, C. 2003.
12 Bennholdt-Thomsen, V. 2005.
13 Data: Literacy: INEGI 2000a; Economic participation: INEGI-STPS 2001; Female municipal presidents: INAFED 2002.
14 SS/DGE 2008.
15 Aguayo Q., S. 2007.
16 INEGI-STPS 2001.
17 INEGI-STPS 2001.
18 INEGI 2000a.

Chapter 30

1 Melville, E.G.K. 2000.
2 Sluyter, A. 2002.
3 Folan, W.J. et al 2000.
4 Denevan, W.M. 1992.
5 Simon, J. 1997.
6 Hunter, R.W. 2009.
7 FAO 2006.
8 SEMARNAT 2006.
9 Barreda, A. 2003; Carlsen, L. 2003.
10 Eakin 2006.
11 UNESCO 2009.
12 MSNBC 2005.
13 Simonian, L. 1995.
14 Toledo, A. et al 1983.
15 SEMARNAT 2009.
16 SEMARNAT 2009.
17 The Economist 2009.
18 LMER, November 2004.
19 Wackernagel and Rees 1996.
20 WWF 2008.
21 WWF 2008.
22 WWF 2008.
23 Chávez-Dagostino, R.M. et al 2008.
24 Chávez-Dagostino, R.M. et al 2008.
25 WWF 2008.
26 Esty, D.C. et al 2005.
27 Esty, D.C. et al 2005; Nef 2009.
28 Esty, D.C. et al 2005.
29 Nef 2009.

Chapter 31

1 IPCC 2007; ISAE 2008.
2 OECD 2009.

Appendix A: Population growth by state, 1950-2005

Data: INEGI 1985; INEI 2009b For related discussion, see chapter 8

State	Population (thousands)			Growth rate per year (%)		
	1950	1970	2005	1950-1970	1970-2000	1950-2005
Aguascalientes	188	338	1 065	2.98	3.33	3.20
Baja California	227	870	2 844	6.95	3.44	4.70
Baja California Sur	61	128	512	3.78	4.04	3.94
Campeche	122	252	755	3.69	3.18	3.37
Chiapas	907	1 569	4 293	2.78	2.92	2.87
Chihuahua	846	1 613	3 241	3.28	2.01	2.47
Coahuila	721	1 115	2 495	2.20	2.33	2.28
Colima	112	241	568	3.91	2.48	3.00
Durango	630	939	1 509	2.02	1.36	1.60
Federal District	3 050	6 874	8 721	4.15	0.68	1.93
Guanajuato	1 329	2 270	4 894	2.71	2.22	2.40
Guerrero	919	1 597	3 115	2.80	1.93	2.24
Hidalgo	850	1 194	2 346	1.71	1.95	1.86
Jalisco	1 747	3 297	6 752	3.23	2.07	2.49
Mexico State	1 393	3 833	14 007	5.19	3.77	4.29
Michoacán	1 423	2 324	3 966	2.48	1.54	1.88
Morelos	273	616	1 613	4.15	2.79	3.28
Nayarit	290	544	950	3.20	1.60	2.18
Nuevo León	740	1 695	4 199	4.23	2.63	3.21
Oaxaca	1 421	2 015	3 507	1.76	1.60	1.66
Puebla	1 626	2 508	5 383	2.19	2.21	2.20
Querétaro	286	486	1 598	2.69	3.46	3.18
Quintana Roo	27	88	1 135	6.09	7.58	7.03
San Luis Potosí	856	1 282	2 410	2.04	1.82	1.90
Sinaloa	636	1 267	2 608	3.51	2.08	2.60
Sonora	511	1 099	2 395	3.90	2.25	2.85
Tabasco	363	768	1 990	3.82	2.76	3.14
Tamaulipas	718	1 457	3 024	3.60	2.11	2.65
Tlaxcala	285	421	1 068	1.98	2.70	2.43
Veracruz	2 040	3 815	7 110	3.18	1.79	2.30
Yucatán	517	758	1 819	1.93	2.53	2.31
Zacatecas	666	951	1 368	1.80	1.04	1.32
MEXICO	**25 779**	**48 225**	**103 263**	**3.18**	**2.20**	**2.56**

Appendix B: Rural population, by state

Data: CONAPO 2000b **For related discussion, see chapter 24**

State	Total population 2000 (thousands)	Rural population 2000 (thousands)	Rural population as % of total population	Percent of total population living in			
				Rural near cities	Rural near towns	Rural near roads	Rural isolated areas
Aguascalientes	944	187	19.8	7.5	1.6	10.7	0.0
Baja California	2 488	208	8.4	1.9	0.8	5.3	0.3
Baja California Sur	424	79	18.6	3.3	0.6	12.3	2.6
Campeche	691	200	29.0	0.4	1.2	21.9	5.5
Chiapas	3 921	2 127	54.2	3.8	4.9	16.2	29.3
Chihuahua	3 053	533	17.5	1.3	0.5	9.5	6.2
Coahuila	2 298	243	10.6	2.1	0.4	7.7	0.3
Colima	543	78	14.4	3.5	0.9	9.8	0.1
Durango	1 449	525	36.2	3.1	1.5	24.0	7.5
Federal District	8 605	20	0.2	0.2	0.0	0.0	0.0
Guanajuato	4 663	1 529	32.8	9.0	1.7	15.8	6.3
Guerrero	3 080	1 368	44.4	4.3	3.5	24.8	11.7
Hidalgo	2 236	1 133	50.7	10.2	5.4	33.6	1.4
Jalisco	6 322	971	15.4	2.0	1.2	6.3	5.9
Mexico State	13 097	1 784	13.6	4.8	3.1	5.6	0.1
Michoacán	3 986	1 379	34.6	5.6	4.2	20.5	4.3
Morelos	1 555	226	14.5	7.0	3.9	3.7	0.0
Nayarit	920	329	35.8	3.9	2.5	13.5	15.9
Nuevo León	3 834	249	6.5	1.2	0.2	4.8	0.3
Oaxaca	3 439	1 889	54.9	2.9	4.2	32.0	15.8
Puebla	5 077	1 598	31.5	6.2	5.5	10.3	9.5
Querétaro	1 404	455	32.4	4.5	4.3	22.4	1.2
Quintana Roo	875	153	17.5	1.1	0.3	15.4	0.6
San Luis Potosí	2 299	942	41.0	3.9	2.3	30.2	4.6
Sinaloa	2 537	826	32.6	4.2	3.5	13.0	11.9
Sonora	2 217	375	16.9	2.3	0.8	11.8	2.0
Tabasco	1 892	875	46.3	9.4	7.1	22.3	7.5
Tamaulipas	2 753	401	14.6	1.5	0.6	9.3	3.2
Tlaxcala	963	194	20.2	10.2	1.8	8.3	0.0
Veracruz	6 909	2 822	40.8	6.8	3.8	25.9	4.4
Yucatán	1 658	308	18.6	2.5	0.8	15.0	0.2
Zacatecas	1 354	632	46.7	3.7	2.0	39.0	1.9
MEXICO	**97 483**	**24 638**	**25.3**	**4.1**	**2.5**	**13.5**	**5.1**

Appendix C: Impact of internal migration on population

Data: INEGI 2000b; INEGI 2001   For related discussion, see chapter 25

| State | 1930 Impact of migration on state population (%) | 1960 Impact of migration on state population (% | 2000 | | |
			Impact of migration on state population (%)	Migrants moving to state	Migrants leaving state	Population gain/loss from migration
Aguascalientes	4.4	−17.6	7.6	187 768	116 039	71 729
Baja California	64.3	52.7	36.1	1 025 754	127 074	898 680
Baja California Sur	−3.5	−20.5	25.5	137 928	29 883	108 045
Campeche	−2.8	−5.5	9.7	156 158	89 223	66 935
Chiapas	2.4	−3.6	−5.4	122 451	336 140	−213 689
Chihuahua	11.9	9.7	10.5	524,897	202 864	322 033
Coahuila	17.3	−4.3	−4.7	317 792	425 338	−107 546
Colima	4.8	6.9	11.2	139 290	78 375	60 915
Durango	−4.2	−18.9	−19.6	163,607	447 731	−284 124
Federal District	47.9	36.3	−30.6	1 827 644	4 457 713	−2 630 069
Guanajuato	−11.6	−19.2	−6.0	389 975	669 729	−279 754
Guerrero	−2.3	−6.3	−15.9	167 115	655 538	−488 423
Hidalgo	−7.0	−19.1	−13.6	276 143	579 937	−303 794
Jalisco	−7.9	−10.4	1.7	835 121	726 021	109 100
Mexico State	−18.4	−10.0	33.6	5 059 089	654 711	4 404 378
Michoacán	−4.0	−17.0	−14.5	332 805	909 120	−576 315
Morelos	−2.8	15.5	18.5	431 003	143 964	287 039
Nayarit	4.7	2.4	−5.6	152 540	204 431	−51 891
Nuevo León	4.7	11.6	15.6	827 453	228 453	599 000
Oaxaca	−3.5	−9.4	−18.7	201 099	843 317	−642 218
Puebla	−4.5	−7.7	−8.8	436 024	884 670	−448 646
Querétaro	−15.4	−27.5	7.8	284 890	174 955	109 935
Quintana Roo	30.0	21.8	51.6	485 255	34 139	451 116
San Luis Potosí	−12.5	−14.5	−16.4	217 042	594 267	−377 225
Sinaloa	−0.5	−5.5	−6.5	303 514	468 353	−164 839
Sonora	8.5	9.9	6.7	356 489	208 016	148 473
Tabasco	−4.2	−7.0	−3.0	178 683	235 392	−56 709
Tamaulipas	18.9	19.3	11.2	678 752	370 722	308 030
Tlaxcala	−6.6	−17.7	−4.5	136 504	179 408	−42 904
Veracruz	5.7	1.5	−10.4	629 180	1 350 282	−721 102
Yucatán	1.6	−8.9	−9.6	113 140	271 734	−158 594
Zacatecas	−19.8	−26.9	−29.4	125 319	522 885	−397 566
MEXICO	na	na	na	**17 220 424**	**17 220 424**	0

Appendix D: Migration to USA from Mexican states

Sources: CONAPO 2004; 2008; Tépach M., R. 2008 For related discussion, see chapter 26

State	Born in Mexico, living in USA				Net out-migration to USA 2004	Remittances 2007	
	1990	2005	% increase 1990-2005	Migrants as % of state's 2005 pop.		$ per inhabitant	$ millions
Aguascalientes	71 038	135 989	91	13.0	6 636	306	339
Baja California	486 173	576 590	19	19.6	1 964	111	333
Baja California Sur	13 637	23 287	71	4.6	411	59	32
Campeche	4 777	10 486	120	5.1	548	83	65
Chiapas	6 318	37 441	492	7.5	1 758	177	780
Chihuahua	338 780	523 050	54	15.2	11 134	128	427
Coahuila	133 986	192 115	43	7.6	4 995	109	282
Colima	57 170	99 605	74	16.8	2 942	319	187
Durango	204 871	384 192	65	24.7	10 694	260	400
Federal District	270 978	445 203	64	5.1	15 597	155	1 372
Guanajuato	400 033	926 718	132	18.3	43 855	429	2 143
Guerrero	107 405	408 759	281	6.4	19 268	394	1 240
Hidalgo	32 977	207 610	530	8.7	16 397	398	953
Jalisco	912 093	1 415 224	55	20.8	41 870	281	1 938
Mexico State	206 566	656 457	218	4.5	35 469	140	2 023
Michoacán	571 002	1 061 867	86	25.1	42 079	567	2 264
Morelos	72 656	243 590	235	14.2	11 650	353	581
Nayarit	99 315	183 508	85	18.4	6 056	363	350
Nuevo León	197 012	335 669	70	7.9	7 863	80	349
Oaxaca	69 574	257 991	271	7.1	14 917	358	1 272
Puebla	85 369	340 102	298	6.1	18 198	270	1 496
Querétaro	47 384	101 690	115	6.4	6 576	263	436
Quintana Roo	12 790	23 542	84	2.7	174	78	95
San Luis Potosí	200 941	393 845	96	16.3	16 069	272	669
Sinaloa	83 135	208 219	150	7.5	8 955	187	496
Sonora	139 996	190 160	36	7.6	2 543	134	331
Tabasco	4 315	14 764	242	5.3	742	81	164
Tamaulipas	137 839	300 680	118	9.5	7 851	157	489
Tlaxcala	4 238	29 708	601	2.8	2 309	255	282
Veracruz	46 614	305 769	556	12.4	20 858	204	1 474
Yucatán	33 824	50 982	51	2.4	1 184	66	125
Zacatecas	360 276	508 924	41	35.9	16 426	431	596
MEXICO	**5 413 082**	**10 593 716**	**96**	**10.0**	**397 988**	**227**	**23 979**

Appendix E: Human Development Index, by state

Data: CONAPO 2000c   For related discussion, see chapter 29

State	Life expectancy at birth (years)	Literacy (% of popn. age 15+)	Students (% of popn. age 6-24)	Adjusted income/ person (US$)	HDI	HDI rank (out of 32)
Aguascalientes	76.4	95.2	63.3	9 443	0.820	5
Baja California	76.3	96.5	61.9	9 571	0.822	4
Baja California Sur	76.3	95.8	63.2	8 722	0.817	9
Campeche	74.7	88.2	64.5	13 153	0.815	10
Chiapas	72.4	77.1	57.0	3 302	0.693	32
Chihuahua	75.8	95.2	61.0	10 324	0.819	7
Coahuila	76.2	96.1	62.6	10 808	0.828	3
Colima	76.4	92.8	63.3	8 048	0.806	11
Durango	74.8	94.6	62.2	6 725	0.790	15
Federal District	77.2	97.1	69.8	17 696	0.871	1
Guanajuato	75.1	88.0	58.6	5 376	0.761	24
Guerrero	73.3	78.4	63.3	4 112	0.719	30
Hidalgo	74.2	85.1	64.7	4 690	0.748	28
Jalisco	76.3	93.5	61.5	7 412	0.801	14
Mexico State	76.3	93.6	64.3	5 672	0.789	16
Michoacán	74.8	86.1	59.0	4 785	0.749	27
Morelos	75.9	90.7	63.1	6 820	0.789	17
Nayarit	75.2	90.9	64.3	4 709	0.767	20
Nuevo León	76.8	96.7	62.2	13 033	0.842	2
Oaxaca	72.5	78.5	63.3	3 489	0.706	31
Puebla	74.1	85.4	60.7	5 976	0.758	25
Querétaro	75.3	90.2	61.8	9 562	0.802	13
Quintana Roo	75.7	92.5	59.4	12 039	0.820	6
San Luis Potosí	74.2	88.7	64.1	5 699	0.767	21
Sinaloa	75.4	92.0	64.2	5 905	0.783	18
Sonora	76.1	95.6	65.2	8 761	0.818	8
Tabasco	75.0	90.3	63.5	4 960	0.766	22
Tamaulipas	75.5	94.9	62.0	7 757	0.803	12
Tlaxcala	75.4	92.2	62.7	4 221	0.763	23
Veracruz	74.0	85.1	63.3	4 535	0.744	29
Yucatán	74.3	87.7	63.9	6 342	0.771	19
Zacatecas	74.4	92.0	60.1	4 210	0.754	26
MEXICO	75.3	90.5	62.8	7 495	0.791	na

Appendix F: Quality of life in places where foreign interest is greatest

Data: CONAPO 2000c; CONAPO 2005 For related discussion, see chapter 29

Place (municipality)	2005 population	2000 Census data			2005 Marginalization data (all figures as %)				
		HDI	Infant deaths /1000	Adjusted income/ person (US$)	Not literate age 15+	Did not finish primary school	Homes with no power	Homes with no piped water	<200% mini- mum wage
Acapulco, Guerrero	717 766	0.806	21	8 280	9	21	1	18	60
Aguascalientes, Ags.	723 043	0.821	21	11 302	3	14	1	2	28
Cancun, QRoo	572 973	0.849	20	15 656	4	15	2	6	26
Chapala, Jalisco	43 345	0.801	21	7 316	6	25	1	1	36
Cuernavaca, Morelos	349 102	0.844	18	10 521	4	12	0	3	28
Ensenada, BC	413 481	0.823	26	8 388	5	19	3	8	22
Guadalajara, Jalisco	1 600 940	0.834	18	8 824	3	12	0	0	28
Guanajuato*, Gto.	153 364	0.797	24	6 979	7	20	2	11	36
Guaymas, Sonora	134 153	0.810	22	7 283	4	18	2	2	32
Hermosillo, Sonora	701 838	0.839	21	10 404	2	13	1	2	24
Juárez, Chihuahua	1 313 338	0.812	21	12 970	2	14	0	2	28
La Paz, BCS	219 596	0.817	22	7 414	3	13	3	6	24
León, Guanajuato	1 278 087	0.798	21	7 080	7	21	1	7	32
Los Cabos, BCS	164 162	0.836	20	15 018	3	15	2	22	16
Manzanillo, Colima	137 842	0.816	21	8 893	5	19	1	2	35
Mazatlán, Sinaloa	403 888	0.815	20	7 019	3	15	1	1	34
Mérida, Yucatán	781 146	0.833	21	9 557	4	16	1	2	49
Mexicali, BC	855 962	0.842	21	11 855	3	14	1	2	14
Mexico City	8 720 916	0.873	20	17 696	3	10	0	2	33
Monterrey, NL	1 133 814	0.834	20	14 769	3	12	0	1	22
Morelia, Michoacán	684 145	0.818	20	7 774	5	17	1	4	39
Nuevo Laredo, Tamps.	355 827	0.815	22	8 986	4	15	2	2	30
Oaxaca, Oaxaca	265 006	0.834	19	8 722	5	13	1	10	40
Playa del Carmen, QRoo	135 512	0.810	26	16 553	6	19	2	3	30
Playas de Rosarito, BC	73 305	0.785	23	5 353	3	18	2	26	16
Puebla, Puebla	1 485 941	0.843	19	11 073	4	12	0	5	37
Puerto Escondido*, Oax.	33 682	0.761	24	5 796	15	34	4	7	57
Puerto Vallarta, Jalisco	220 368	0.824	21	9 692	4	15	0	3	24
Querétaro City, Qro.	734 139	0.853	20	17 479	4	12	1	2	27
San Miguel de Allende*, Gto	139 297	0.741	28	5 322	15	35	3	13	46
Tepic, Nayarit	336 403	0.817	20	6 774	4	15	1	2	41
Tijuana, BC	1 410 687	0.825	21	9 815	3	14	1	4	12
Veracruz, Veracruz	512 310	0.827	19	8 118	4	15	0	7	38
Xalapa, Veracruz	413 136	0.825	20	8 110	5	15	0	1	41
Zapopan, Jalisco	1 155 790	0.839	20	10 619	3	13	0	6	26
National	103 263 388	0.790	25	7 495	8	23	2	10	45

* over 30% of each of these municipalities is rural; this significantly lowers their quality of life values

Bibliography

Note: for all URLs, the date last accessed is in square brackets: eg [15 September 2009]

AFT Breitbart 2009 *Germany, Mexico, US top smart energy list.* AFT Breitbart 5 November 2009. http://www.breitbart.com/article.php?id=CNG.97b3a5404235ab56d84cc3c153ecf9b6.01&show_article=1 [8 November 2009]

Aguayo Q., S. (ed) 2000 *El Almanaque Mexicano Hechos Confiables,* 2000. Mexico City.

———— 2003 *México a la Mano, Hechos Confiables,* 2003, Mexico City.

———— (ed) 2007 *El Almanaque Mexicano, 2007.* Mexico City: Editorial Santillana.

Aguilera Reyes, S. 2004 "Desarrollo, Población y Uso de los Recursos Naturales en el Valle de Uxpanapa." *Universidad Veracruzana Facultad de Sociología thesis.* Xalapa,Veracruz. Marzo 2004. www.ciesas-golfo.edu.mx/istmo/docs/tesis/UXPANAPA%20S.%20AGUILERA/CAPITULO%20III.PDF [10 October 2009]

AMIA (Associacion Mexicana de la Industria Automotriz) *2009 Website* homepage: www.amia.com.mx/estadisticas.html [19 August 2009]

AMMT (Asociación Mexicana de Marinas Turísticas) undated *Website homepage:* www.ammt.org/index.html [8 August 2009]

Angeles-Castro, G. 2007 *Factors driving changes in income distribution in post-reform Mexico.* May ftp://ftp.ukc.ac.uk/pub/ejr/RePEc/ukc/ukcedp/0706.pdf [18 August 2009]

Ariza, M. and Ramírez, J.M. 2005 Urbanización, mercados de trabajo, y escenarios sociales en el México finisecular, in Portes, A., Roberts, B. and Grimson, A. (compilers) 2005 *Ciudades latinoamericanas. Un análisis comparativo en el umbral del nuevo siglo*: 299-361. Buenos Aires: Prometeo Libros. www.prc.utexas.edu/urbancenter/documents/ArizaRamirez51.pdf [18 August 2009]

A.T. Kearney 2006 *The A.T. Kearney Index of Globalization 2006.* http://www.atkearney.com/images/global/pdf/Globalization-Index_FP_Nov-Dec-06_S.pdf [29 August 2009]

Bakewell, P.J. 2002 *Silver Mining and Colonial Society in Mexico: Zacatecas, 1546-1700.* Cambridge University Press.

Banco de México 2005 Loss of Share of Mexican Products in International Markets. *Inflation Report July – September 2005.* Mexico City: Banco de México

Barreda, A. 2003 Biopiracy, Bioprospecting, and Resistance: Four Cases in Mexico, in Wise, T.A., Salazar, H. and Carlsen, L. (eds) *Confronting Globalization. Economic Integration and Popular Resistance in Mexico.* Bloomfield, Connecticut: Kumarian Press: 101-125

BBVA 2009. "Which states will be most affected by the recession?" *BBVA, Mexico Economic Research Department,* July 8, 2009. http://serviciodeestudios.bbva.com. http://serviciodeestudios.bbva.com/KETD/fbin/mult/090708_ObserSectorialMexico_5_eng_tcm348-197869.pdf

Beals, R.L. 1975 *The Peasant Marketing System of Oaxaca, Mexico.* University of California Press.

Bennholdt-Thomsen, V. 2005 A matriarchal society in the age of globalization: Juchitán/Southern Mexico. Paper presented at *2nd World Congress on Matriarchal Studies,* San Marcos and Austin, Texas. 2005 www.second-congress-matriarchal-studies.com/bennholdtthomsen.html [2 November 2009]

Blackman, A., Batz, M. and Evans, D. 2004 "Maquiladoras, Air Pollution, and Human Health in Ciudad Juárez and El Paso. April 2003, updated July 2004." *Discussion Paper 03-18.* Washington D.C.: Resources for the Future. http://www.rff.org/documents/RFF-DP-03-18.pdf [10 Ocotber 2009]

Blanke, J. and Chiesa, T. (eds) 2008 *The Travel & Tourism Competitiveness Report 2008* World Economic Forum [20 January 2009] at www.weforum.org/ttcr08browse/index.html

Boehm S., B. 2001 El Lago de Chapala: su Ribera Norte. Un ensayo de lectura del paisaje cultural. 2001. *Relaciones* 85, Invierno, 2001. Vol XXII: 58-83.

Borroto R.J. and Martinez-Piedra R. 2000 Geographical patterns of cholera in Mexico, 1991–1996, *International Journal of Epidemiology,* Vol 29 (4), August 2000: 764-772

Brown, L.A. and Lentnek, B. 1973 Innovation diffusion in a Developing Economy: a mesoscale view, *Economic Development and Cultural Change* 21: 274-92.

Burton, T. 1982 Sun and Sombreros; some observations on fieldwork in Mexico. *Teaching Geography*, April 1982: 171-5.

—— 1994 Los estudiantes estudian a la comunidad local. *El Ojo del Lago* (Chapala, Mexico), September 1994.

—— 2003a Chihuahua caves house world's largest crystals. *MexConnect e-zine*, March 2003. http://www.mexconnect.com/articles/1221. [12 November 2008]

—— 2003b Archaeologists have found fifteen-hundred-year-old kitchens. *MexConnect e-zine*, November 2003 http://mexconnect.com/articles/1188 [21 August 2009]

—— 2004 An enchanted lake in Veracruz rises every dry season, but falls again during the wet season, *MexConnect e-zine*. 14 March 2004, www.mexconnect.com/articles/1219 [20 August 2009]

—— 2008a Mexico has the deepest water-filled sinkhole in the world, in Tamaulipas. *MexConnect e-zine*, March 2008. http://mexconnect.com/articles/3026 [10 November 2008]

—— 2008b *Lake Chapala Through the Ages, an Anthology of Travellers' Tales*. Canada: Sombrero Books.

Butler, R.W. 1980. The Concept of the tourist area cycle of evolution: Implications for management of resources. *Canadian Geographer* 24 (1): 5-12.

Byerlee, D. and Hesse de Polanco, E. 1986. Farmers' Stepwise Adoption of Technological Packages: Evidence from the Mexican Altiplano, *American Journal of Agricultural Economics*, vol. 68 (3) August 1986:519-557

Carlsen, L. 2003 Biopiracy on the Border: The Battle for the Yellow Bean, in Wise, T.A., Salazar, H. and Carlsen, L. (eds) *Confronting Globalization. Economic Integration and Popular Resistance in Mexico*. Bloomfield, Connecticut: Kumarian Press: 81-99

Castillo, A. and Toledo, V.M. 2000 "Applying Ecology in the Third World: The Case of Mexico." *BioScience*, vol. 50, 1, January 2000: 66-76

Cato Institute 1995 *Immigration: The Democratic and Economic Facts. 4. Effects of Immigration on Native Unemployment.* Cato Institute and the National Immigration Forum. http://www.cato.org/pubs/policy_report/pr-imnative.html [22 August 2009]

CDI (Comisión Nacional para el Desarrollo de los Pueblos Indígenas) 2006 *Indicadores con perspectiva de género para los pueblos indígenas.* Mexico City. http://www.cdi.gob.mx/indica_genero/indicadores_perspectiva_genero_2006.pdf [23 AUgust 2009]

CENAPRED (Centro Nacional de Prevención de Desastres) 2008 *Atlas Nacional de Riesgos* http://www.cenapred.gob.mx/es/Atlas/ Mexico: CENAPRED [15 April 2008]

CESOP (Centro de Estudios Sociales y de opinión Pública) 2004 *El impacto de las remesas familiares en México y su uso productivo,* December 2004. http://www.cddhcu.gob.mx/cesop/doctos/EL%20IMPACTO%20DE%20LAS%20REMESAS%20FAMILIARES%20EN%20MEXICO%20Y%20SU%20USO%20PR%85.pdf

CESTUR 2002 *Estudio Estratégico de viabilidad del segmento de turismo de retirados. Sintesis Ejecutiva.*

—— 2005 *Estudio "Hábitos de Consumo del Turista Nacional" Temporada vacional de verano, 2005.* Reporte total. www.turismo.gob.mx/work/sites/sectur/resources/LocalContent/14616/5/HabitosVeranoCompleto.pdf [16 June 2009]

—— 2007 *Elementos para Evaluar el Impacto Económico, Social y Ambiental del Turismo de Naturaleza en México.* December 2007.

Chávez-Dagostino, R.M., Cifuentes-Lemus, J.L., Andrade-Romo, E., Espinoza-Sánchez, R., Massam, B.H. and Everitt, J. 2008 "Huellas ecológicas y sustentabilidad en la costa norte de Jalisco, México", *Teoría y Praxis* 4:137-144. http://www.teoriaypraxis.uqroo.mx/doctos/Numero5/Chavez-Andrade.pdf [10 october 2009]

CIA 2003 *The World Factbook 2003*. Washington, D.C.: CIA.

—— 2009 *The World Factbook 2009*. Washington, D.C.: CIA. https://www.cia.gov/library/publications/the-world-factbook/index.html [2 May 2009]

CIESEN (Center for International Earth Science Information Network) 2009 *World Data Center for Human Interactions with the Environment.* New York: Columbia University http://sedac.ciesin.columbia.edu/wdc/geonetSearch?geonetService=wdc.home&extended=off&remote=off&attrset=geo&any=&title=&author=&abstract=&themckcy=&hitsPerPage=10&siteId=WDC [21 August 2009]

Clark, J. 2005 Mormon church charts rapid growth in Mexico. *The Miami Herald*, Mexico edition, 29 November 2005.

Cohen, M.J., Henges-Jeck, C and Castillo-Moreno, G 2001 A preliminary water balance for the Colorado River delta, 1992–1998, *Journal of Arid Environments* 49: 35-48.

CONABIO (Comisión nacional para el conocimiento y uso de la biodiversidad) 2008 Mexico City: CONABIO. www.conabio.gob.mx [10 November 2008]

CONAGUA/CNA (Comisión Nacional del Agua) 2006 *Water in Mexico.* Mexico City: CONAGUA www.worldwaterforum4.org.mx/uploads/TBL_DOCS_115_40.pdf

———— 2008a *Datos Históricos de Ciclones Tropicales.* Mexico City: CONAGUA, via http://smn.cna.gob.mx/ [11 Nov. 2008]

———— 2008b *Estadísticas del agua en México.* Edición 2008. Mexico City: CONAGUA.

CONAPO (Comisión Nacional de la Población) 1999 *Veinticinco anos de cambio de la migración interna en México*, Mexico City: CONAPO www.conapo.gob.mx/publications/1999/PDF/99006.pdf. [20 April 2009]

———— 2000a *Índices de marginación*, Mexico City: CONAPO www.conapo.gob.mx/00cifras/2000.htm.

———— 2000b *Localidades Rurales*, Mexico City: CONAPO www.canpo.gob.mx/distribution_tp/04.htm.

———— 2000c *Índices de de desarrollo humano*, Mexico City: CONAPO www.conapo.gob.mx/00cifras/6.htm.

———— 2001 *Migración Interna; cuadro 1* Mexico City: CONAPO www.conapo.gob.mx/index.php?option=com_content&view=article&id=7&Itemid=247

———— 2004 *La nueva era de las migraciones*, December, 2004. Mexico City: CONAPO www.conapo.gob.mx/publicaciones/nuevaera/era.htm.

———— 2005 *México en cifras, Índices de Marginación, Anexó B, índices de marginación por municipio, 2005* Mexico City: CONAPO http://www.conapo.gob.mx/publicaciones/margina2005/AnexoB.pdf [28 October 2009]

———— 2006 *Proyecciones de la población de México 2005-2050* Mexico City: CONAPO.

———— 2008 *Series sobre migración internacional*. Mexico City: CONAPO. http://www.conapo.gob.mx/index.php?option=com_content&view=article&id=31&Itemid=295 [23 August 2009]

———— 2009 *De la población de México 2005-2050.* Mexico City: CONAPO. *http://conapo.gob.mx/index.php?option=com_content&view=article&id=36&Itemid=234* [31 August 2009]

Conde, C. and Gay, C. 1999 Impacts of Climate Change and Climate Variability in Mexico. *Acclimations,* September-October, 1999. www.usgcrp.gov/usgcrp/Library/nationalassessment/newsletter/1999.10/Mexico.html [20 August 2009]

Cone, C.A. 1995 Crafting Selves: the lives of two Mayan women. *Annals of Tourism Research*, vol 22, No 2: 314-327.

Conkling, A.R. 1886 *Appleton's Guide to Mexico.* New York: Appleton.

Connolly, P. 1999 Mexico City: Our Common Future, *Environment and Urbanization*, VII, No. 1, April 1999.

———— 2003 *Understanding Slums: Case Studies for the Global Report 2003: The Case of Mexico City, Mexico,* www.ucl.ac.uk/dpu-projects/Global_Report/pdfs/Mexico.pdf

Corona Vázquez, R. 1992 *Estimación de la población de origen mexicano que reside en Estados Unidos.* Tijuana: El Colegio de la Frontera Norte, November, 1992;

de Lizaur, B. 1997 Telenovelas, in Werner, M.S. (ed) 1997. *Encyclopedia of Mexico: History, Society, & Culture.* Chicago: Fitzroy Dearborn.

de Moura, C., Wolf, L. and García, N. 1999 Mexico's Telesecundaria–Bringing Education by Television to Rural Areas. *TechKnowLogia.* September/October 1999. www.techknowlogia.org/TKL_active_pages2/CurrentArticles/main.asp?IssueNumber=1&FileType=PDF&ArticleID=6 [2 May 2009]

Denevan, W.M. 1992 "The Pristine Myth: The Landscape of the Americas in 1492", *Annals of the Association of American Geographers*, 82 (3), September 1992: 369-385.

Deutsche Bank Research 2006. *Mexico 2020: Tequila sunrise. A medium-term growth perspective.* www.dbresearch.com/PROD/DBR_INTERNET_ENPROD/PROD0000000000196419.pdf [accessed April 13, 2009]

DGE (Dirección General de Estadística) 1975 *V Censos Agrícola, Ganadero y Ejidal, México 1970.* Mexico City: DGE.

Diamond, J. 1998 *Guns, Germs and Steel.* New York: W.W. Norton & Company.

Dickerson, M. 2005 Shoehorns in Hand, Mexicans Move into Their Dream Homes. *Los Angeles Times,* 7 October 2005. http://articles.latimes.com/2005/oct/07/business/fi-mexhomes7 [24 August 2009]

Díez, J. 2008. "The Rise and Fall of Mexico's Green Movement", *European Review of Latin American and Caribbean Studies* 85, October 2008, 1: 81-99.

Dodge, D. 1969 *The best of Mexico by car.* Toronto: The Macmillan Company.

Dow, J.W. 2003 The Growth of Protestant Religions in Mexico and Central America. *Society for the Scientific Study of Religion Annual Meeting 2003*, Norfolk, Virginia, October, 2003.

Dow, J.W. and Sandstrom, A. R. (eds) 2001 *Holy Saints and Fiery Preachers: The Anthropology of Protestantism in Mexico and Central America.* Westport, Connecticut: Praeger.

Doxey G.V. 1975 A causation theory of visitor-resident irritants: methodology and research inferences. *Proceedings of the Travel Research Association, 6th Annual Conference,* San Diego, California, USA: 195-8.

Durand, J, Massey, D.S. and Zenteno, R.M. 2000 Mexican Immigration To The United States: Continuities and Changes. *Latin American Research Review*, Volume 36, Number 1, 107-127. www.pacificcouncil.org/public/Studies/Naf/latin1.htm.

Eakin, H. 2006 *Weathering Risk in Rural Mexico. Climatic, institutional and economic change*. Tucson: The University of Arizona Press.

EIA (Energy Information Administration) 2009 *Country Analysis Briefs: Mexico*. Washington D.C.: EIA http://www.eia.doe.gov/cabs/Mexico/Full.html [31 August 2009]

Endfield, G.H. 2008 *Climate and Society in Colonial Mexico, A Study in Vulnerability*. Blackwell.

Época 1994 Sigue abierta la herida que dejó el sismo del 85. *Época* 19 Sep. 1994.

Esty, D.C., Levy, M., Srebotnjak, T. and de Sherbinin, A. 2005. 2005 Environmental Sustainability Index: Benchmarking National Environmental Stewardship. New Haven: Yale Center for Environmental Law & Policy.

Esty, D.C., Levy, M.A., Kim, C. H., de Sherbinin, A., Srebotnjak, T. and Mara, V. 2008. *2008 Environmental Performance Index*. New Haven: Yale Center for Environmental Law & Policy.

Expansión 2009 *Expansión 500 Las empresas más importantes de México*. www.cnnexpansion.com/XPA5002009/?uid=1 [15 October 2009]

FAO (Food and Agriculture Organization) 2006 *Forest Resources Assessment 2005*. Rome, Italy: FAO.

———— 2009 *Information System on Water and Agriculture, Aquastat*. http://www.fao.org/nr/water/aquastat/main/index.stm [8 August 2009]

FAO/AGL 2007 *World Reference Base for Soil Resources*, www.fao.org/ag/agl/agll/wrb/ [20 August 2009]

Fernández H., P., Embriz O., A, Medina D., M.E. and Serrano C., E. (coordinators) 2006 *Indicadores con perspectiva de género para los pueblos indígenas*. Mexico City: Comisión Nacional para el Desarrollo de los Pueblos Indígenas. http://www.cdi.gob.mx/indica_genero/indicadores_perspectiva_genero_2006.pdf [21 August 2009]

Fix, M., Zimmerman, W and Passel, J.S. 2001 *The Integration of Immigrant Families in the United States*, The Urban Institute, July 2001, www.urban.org/UploadedPDF/immig_integration.pdf [18 August 2009]

Folan, W.J., Faust, B., Lutz, W. and Gunn, J.D. 2000 "Social and Environmental Factors in the Classic Maya Collapse", in Lutz, W., Prieto, L. and Sanderson, W. (eds) *Population, Development, and Environment on the Yucatán Peninsula: From Ancient Maya to 2030*. Laxenburg, Austria: International Institute for Applied Systems Analysis.

FONATUR 2009. *Invierta en FONATUR*. www.fonatur.gob.mx/es/IF/index_IF.asp [8 August 2009]

Freedom House. undated, via http://www.freedomhouse.org/template.cfm?page=1

Gabinete de Desarrollo Humano y Social/Comisión Intersecretarial de Desarrollo Social. 2006. *Los Objetivos de Desarrollo del Milenio en México: Informe de Avance 2006*. http://www.objetivosdelmilenio.org.mx/PDF/ODM%202006.pdf [23 August 2009]

García, E. 1973 *Modificaciones al sistema de clasificación climática de Koeppen*. Mexico City: Universidad Nacional Autónoma de México, Instituto de Geografía.

Garza, G. 2003 "The transformation of the urban system in Mexico", in Champion, T. and Hugo, G. (eds) 2003 *New forms of urbanization: beyond the urban-rural dichotomy*.Burlington, VT, USA: Ashgate Publishing Company: 153-170.

Ginsberg, S. 2000 *Report from Uxpanapa. Can bromeliads save Veracruz's last rainforest?* www.planeta.com/planeta/00/0004veracruz.html [6 September 2009]

Global Footprint Network. undated *World Footprint*. http://www.footprintnetwork.org/en/index.php/GFN/page/world_footprint/ [9 July 2009]

Gobierno de los Estados Unidos Mexicanos 2008a *Segundo Informe del Gobierno, Gobierno de los Estados Unidos Mexicanos, 2008* www.informe.gob.mx/informe/ [21 January 2009].

———— 2008b *Segundo Informe del Gobierno, Gobierno de los Estados Unidos Mexicanos, 2008; anexo estadístico*. www.informe.gob.mx/informe/?contenido=14 [10 February 2009].

———— 2009a *Tercer Informe del Gobierno, Gobierno de los Estados Unidos Mexicanos, 2009* www.informe.gob.mx/informe/ [4 Sept. 2009]

———— 2009b *Tercer Informe del Gobierno, Gobierno de los Estados Unidos Mexicanos, 2009; anexo estadístico*. www.informe.gob.mx/anexo_estadistico [4 September 2009].

González, D. and Carroll, S. 2005 Siege on border: Costly fortifications fail to deter immigrant flow". *The Arizona Republic*, 19 June 2005. www.polisci.ucsd.edu/cornelius/Siege%20on%20border--AZ%20Republic.htm.

Gosline, A. 2005 Tourist Hotter Spots. *New Scientist,* 21 May 2005

Gössling, S., et al. 2002 Ecological footprint analysis as a tool to assess tourism sustainability. *Ecological Economics*, 43: 199-211.

Graham, S. 1998 The end of geography or the explosion of space? Conceptualizing space and information technology. *Progress in Human Geography* 22, 2 165.

Haggett, P. 1965 *Locational Analysis in Human Geography*. London: Edward Arnold.

Haggett, P. 2001 *Geography (A Global Synthesis).* Prentice Hall.

Harris, C.D. and Ullman, E.L. 1945 The Nature of Cities. *Annals of the American Academy of Political Science* 242: 7-17.

Harvey, D. 1989 *The Condition of Postmodernity: an Enquiry into the Origins of Cultural Change.* Oxford: Blackwell.

Hernández C., R.A. 2001 *Histories and Stories from Chiapas. Border Identities in Southern Mexico.* University of Texas Press.

Hewitson, B. and Crane, R. 1992 Large-scale atmospheric controls on local precipitation in tropical Mexico. *Geophysical Research Letters* 19: 1835-38.

Hoekstra, A.Y. and Chapagain, A.K. 2008 *Globalization of water: Sharing the planet's freshwater resources.* Oxford, U.K.: Blackwell Publishing.

Hoyt, H. 1939 *The Structure and Growth of Residential Neighborhoods in American Cities.* Washington D.C., Federal Housing Administration.

Hunter, R.W. 2009 "People, Sheep, and Landscape Change in Colonial Mexico: the Sixteenth Century Transformation of the Valle del Mezquital", *PhD dissertation, LSU Dept. of Geography and Anthropology*, May 2009. http://etd.lsu.edu/docs/available/etd-04022009-230601/unrestricted/Hunterdiss.pdf [10 October 2009]

IBWC (International Boundary and Water Commission) 2009 *Colorado River at Southerly International Boundary in Cubic Meters per Second.* http://www.ibwc.state.gov/wad/DDQSIBCO.htm [4 September 2009]

IFE (Instituto Federal Electoral) 2009 *Estadísticas Lista Nominal y Padrón Electoral.* http://www.ife.org.mx/portal/site/ifev2/Estadisticas_Lista_Nominal_y_Padron_Electoral/ [22 August 2009]

INAFED 2002 *Resumen nacional de la filiación política de los presidentes municipales de México.* http://www.elocal.gob.mx/work/resources/LocalContent/9523/1/filiacion.htm.orig [15 April 2009]

INEGI (Instituto Nacional de Estadística y Geografía) 1984 *Geología de la República Mexicana.* Mexico City: INEGI.

———— 1985 *Estadísticas Históricas de México.* Mexico City: INEGI.

———— 2000a *XII Censo General de Población y Vivienda. 200*0. Aguascalientes, Mexico: INEGI.

———— 2000b *México en el siglo XX (Panorama estadístico), Dinámica Demografía.* Aguascalientes, Mexico: INEGI. http://www.inegi.org.mx/prod_serv/contenidos/espanol/bvinegi/productos/integracion/especiales/mexsigloxx/est1w.pdf [21 August 2009]

———— 2001 *XII Censo General de Población y Vivienda, 2000. Tabulados Básicos.* Aguascalientes, Mexico: INEGI, via www.inegi.org.mx

———— 2002 *Anuario estadístico de los Estados Unidos Mexicanos 2001* Aguascalientes, Mexico: INEGI.

———— 2003a *Anuario estadístico de los Estados Unidos Mexicanos 2002* Aguascalientes, Mexico: INEGI.

———— 2003b *Anuario de Estaisticas por Entidad Federativo, Edición 2003,* Aguascalientes, Mexico: INEGI.

———— 2004a *Anuario de Estadísticas por Entidad Federativa.* Aguascalientes, Mexico: INEGI.

———— 2004b *Estadísticas Históricas de México* Aguascalientes, Mexico: INEGI.

———— 2004c *Anuario estadístico de los Estados Unidos Mexicanos 2003,* Aguascalientes, Mexico: INEGI.

———— 2004d *Encuesta Nacional Sobre la Dinámica de las Relaciones en los Hogares, 2003.* Aguascalientes, Mexico: INEGI. www.inegi.gob.mx/est/contenidos/espanol/rutinas/ept.asp?t=mvio33&c=5521

———— 2005 *II Conteo de Población y Vivienda 2005.* Aguascalientes, Mexico: INEGI, via www.inegi.org.mx

———— 2006a *Anuario estadístico de los Estados Unidos Mexicanos 2005.* Aguascalientes, Mexico: INEGI. www.inegi.org.mx

———— 2006b *Población total por entidad federativa según sexo, 2000 y 2005.* Aguascalientes, Mexico: INEGI. www.inegi.org.mx/est/contenidos/espanol/rutinas/ept.asp?t=mpob02&c=3179

———— 2007a *Anuario estadístico de los Estados Unidos Mexicanos 2006.*Aguascalientes, Mexico: INEGI.

———— 2007b *Anuario de Estadísticas por Entidad Federativa, Edición 2007.* Aguascalientes, Mexico: INEGI.

———— 2007c *Sistema de Cuentas Nacionales. Producto Interno Bruto por Entidad Federativa para el periodo 2001-2006.* Aguascalientes, Mexico: INEGI.

———— 2008a *Anuario de Estadísticas por Entidad Federativa, Edición 2008.* Aguascalientes, Mexico: INEGI.

———— 2008b *Mexico at a Glance 2008.* Aguascalientes, Mexico: INEGI.

———— 2009 *Población de 5 y más años inmigrantes y emigrantes y saldo neto migratorio estatal por entidad federativa según el lugar de residencia cinco años antes, 2000 y 2005.* Aguascalientes, Mexico: INEGI. www.inegi.org.mx/est/contenidos/espanol/rutinas/ept.asp?t=mpob61&s=est&c=3238

———— undated (various years) Cartas de Uso de Suelo y Vegetación, Escala 1: 1 000 000. Aguascalientes, Mexico: INEGI

INEGI-STPS 2001 *Encuesta Nacional de Empleo, 2001.* via .inegi.org.mx/ [13 April 2009]

IPCC 2007 "Regional Climate Projections", in *Climate Change 2007:The Physical Science Basis. Contribution of Working Group I to the Fourth Assessment Report of the Intergovernmental Panel on ClimateChange.* Cambridge, UK: Cambridge University Press, http://ipcc-wg1.ucar.edu/wg1/Report/AR4WG1_Print_Ch11.pdf [15 October 2009]

ISAE (Iowa State Agriculture Extension) 2008 "Global Warming – Impact Of Climate Change On Global Agriculture", *Cattlenetwork*, Nov. 13, 2008, www.cattlenetwork.com/Content.asp?ContentID=260049 [15 October 2009]

ITU (International Telecommunication Union) 2003 *ITU Digital Access Index: World's First Global ICT Ranking.* ITU. www.itu.int/newsroom/press_releases/2003/30.html [2 May 2009]

———— 2008 *ITU Eye; statistics.* ITU. www.itu.int//ITU-D/ict/statistics/index.html [2 May 2009]

Jacoby, E. R. 2004 PAHO regional consultation of the Americas on diet, physical activity and health. *Food and Nutrition Bulletin* 25 (2): 172-174.

Janelle, D. 1968 Central place development in a time-space framework. *Professional Geographer* 20, #1, 5-10.

Janoschka, M. 2004 Modelling the Dynamics, of Latin American Cities: from Polarisation to Fragmentation, *Memories of the 11th Planning Conference of the International Planning History Society,* Barcelona. www.michael-janoschka.de/pdfs/Communication%20Barcelona.pdf.

Jauregui, E. 2003 Impact of Increasing Urbanization on the Thermal Climate of Large Mexican Cities. *Paper presented at 5th International Conference on Urban Climate, Lodz, Poland.* www.geo.uni.lodz.pl/~icuc5/text/O_22_3.pdf [November 2008]

———— 2004 Impact of land-use changes on the climate of the Mexico City Region. *Investigaciones Geográficas, Boletín del Instituto de Geografía.* Mexico City: Universidad Nacional Autónoma de México: Instituto de Geografía.

Jazcilevich, A., Fuentes, V., Jáuregui, E. and Luna, E. 2000 Simulated Urban Climate Response to Historical Land Use Modification in the Basin of Mexico. *Climatic Change* 44.

Juvenil Obrera, P. 2003 "The Struggle for Justice in the Maquiladoras: The Experience of the Autotrim Workers" in Wise, T.A., Salazar, H. and Carlsen, L. (eds) *Confronting Globalization. Economic Integration and Popular Resistance in Mexico.* Bloomfield, Connecticut: Kumarian Press: 173-194

Kandell, J. 2005 Cross Purposes, *Smithsonian,* June, 2005: 90-96.

Katel, P. 1997 Bordering on Chaos–the Cemex story, in *Wired Magazine* May 1997.

Kemper, R.V. and Royce, A.P. 1979 Mexican Urbanization Since 1821: A Macro-Historical Approach, *Urban Anthropology* 8(3/4): 267-289.

———— 1983. Urbanization in Mexico: Beyond the Heritage of Conquest, in Kendall, C. Hawkins, J. and Bossen, L. (eds) *Heritage of Conquest: Thirty Years Later,* Albuquerque: Univ. of New Mexico Press: 93-128.

Kennelly, R.A. 1954, 1955 Location of Steel Mills in Mexico, *Revista Geografía,* 15:109-129; 16: 199-213; 17:60-77.

Kochhar, R., Suro, R. and Tafoya, S. 2005 *The New Latino South: The Context and Consequences of Rapid Population Growth,* Pew Hispanic Center. http://pewhispanic.org/files/reports/50.1.pdf [20 August 2009]

KOF 2009 *KOF Index of Globalization.* Zurich, Switzerland: KOF/ETH.

Kuznets, S. 1955 Economic Growth and Income Inequality. *American Economic Review* 45: 1-28.

Kyle, C. 1997 Transport and Communications 1910-96, in Werner, M.S. (ed) 1997 *Encyclopedia of Mexico: History, Society, & Culture.* Chicago: Fitzroy Dearborn.

Lagarda L, I. undated *Historia de los Menonitas de Cuauhtemoc, Chihuahua,* México. www.monografias.com/trabajos11/menonit/menonit.shtml#CUAU [29 January 2007]

Lamont, R. 1988 *Siete llaves para abrir un nuevo 'tesoro turístico' en Guadalajara y alrededores.* Guadalajara: American Chamber of Commerce.

Lanegran, D.A. and Natoli, S. 1984 *Guidelines for Geographic Education in the Elementary and Secondary Schools.* Washington, DC: Association of American Geographers; National Council for Geographic Education. http://www.nationalgeographic.com/resources/ngo/education/themes.html [15 October 2009]

Lee, E.S. 1966 A Theory of Migration, *Demography* 3: 47-57, 1966.

Linquist, D. 2000 Plenty of jobs, not enough workers: NAFTA's bittersweet boom, *The San Diego Union Tribune,* 31 July 2000.

Liverman, D. 1991 Global change and Mexico. Earth and Mineral Sciences, 60: 71-76, cited in Eakin, H. 2006 *Weathering Risk in Rural Mexico. Climatic, institutional and economic change.* Tucson: The University of Arizona Press.

LMER (*Lloyd Mexican Economic Report*) Published monthly from 1966 to 2006. Guadalajara, Mexico: Operadora de Fondos Lloyd, S.A.

MacKenzie, D. 2009 Wheat in shining armor arives. *New Scientist.* Volume 201, No 2700, 21 March 2009.

MacLachan, C.M. and Rodriquez O., J.E. 1980 *The Forging of the Cosmic Race: A Reinterpretation of Colonial Mexico.* Berkeley: University of California Press.

Malkin, E. 2005 Mexico Confronts Sudden Surge in Obesity, *New York Times,* 29 June 2005.

Manrique C., L (coordinator) 1988 *Atlas Cultural de México: Lingüística.* Mexico: SEP/INAH/Planeta.

Manzanilla, L. 1996 Soil analyses to identify ancient human activities. *Canadian Journal of Soil Science,* vol. 76 (2), May 1996: 107-108.

Martínez M., L.A. 2008. Nafta, Tourism and the Environment in Mexico. *Research Paper 08 for the Fourth North American Symposium on Assessing the Environmental Effects of Trade.* Phoenix. www.cce.cec.org/files/PDF/ECONOMY/MartinezLuz-Symposium08-21apr_en.pdf [20 January 2009]

Massey, D.S. 2006. Illegal immigrants: Are they freebies or freeloaders? *The San Diego Union-Tribune*, June 2, 2006. http://www.signonsandiego.com/uniontrib/20060602/news_lz1e2massey.html [22 August 2009]

McCool, S.F. 1994 Planning for sustainable nature dependent tourism develoment: The limits of acceptable change system in *Tourism Recreation Research*, vol XIX, No 2.

McHugh, M. 2009 Overfishing in the Sea of Cortez: Are sustainable fish farms the solution? *MexConnect*, 16 March 2009. www.mexconnect.com/articles/3157 [10 September 2009]

Melville, E.G.K. 1994 *A plague of Sheep. Environmental consequences of the conquest of Mexico*. Cambridge University Press.

——— 2000 "Disease Ecology and the Environment", in Meyer, M.C. and Beezley, W.H. (ed) 2000 *Oxford History of Mexico*: 213-243. Oxford University Press.

Moats, L. B. and Moats, A-L. 1935 *Off to Mexico*. New York: Charles Scribner's Sons.

Molina, D.J. and Peach, J. 2005 Mexico's Changing Distribution of Income, *Journal of Political Issues*, Vol. 39, 2005.

Molina, L.T. and Molina, M.J. 2003 Improving urban air quality, Revista, *Harvard Review of Latin America*, Winter 2003.

Molina, L.T., de Foy, B., Vázquez M., O., Páramo F., V.H. 2009 Air quality, weather and climate in Mexico City. *Bulletin, the Journal of the World Meteorological Orgnanization,* vol 58 (1), January 2009: 48-53.

Morrison, A. no date *The Tramways of Mexico*, www.tramz.com/mx/mc/mcml.html.

MSNBC 2005 "Mexico oil spills reflect crumbling network", *msnbc.com* January 27, 2005. http://www.msnbc.msn.com/id/6861084/ [14 October 2009]

Muller, A. 2007. *Mexico City's Green Referéndum*. www.worldchanging.com/archives/008696.html [20 August 2009]

Nationmaster.com – Various statistics, including:2008 Severe Water Stress by Country at www.nationmaster.com/graph/env_wat_sev_wat_str-environment-water-severe-stress [21 August 2009] and Agricultural grain imports at www.nationmaster.com/graph/agr_gra_cor_imp-agriculture-grains-corn-imports.

Nef (New Economics Foundation) 2009 *The Happy Planet Index 2.0*. http://www.happyplanetindex.org/learn/download-report.html [10 October 2009]

Norman, J. 1966 *Terry's Guide to Mexico*. New York: Doubleday & Company.

OAS (Organization of American States) 1998 *Report on the Situation of Human Rights in Mexico,* Chapter VII: the Situation of indigenous Peoples and Their Rights. Inter-American Commission on Human Rights. http://www.cidh.oas.org/countryrep/Mexico98en/Chapter-7.htm [21 August 2009]

OECD (Organisation for Economic Co-operation and Development) 2005 Mexico. *OECD Economic Survey*. Paris, France: OECD

——— 2008. *OECD Environmental Data. Compendium 2006/2008*. Paris, France: OECD http://www.oecd.org/dataoecd/22/58/41878186.pdf [12 October 2009]

——— 2009 "Growing unequal, poverty and incomes over 20 years," in *OECD DELSA Newsletter* Issue 7, 2009, http://www.oecd.org/dataoecd/13/54/42255285.pdf [15 October 2009]

Ooska News Weekly Water Report for Latin America and the Caribbean. 2008 Energy and Water Research Institute Created in Tabasco. Ooska News Weekly Water Report vol 1 #8, 2 December 2008.

O'Rourke and Associates 2009 *Mexican Economic Report*. September 2009. Guadalajara, Mexico: O'Rourke and Associates.

PAHO 1997 (Pan American Health Organization) Cholera Situation in the Americas 1996, *Epidemiological Bulletin*, vol 18 (1) http://www.paho.org/english/sha/epibul_95-98/be971cho.htm [4 September 2009]

Palma M., M. 2006 Estadounidenses en México: notas sobre su inmigración en el siglo XX in *Material inestable: reflexiones sobre historia reciente*. CONACULTA/INAH. Suplemento #37, 2006. www.antropologia.inah.gob.mx/pdf/pdf_diario/mayo_06/sup_mayo_06.pdf [13 November 2008]

Park, K. 2001 *World Almanac and Book of Facts 2002*. New York: World Almanac.

Park, R.E., Burgess, E.W. and McKenzie, R.D. 1925 *The City*. Chicago: University of Chicago Press.

Parnreiter, C. 2003 Global City Formation in Latin America: Socioeconomic and Spatial Transformations in Mexico City and Santiago de Chile. *GaWC Research Bulletin* 103, www.lboro.ac.uk/gawc/rb/rb103.html [20 August 2009]

Partida B, V. 2003 *Proyecciones de la población de México, de las entidades federativas, de los municipios y de las localidades, 2000-2050 (Documento Metodológico)* Mexico: Consejo Nacional de la Población: 139-148

Passel, J.S. and Cohn, D. 2009 *Mexican Immigrants: How Many Come? How Many leave?* Pew Hispanic Center. July 2009. http://pewhispanic.org/reports/report.php?ReportID=112 [3 September 2009]

Passel, J.S. and Suro, R. 2005 *Rise, Peak, and Decline: Trends in U.S. Immigration 1992–2004* Pew Hispanic Center, Washington, D.C., September 27, 2005. http://pewhispanic.org/files/reports/53.pdf.

Pew Hispanic Center 2009a *State and County Databases*. Washington DC. http://pewhispanic.org/states/ [22 August 2009]

——— 2009b *Mexican Immigrants in the United States 2008*. Washington DC. http://pewhispanic.org/files/factsheets/47.pdf [22 August 2009]

Prescott-Allen, R. 2001 *The Wellbeing of Nations*, Washington, DC: Island Press.

Rhoda, R. 1983 Rural Development and Urban Migration: Can We Keep Them Down on the Farm? *International Migration Review*, volume 17, Spring 1983.

Rose, W.I. and Durant, A.J. 2008 El Chichón volcano, April 4, 1982: volcanic cloud history and fine ash fallout. *Natural Hazards* 2008.

Rosenberg, T. 2008 A Payoff Out of Poverty? *New York Times*, 19 December 2008.

SCT (Secretaría de Comunicaciones y Transportes) undated *Chronology of transport in Mexico*. Mexico City: http://info.sct. gob.mx/index.php?id=443 [27 April 2009]

——— undated Road trip calculator: http://aplicaciones4.sct.gob.mx/sibuac_internet/ControllerUI?action=cmdEscogeRuta [27 April 2009]

——— 2008 *Anuario Estadístico de los Puertos de México*. www.sct.gob.mx/fileadmin/CGPMM/estadisticas/anuarios/2008/index.htm [8 August 2009]

Seawatch 2009 *The Problem: Destruction of the Sea of Cortes*. *"Owned by All Mexicans and Managed by None"*. www.seawatch. org/reports/sea_of_cortez.php [17 October 2009]

SECTUR (Secretaría de Turismo) 2006 *Turismo de internación 2001-2005, Visitantes internacionales hacia México*. Mexico: Secretaría de Turismo [26 July 2008]

——— Datatur statistics system [8 August 2009]

SEGOB (Secretaría de Gobernación) 2009 Sistema de Información Legislativa. http://sil.gobernacion.gob.mx/Numeralia/Legisladores/index.php [4 September 2009]

SEGOB-CENAPRED 2006a Impacto Socioeconómico de los Ciclones Tropicales 2005. *Ponencia presentada en el Taller sobre Análisis de posibles impactos del cambio climático en Cancún, Quintana Roo, México,* 13 de septiembre de 2006 Mexico: Secretaría de Gobernación–Centro Nacional para la Prevención de Desastres.

——— 2006b *Mexico's Third National Communication to the UNFCCCC*. Mexico: Secretaría de Gobernación–Centro Nacional para la Prevención de Desastres.

Selee, A. 2009 *Mexico's 2009 Midterm Elections: Winners and Losers,* Woodrow Wilson International Center for Scholars: Mexico Institute, July 2009. http://wilsoncenter.org/topics/pubs/Mexico's%20Midterm%20Elections%20F.pdf [20 August 2009]

SEMARNAT (Secretaría de Medio Ambiente y Recursos Naturales) *2006 Información ambiental.* Mexico City: SEMARNAT www.semarnat.gob.mx/INFORMACIONAMBIENTAL/Pages/index.aspx 2006 [November 2008]

SEMARNAT (Secretaría de Medio Ambiente y Recursos Naturales) 2009 *Informe de la Situación del Medio Ambiente en México. Edición 2008. Compendio de Estadísticas Ambientales.* Mexico City: SEMARNAT. http://app1.semarnat.gob.mx/dgeia/informe_2008/00_intros/pdf.html [4 October 2009]

Siemens, A. H. 1990 *Between the Summit and the Sea. Central Veracruz in the Nineteenth Century.* Vancouver: University of British Columbia Press.

Simon, D. 2002 *Another 50 Years of Mass Mexican Immigration: Mexican Government Report Projects Continued Flow Regardless of Economics or Birth Rates,* March 2002. Center for Immigration Studies, March 2002. www.cis.org/articles/2002/back202.html [12 April 2009]

Simon, J. 1997 *Endangered Mexico: An Environment on the Edge.* San Francisco: Sierra Club Books.

Simonian, L. 1995 *Defending the land of the jaguar: a history of conservation in Mexico.* Austin, Texas: University of Texas Press.

Sluyter, A. 2002 *Colonialism and Landscape. Postcolonial theory and applications.* Lanham, Maryland: Rowman and Littlefield.

Smith, D. M. 1971 *Industrial location: an economic geographical analysis.* New York.

SMN (Servicio Meteorológico Nacional) 2008 *Datos Históricos de Ciclones Tropicales,* via http://smn.cna.gob.mx/ [21 Augut 2009]

SPP (Secretaría de Programación y Presupuesto) 1981 *México: información sobre aspectos geográficos, sociales y económicos.* Vol 1: Aspectos geográficos. Mexico City: SPP.

——— 1982 *México: información sobre aspectos geográficos, sociales y económicos.* Vol III: Aspectos económicos. Mexico. Mexico City: SPP.

SS/DGE 2008 Registro Nacional de Casos de SIDA. 2008.

SSN (Servicio Sismológico Nacional) undated *Sismicidad Histórica,* consulted online via www.ssn.unam.mx/ [12 April 2008]

Stokes, E.M. 1981 La Colonia Extranero: An American retirement Community in Ajijic, Mexico. *PhD dissertation, University of New York*, Stony Brook, cited in Truly, D. 2002.

Stouffer, S.A. 1940 Intervening Opportunities: A Theory Relating to Mobility and Distance. *American Sociological Review* 5: 845-867.

Stratfor 2008 Mexican Drug Cartels: Government Progress and Growing Violence. Austin, Texas: *Stratfor Global Intelligence.* 11 December 2008 www.stratfor.com/memberships/128691/analysis/20081209 [18 October 2009]

Suro, R. 2005a *Attitudes about Immigration and major Demographic Characteristics.* Pew Hispanic Center, 2 March 2005.

http://pewhispanic.org/reports/report.php?ReportID=41

———— 2005b *Attitudes towards Immigrants and Immigration Policy: Surveys among Latinos in the U.S. and in Mexico*. Pew Hispanic Center, 16 August 2005. www.pewhispanic.org/files/reports/52.pdf.

Tejeda M., A. and Rodríguez V., L. 2007 Estado de la investigación de los aspectos físicos del cambio climático de México. *Investigaciones Geográficas, Boletín del Instituto de Geografía*. Mexico City: Universidad Nacional Autónoma de México, Instituto de Geografía.

Tépach M., R. 2008. *La importancia de las Remesas Familiares en la economía mexicana, 1990–2007. (Actualizado)*. Mexico City: Camara de Diputados. LX Legislatura, Centro de Documentación Información Análisis. www.diputados.gob.mx/cedia/sia/se/SE-ISS-06-08.pdf

Terry, T.P. 1909 *Terry's Mexico Handbook for Travellers*. Mexico City: Sonora News Company.

Terry, T.P. 1947 *Terry's Guide to Mexico*. Hingham, Massachusetts.

The Economist. Mexico and climate change. What's hot, green and Mexican? *The Economist*, 391, no. 8627, April 16, 2009.

The Miami Herald 2005 Guatemalan scavengers endure toxins, *The Miami Herald*, Mexico Section, 31 July 2005: 3.

Toledo, A., Nuñez, A. and Ferreira, H. 1983 *Cómo destruir el paraíso, el desastre ecológico del sureste*. Mexico City: Océano/Centro de ecodesarrollo.

Toledo, V.M., Batis, A.I., Becerra, R., Martínez E. and Ramos, C.H. 1995. La selva util: etnobotánica cuantitativa de los grupos indígenas del trópico húmedo de México. *Interciencia* 20: 177-187.

Townroe, P (1971) *Industrial location decisions, a study in management behaviour*. Univ. of Birmingham Centre for Urban and Regional Studies, Occasional Paper 15, cited in Hodder, B.W. and Lee, R. 1974 *Economic Geography*, London: Methuen.

Truly, D. 2002 International Retirement migration and tourism along the Lake Chapala Riviera: developing a matrix of retirement migration behavior. *Tourism Geographies*. Vol 4 # 3, 2002: 261-281.

———— 2006 The Lake Chapala Riviera: The evolution of a not so American foreign community, in Bloom, N.D. (ed) 2006 *Adventures into Mexico: American Tourism beyond the Border* Rowman & Littlefield: 167-190

UNAM (Universidad Nacional Autónoma de México) 1990 *Atlas Nacional de México*, Mexico City: UNAM.

UNESCO 2009 World Heritage Centre. *World heritage List*. http://whc.unesco.org/pg.cfm?CID=31&l=EN [8 August 2009]

UNDP (United Nations Development Programme) 2007 *2007/2008 Human Development Report* via http://hdr.undp.org/en [22 August 2009]

UNEP (United Nations Environment Programme) 2007 *Global Environmental Monitoring System/Water Quality Monitoring System*. www.unesco.org/bpi/wwdr/WWDR_chart2_eng.pdf [Dec 6, 2008]

UNESCO 2009 - web-page - http://whc.unesco.org/pg.cfm?CID=31&l=EN [August 18, 2009]

UNESCO-WWAP 2003 *Water for People, Water for Life*. Paris, France: UNESCO via http://www.unesco.org/water/wwap/ [21 August 2009]

UNPIN (United Nations Population Information Network) 2009 *A guide to population information on UN system web sites*. http://www.un.org/popin/ [21 August 2009]

UNWTO (United Nations World Tourism Organization) 2001 *Tourism 2020 Vision*. http://www.unwto.org/facts/eng/vision.htm [14 June 2008]

———— 2007 *UNWTO Tourism Highlights, Edition 2007*. World Tourism Organization. http://www.unwto.org/facts/eng/highlights.htm [14 June 2008]

———— 2008 *World Tourism Barometer* June 2008, http://www.unwto.org/facts/eng/barometer.htm [14 June 2008].

UN Millennium Development Goals 2009 *The Millennium Development Goals Report 2009*. New York: United Nations. http://www.un.org/millenniumgoals/pdf/MDG_Report_2009_ENG.pdf [24 October 2009]

US Census Bureau 2001 *The Hispanic Population. Census 2000 Brief*. www.census.gov/prod/2001pubs/c2kbr01-3.pdf [10 May 2009]

———— 2009a *Current Population Surveys (for years 1998-2008)*, via www.census.gov/population/www/socdemo/migrate.html [10 May 2009]

———— 2009b *Geographical Mobility/Migration*, via www.census.gov/population/www/socdemo/migrate.html [9 May 2009]

———— 2009c. *American Community Survey, US Census of 2000 supplementary survey (C2SS)*, via www.census.gov/acs/www/ [10 May 2009]

Vallarta Opina 2009 Punta de Mita, entre la opulencia y la marginación de su gente. *Vallarta Opina*, 4 April 2009. Puerto Vallarta, Mexico. www.vallartaopina.net/index.php?mod=sec&cat=ens&ele=1825 [13 October 2009]

van den Berghe, P. L. 1995 Marketing Mayas - Ethnic Tourism Promotion in Mexico. *Annals of Tourism Research*, vol 22, no 3: 568-588

Veenhoven, R., 2009 *World Database of Happiness*. Rotterdam: Erasmus University http://worlddatabaseofhappiness.eur.nl [20 August 2009]

Vinson III, B. and Vaughn, B. 2004 *Afroméxico*. Mexico: CIDE/CFE.

Volpe P. 2000 Nations, Regions, and the Global Economy. *Unpublished manuscript*, Durham, North Carolina: Duke University.

Wackernagel, M. and Rees, W.E. 1996 *Our Ecological Footprint: Reducing Human Impact on the Earth*. Gabriola Island, B.C., Canada: New Society Publishers.

WAN (World Association of Newspapers) 2008 *World Press Trends 2008 Edition*. Paris, France: World Association of Newspapers.

Weber, A. 1909 (translated 1929) *Theory of the Location of Industries*. Chicago.

Weidensaul, S. 2009 "Meet Me at the Oasis", *Audubon*, May-June 2009: 52-58.

Wellington, A.M. 1886 The American line from Vera Cruz to the city of Mexico, via Jalapa, with notes on the best methods of surmounting high elevations by rail. *American Society of Civil Engineers,* Transactions, XV, 791.

Werner, M.S. (ed) 1997 *Encyclopedia of Mexico: History, Society, & Culture*. Chicago: Fitzroy Dearborn.

West, R.C. and Augelli, J.P. 1966 *Middle America, its lands and people*s. Englewood Cliffs, New Jersey: Prentice-Hall.

White, M., Salas, C. and Gammage, S. 2003 *Trade Impact Review: Mexico Case Study. NAFTA and the FTAA: A Gender Analysis of Employment and Poverty Impacts in Agriculture*. Women's Edge Coalition, November, 2003. http://www.tradeobservatory.org/library.cfm?refID=26000 [21 August 2009]

Whyte, A.V.T. 1977 *Guidelines for field studies in environmental perception*. MAB Technical Note 5. Paris: UNESCO.

Wikipedia undated Entry on Regional styles of Mexican music http://en.wikipedia.org/wiki/Regional_styles_of_Mexican_music [25 April 2009]

World Bank 2002 Mexico Urban Development: *A Contribution to a National Urban Strategy*, Washington, D.C. http://www-wds.worldbank.org/external/default/WDSContentServer/WDSP/IB/2002/09/06/000094946_02081904011340/Rendered/PDF/multi0page.pdf [21 August 2009]

World Resources Institute 2007 *EarthTrends, the Environmental Information Portal*. http://earthtrends.wri.org/searchable_db/index.php [24 October 2009]

WWF (WorldWide Fund for Nature) 2008 *2008 Living Planet Report*. Gland, Switzerland: WWF. http://www.footprintnetwork.org/download.php?id=505 [11 October 2009]

Yarza, E. 1992 *Volcanes de México*. Mexico City: Universidad Nacional Autónoma de México, Instituto de Geografía.

Zeder, M.A, Emshwiller, E., Smith, B. D. and Bradley, D.G. 2006 Documenting domestication: the intersection of genetics and archaeology. *Trends in Genetics*, vol. 22, no. 3, March 2006, 139-155. http://anthropology.si.edu/archaeobio/Zederetal.2006.TIG.pdf [2 May 2009}

Index

Acknowledgments

Several people helped bring this book into being. Valerie Rhoda suggested the initial idea and subsequently identified a wide range of relevant information which has greatly enhanced its quality. Together with Jim Brown and Gwen Burton, she also provided insightful feedback on chapter drafts. All three offered support and encouragement during all phases of the project.

We would also like to give our sincere thanks to Anne Harris Baker for her rigorous proof reading of the final manuscript. Any remaining errors or omissions are entirely our own.

Made in the USA
Coppell, TX
08 January 2021